Systems and Simulation

MATHEMATICS IN SCIENCE AND ENGINEERING

A SERIES OF MONOGRAPHS AND TEXTBOOKS

Edited by Richard Bellman

University of Southern California

MATHEMATICS IN SCIENCE AND ENGINEERING

In preparation

Systems
and
Simulation

DIMITRIS N. CHORAFAS

CORPORATE CONSULTANT IN ENGINEERING AND MANAGEMENT, PARIS
VISITING PROFESSOR, INFORMATION SCIENCE AND BUSINESS ADMINISTRATION,
WASHINGTON STATE UNIVERSITY

1965

New York   ACADEMIC PRESS   London

To F. GORDON SMITH

ACADEMIC PRESS INC.
111 Fifth Avenue, New York, New York 10003

United Kingdom Edition published by
ACADEMIC PRESS INC. (LONDON) LTD.
Berkeley Square House, London W.1

Library of Congress Catalog Card Number: 64-24654

First Printing 1965
Second Printing 1967

PRINTED IN THE UNITED STATES OF AMERICA

Foreword

That the history of science and mathematics is intimately entwined with the history of mankind has been emphasized by many historians of science; Sarton, in particular. Great political and cultural surges have always reflected themselves in corresponding bursts of scientific and mathematical creativity. This has been the case from the time of Archimedes through the times of Newton and Leibniz to the present. One aspect of the current intellectual explosion has been that fields far removed from the conventional domains of mathematics and its applications are now being studied and cultivated with great zeal. Among these fields, we may mention economics, management, organization theory, psychology, and biology and medicine.

Actually the beginning efforts in these areas stretch back into time. At the end of the eighteenth and the beginning of the nineteenth century, for example, there was a great deal of interest in what is now called "operations research" and mathematical economics. But a lack of computers and a lack of urgency combined to prevent any extensive development. World War II created the urgency, and the hasty work done during that period under great pressure of time gave some idea of what could be accomplished in these areas using sophisticated concepts and modern mathematical techniques. In the years following the war, there has been an opportunity to examine the problems and solutions with the care and effort required to produce a new discipline called systems analysis.

The book by Chorafas is a building block in the firm foundation of this new discipline. Ideas, concepts, and methods have been borrowed from the traditional domains, and new types of problems have been treated in this fashion. From this amalgam has emerged new ideas, concepts, and techniques which have been applied to treat the more complex questions and which have then been applied to problems within the classical domain. This is the usual feedback that occurs when a new field is explored. It is a fair exchange for both sides.

Many of the most important problems confronting our society are related to the analysis, behavior, design, and control of systems. The reader forced to face the complexities of reality will find this volume of great value; the mathematician looking for new fields to conquer

vii

and new categories of problems to tame will equally find it of interest and value. It is with pleasure that I welcome this book into our series.

RICHARD BELLMAN
Santa Monica, California

Preface

Professor Chorafas has again rendered an invaluable service to many of us in describing some very real problems which arise in our modern world, and the means now at hand for rapid, accurate and comprehensive solution. For the technical planner, and the engineer, this book must surely become a ready reference work of great worth. Business and industrial management will find that it outlines new methods of attack on their unsolved difficulties which are created by the complexities of living in a highly developed and competitive economy. Professor Chorafas feels that we have reached a point in almost every sphere of human activity and quasi-achievement where all major problems of business, industry, and government can be formulated and presented as systems of mathematical logic.

A system is defined broadly as a "group of interdependent elements acting together to accomplish a predetermined task." The objectives, interrelationships, and constraints of the system are recognized and isolated, and in turn stated through the true and universal language of mathematics. When we have the problems of the age reduced to the form of equations and quantitative data, we have the abstract and the real, which is the true concern of mathematical analysis and mathematical systems.

The new and promising discipline of *system analysis* seeks to determine the optimum means for accomplishing the task described in the problem statement. The *system analyst* is more than an engineer, a mathematician or an accountant. His education involves these subjects and many others, including psychology and the general theory of knowledge. System analysis presents a rewarding and exciting career opportunity for the bright members of the new generation; clear conceptual thinking, analytical ability, and the power of synthetizing many different factors into an organic whole are required to excel in this new discipline. Knowledge in many fields is necessary, but narrow specialization in any specific area must be avoided, in order to maintain an unbiased "generalist" approach to the entire problem.

Once the system has been defined in mathematical terms, its solution may be found by the technique of simulation, that is, by investigating the performance of the actual system through an analogous system, more accessible to the system analyst. Through the observations made on the simulated system, we can study the characteristics, test the reaction, and predict the performance of the original system.

Because of the complexity of the system studied, analog and digital computers are almost always necessary for simulation studies. A simulator is a device that puts a physical process or concept or a mechanical, electronic, biological or social system into such a representative form that the phenomenon can be imitated with a computer where there is correspondence between problem parameters and variables and those of the computer. Professor Chorafas's examples of successful simulations are widely drawn, thoroughly explained, and cover a significant number of civil and military applications.

Many complex industrial processes are ideally simulated on digital computers, particularly where the product is made up of many parts. For such a simulation, it is necessary to describe all parts required in the finished product, the machines used to produce each part, the time used for each operation, the relationships between operations, and the capacity of each machine. The computer program will determine the operations sequence, bottlenecks in the production flow, schedules of optimal nature, so that the production time and costs are reduced.

Management gaming lends itself to digital computer simulation. The human player in the game determines the various controllable aspects of his business such as budgets for advertising, for engineering, for research, volume of production, etc.

Programs are fed into the computer which then simulates the business operation and prints reports which may indicate sales volume, inventory, production capacity, and the state of profitability of the business in the future.

Professor Chorafas elucidates some of the most challenging problems of systems engineering and some of the pitfalls. They include, as we learn, the need for designing, predicting performance, building and operating vast and complicated elements in many combinations.

The definition of the word "system" presented above is disarmingly simple and very general. But systems engineering emphasizes the requisites that are necessary for optimum performance under varying conditions of load, environment, information inputs, and even, perhaps, the metabolism of the engineer. When total systems are brought into play, system design, realization, and analysis may require the engineer to be scientist, both natural and social, with the hint of the "specialist." The systems analyst or engineer must have a very broad outlook indeed.

The book itself encompasses broad fields. It takes us through Industrial Operations, Inventory Controls, Tools for Data Generation, Management Data in Mathematical Form, etc. It will make a good book for reading by the computer industry itself which is ever more concerned with solving the problems of business (including its own ?).

The computer is becoming an essential component of modern management information systems, and an indispensable aid in decision making for business fighting its way through the competitive flood, on an international scale. Parallel to the explosive development of the computer, the techniques used by modern business management must become more advanced and sophisticated, and must be based on the most recent developments of science and technology. The book of Professor Chorafas is a timely and worthy contribution toward this goal.

F. GORDON SMITH
*Vice President, UNIVAC Operations
Europe, Middle East and Africa*

Contents

PART V

Research on Traffic and Cargo Problems

PART VI

Hydrological Applications

PART VII

Simulation by Analog Means

Introduction

As the achievements of science become more numerous, more inspiring, more divorced from the little corner of common sense familiar to all of us, it becomes increasingly more necessary as well as increasingly more difficult for an individual scientist to maintain a firm intellectual grip on the various ramifications of a chosen field of knowledge. In a certain way, the individual scientist either becomes dependent on his fellow scientists for an understanding of allied fields, or he finds himself obliged to get acquainted with at least the fundamentals of new theories and new applications. This is not always an easy task since along with the increasing complexities in the sciences themselves comes an increased volume of routine work and of record keeping.

The purpose of this book is to present, explain, and discuss in a fundamental manner, some of the mathematical systems which have become popular in professional practice in recent years. Since World War II we have experienced an increasing development in all the domains of man-made systems, from pure theory to technological and other applications. The wide range of these applications defines the subjects to be discussed in the present work, both practical and theoretical in nature; they have been selected because they constitute the keys to a great variety of fields in science, technology, and management.

This work starts with a discussion of certain fundamental notions— notions concerning mathematical abstraction and systems work, the nature of simulation studies, and the development and use of analytical models. It is only logical that this general-type discussion be followed by a group of chapters that dig deep into the mathematics of the simulator. The writing, developing, and testing of equations are given roles of first importance. This is also true for data generation, data reduction, and the use of certain methods for the solution of equations.

The applications part of the present book is divided into two major groupings. One deals with the simulation of managerial systems, and it involves eight chapters. The other treats applications characterized by their technological nature. This last subject involves six chapters, three of which concern the flow of distinct particles and the other three center on hydrological applications. To bring another facet of this great art under proper perspective, the work closes with two chapters on analog simulation.

This text has been prepared with due consideration to the fact that, in the course of the last ten years, our ways of thinking about performance of integral, purpose-accomplishing systems have evolved virtually to the point of creating a new technical discipline. The ways of thinking are not new in the sense that they consider the contribution of all elements of a system toward the accomplishment of a specific purpose. Such considerations, in varying degrees of refinement, have always been a part of planned endeavors. Essentially, what is new is the ability of modern scientists, mathematicians, and engineers to penetrate into the unknown through systematic experimentation and an analysis of the crucial factors. This analytic thinking is part of the foundation of the amazing technological development we are experiencing.

Some argue that our new technology needs a "new kind" of people. What nonsense! Our technology needs people well educated in the latest theories, methods, and techniques; people possessing the marvelous mixture of a broad background and a good deal of creative imagination. For people with creative imagination, any sphere of human activity will do. To some extent, whether they become officers, priests, tradesmen, managers, engineers, or scientists depends on circumstances.

DIMITRIS N. CHORAFAS

December, 1964

PART I

Basic Notions

CHAPTER 1

Mathematical Abstraction and Systems Work

One of the strongest motives that lead men to art and science is escape from everyday life with its painful crudity and hopeless dreariness, escape from the fetters of one's own ever-shifting desires.

A finely tempered nature tends to slip from personal life into the world of objective perception and thought. This desire may be compared with the townsman's irresistible longing to leave his noisy, cramped surroundings for the silence of high mountains, where the eye ranges freely through the still, pure air and fondly traces out the restful contours apparently built for eternity.

Man tries to make for himself in the fashion that suits him best a simplified and intelligible picture of the world. He then tries to substitute this cosmos of his own for the world of experience, and thus to overcome it. This is what the painter, the poet, the speculative philosopher, the writer, the natural scientist, and the systems analyst[1] do, each in his own fashion.

Each one of these men is an artist in his own sphere of endeavor; and, the greater the artist the greater the art. The philosopher, the writer, the researcher all work on those subjects which stimulate them the most, which answer their mental worries, which generate for them the most thought and promote the human search into the mental unknown—the highest activity a human being can perform.

People of this kind make the cosmos they conceive and its construc-

---

[1] Webster defines "system" as "an assemblage of objects united by some form of regular interaction or interdependence." In the discussion to follow, our reference will be to medium or large scale physical, technological, or administrative ensembles, whose study requires the work of the specialist.

We will use the words "systems analyst," "systems engineer," and "systems specialist," to identify a scientific discipline; persons versatile in conceiving, analyzing, experimenting, evaluating, and designing man-machine–environment systems made for a predetermined objective and according to preestablished criteria. We will use the words "researcher" and "experimenter" more precisely for persons involved in these aspects concerning simulation work and experimentation.

tion the pivot of their emotional life, to find in this way the peace and security they cannot find in the narrow whirlpool of personal experience. But work in the field of mental abstraction demands the highest possible standard of rigorous precision in the description of relations. Here exactly is the point where the two different cosmos separate. That of the poet, the painter, and the writer will continue to be expressed in a qualitative manner; while the natural scientist and the systems analyst require for their expression a quantiative form that only mathematical language can provide.

Abstraction and Reality

In the broadest sense, mathematics may be separated into two classes. One class deals with the symbols, their combinations and properties, in a formal way. The other class concerns itself with the meaning of the symbols: the significance of the system related to the real world. Of the three theoretical sciences—philosophy, mathematics, physics—mathematics made the earliest advances with respect to accuracy and truth. The aim of theoretical science is neither action nor production, but the acquiring of a scientific truth.

Man with his receptors has no deep contact with physical reality. The interaction of his senses with nature gives him the impression he calls empirical knowledge. This empirical knowledge is only what his senses and their extensions can observe and describe. With the data he obtains, he is led to abstraction and idealization, and at that point mathematical analysis takes over. The aim is to formulate a comprehensive theory that will describe observable phenomena and lead to verifiable predictions.

Research workers are often required, by the nature of their profession, to spend years of anxious searching in the dark, with nothing else to warm them but their own fears, with continuous extensions in their search, with alterations of confidence and doubt. Behind the tireless efforts of the investigator there is a stronger, more mysterious drive. It is existence and reality that he wishes to comprehend.

In the course of the evolution of human knowledge we have experienced the growth of new and promising disciplines. One of them is systems analysis. Its foundations have been derived from studies of dynamic systems and their functioning components. A system is a group of interdependent elements acting together to accomplish a predetermined purpose. *Systems analysis* is an attempt to define the most feasible, suitable, and acceptable means for accomplishing a given purpose.

The systems analyst, like the natural scientist, must limit his range of endeavor. The natural scientist contents himself with describing the most simple events that can be brought within the domain of his experience. All events of a more complex order are beyond the power of the human intellect to reconstruct with the subtle accuracy and logical perfection which the theoretical physicist demands. For his part, the systems engineer must content himself with the study and analysis of complex technological systems, with the understanding of the nature and the workings of systems components, and with their synthesis into a working ensemble.

The study of systems behavior is not another whim. On the basis of his experience of the systems of today and by using his creative imagination, man needs to project into the future, to speculate on the systems of tomorrow. Projection into the unknown is based on unproven hypotheses. In our fast-developing technology we can never be sure of what the scientific truth of tomorrow will be. To say that we know tomorrow is to expose ourselves to bitter disappointments.

But what can be the attraction of getting to know the technological future only in a speculative manner? Does the product of such an effort deserve to be called a science or a great art? To answer such questions one should realize that even in the world of today we can never be sure that our conceptions represent the truth or that our formulations are unique and solidly determined. We are living in a world of shifting ideas. What we do know is sample data on a universe. Due to our human limitations we will probably never know the universe in its totality and the "truth" behind it, whatever that may be.

Systems study is very often confronted with problems of inference. On the basis of a sample we are required by the nature of our work to generalize as to the structure and the behavior of the whole; to speculate in the time domain with information from sample data obtained in a finite population.

In this tedious and uncertain work, the scientist is assisted by the fact the general laws on which the structure of natural and man-made systems are based claim to be valid for any phenomenon. With them it ought to be possible to arrive at the description or, in other words, the theory of every natural process including life. Man has often attempted to arrive at such a description. Conceivably, he might have arrived by means of pure deduction if that process of deduction were not far beyond the capacity of the human intellect. This is the approach taken by philosophers and some of the artists.

The state of mind which enables a man to perform work of this kind is akin to that of the religious worshipper or lover. The daily effort comes from no deliberate intention or program, but straight from the heart. To analyze and project, the human mind should be neither restricted nor biased but open to new ideas. It should be fertile in its ability to abstract, imagine, and idealize.

The Development of Mathematical Systems

We will consider the development of a theoretical system, paying special attention to the relation between the content of the theory and the totality of empirical fact.

Ancient Greece is credited with the birth of the first mathematical system. There the world for the first time witnessed a logical, man-made ensemble which proceeded from step to step with such precision that every one of its propositions was absolutely indisputable. Since that time, Euclidean geometry has become the model for every other system of man-made laws.

Reviewing the history of accomplishments of the human intellect, we see that in the year 300 BC the Greek philospher and mathematician Euclid gathered together the geometrical knowledge then available, consisting of the Pythagorean and other theorems, and combined that knowledge into a *system*, which has been the model for all scientific systems since. The main characteristic of such a system is the setting off of some theorems as *postulates* or axioms from which, by logic, all remaining theorems may be derived. Postulates or axioms do not necessarily imply a self-evident truth.

In mathematics, when talking of systems we mostly have in mind a set of laws. In the physical sciences we use the word *system* to mean a portion of the universe around which we draw an imaginary boundary, for the purpose of study of what is enclosed inside this boundary. In engineering the word "system" is mostly interpreted as meaning an organized working total, an assemblage of objects united by some form of regular interaction or interdependence. Systems may themselves be subsystems of other larger ensembles. Hence, the idea of drawing an imaginary boundary holds true with every usage of the systems concept.

Since proof of a theorem means derivation from previous theorems, obviously the first group of theorems (or postulates) cannot be proved. Thus any system must start with *unproved theorems* from which all other theorems will be proved. Euclid's system rested on unproved propositions. Though today we may disagree with the idea of a self-evident truth, fundamentally, Euclid believed any proposition is either a self-evident truth, or something which must be derived logically from self-evident truths (theorems). This can be demonstrated by the relationship

$$\text{self-evident thoughts} \rightarrow \text{logic} \rightarrow \text{theorems}.$$

Among Euclid's postulates or self-evident truths was the parallel postulate: "Through any given point which is not on a given line, one, and only one, line can be drawn which is parallel to the given line." Because this postulate was not as self-evident as many of the others, Euclid reluctantly listed it as such only after unsuccessfully trying to prove it from his other postulates. Other mathematicians were also dissatisfied, and they likewise tried to prove the proposition. Over a period of several centuries, however, they, too, failed.

After 2000 years of failure, early in the nineteenth century several mathematicians came to the conclusion that the reason for this failure was a wrong attitude towards the nature of the postulates. They reasoned that the postulates were not self-evident truths at all, but rather man-made assumptions. Schematically, they believed the procedure of proving theorems was

$$\text{man-made assumptions} \rightarrow \text{logic} \rightarrow \text{theorems}.$$

This in itself provided a great freedom of the mind, for in a man-made system we can prove any theorem if we are allowed to pick out our axioms. Furthermore, if we keep the man-made assumptions constant and vary logic we will obviously arrive at a different set of theorems.

Nevertheless, even a complete mathematical system cannot solve the problem of organized abstraction unless it has its *pawns* to play with. These *pawns* are the numbers. Perhaps feeling this need, men have tried since the early ages to develop number systems. A number system must be complete, self-defined, and noncontradictory in itself, which of course is true for every mathematical system. But, no matter how complete in itself, a number system in essence is only a subsystem of the mathematical system which it serves. This is in conformity with the fundamental principle we have expressed, that any system is a subsystem of another larger ensemble.

Let's consider again the example of the Euclidean system, replacing the parallel postulate with the following: "Through any given point which is not on a given line, two lines can be drawn which are *both* parallel to the given line." We would then deduce a different set of theorems. In fact, the very concept of a man-made assumption gives us the freedom to change these assumptions, state new ones entirely different, and then follow through logically to derive new theorems which are the consequences of these new assumptions. This is what was concluded at the beginning of the nineteenth century by the mathematicians Gauss, Lobachevsky, and Bolyai, each working independently of the others.

The change in the Euclidean system, which showed that postulates are independent in nature and therefore that contradictory postulates may exist in complete harmony, led to the examination of the postulates of algebra. This gave rise to new algebras as well as other new mathematical systems.

One of the new algebras, probably the most important, was Boolean algebra established by George Boole in 1847. Boole based his algebra on a set of eleven postulates. Comparing Boolean algebra to ordinary algebra, we see that some of its postulates hold, some do not hold, and some others are meaningless. Because it has been established, however, that postulates are simply man-made assumptions, we have the right to make them and derive theorems from them, provided there are *no contradictions* in the system.

Time Requirements and the Scientific Thought

Man proceeds in understanding concepts by means of logical analysis. In answering the question: "How do concepts and judgements depend on one another?," logical analysis projects the rationality with which we are so much impressed in mathematics. This rationality, however, has inherent in it the liability of a certain lack of qualitative content. Concepts can only acquire content when they are in some way connected with logical experience. But logical investigations do not reveal such connections in an unique and undisputed manner. They can only indicate their possible existence. From then on, hypotheses start (see Fig. 1).

It might be added that science as something existing and complete is the most objective field of endeavor known to man. But science in the making, science as an end to be pursued, is as subjective and psychologically conditioned as any other branch of human endeavor. And yet the scientist has to establish connections between the facts of experience. He has to establish fundamental laws which will enable him to predict further occurrences, to detail possible accomplishment in the domain of his task.

Here the great challenge starts. Examining the history of scientific and technical discovery we see that we are rather poor in master brains capable of independent thinking and creative imagination. Even when requirements for the birth of an idea have long been in existence, man generally needs a great stimulus to make things actually happen. He has to probe into his mental unknown before he is able to formulate ideas about the physical universe, and has to come, in a way, up against a physical constraint before he is pushed to investigate his own mind. Scientific achievements, like all other achievements, are accelerated by the handicaps found in the way of human progress, provided there exists a strong human willingness and determination to overcome them.

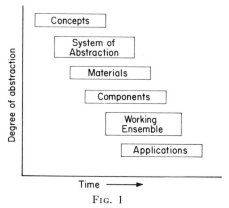

Fig. 1

This task is difficult. But it is not impossible. It has been accomplished before. A tremendous amount of pure mathematical thinking was necessary before analytic tools, of a nature that man could use to advantage in his work, were developed. We are, for instance, so accustomed today to the use of derivatives that we can hardly grasp any longer what a remarkable power of abstraction was needed to reach the general differential law. This was a spectacular crossing of frontiers in mathematical analysis, in the course of which the concept of mass had, in addition, to be invented.

Mathematical analysis as applied to problems of large technological systems does not differ in its conception from the type of analysis used in the physical sciences. When we say that we have succeeded in understanding a group of natural processes, we invariably mean that a constructive theory has been found which covers the processes in question. The great difference, then, in the challenge is in plurality.

Never before has the scientific man been confronted with so many problems at once. Never before have the frontiers of his knowledge been pushed so far that the thrust of the existing powerful minds would be insufficient to carry them farther in a frontal attack. Never before has the urgency for this "new push" been so great. In the centuries of scientific thought which preceded our time, problems of the intellect were allowed and often welcomed to wait. Today, however, we cannot tolerate delays for long.

That's exactly where mathematical simulation[2] comes in. We use it as a tool in experimentation, as an extension of the scientist's penetrating power in problems of complexity. We use it as a means for testing solutions, to find the "truth." We use it as the electronic microscope of technological and other studies. Most important of all, we use it as a lever in compressing time. For today, time is at a premium.

The elements which form the basis of a systems theory are not hypothetically constructed but experimentally discovered. General characteristics of technological processes must be at hand before a system is even constructed. The same is true of the principles that give rise to mathematically formulated criteria which the process or the theoretical representation of the process has to satisfy. Simulation work is one of the most important means of approach to scientific study and experimentation.

Development of a Systems Profession

Advancements in mathematical analysis are at the core of the work of the technologist. The scientific man will be increasingly guided by mathematical considerations in his search for new systems and processes. The predominantly inductive methods appropriate to the youth of science are giving place to tentative deductions. In his research work the systems analyst gets nearer to the grand aim of science, which is to cover the greatest possible number of empirical facts by logical deductions from the smallest possible number of hypotheses or axioms.

The theoretical structure built by the systems analyst needs to be very thoroughly elaborated before it leads to conclusions which can be compared with experience. Until the respective theoretical system is seasoned there is no doubt that the observed fact will be the arbiter. This observed fact, however, cannot pronounce sentence until the wide chasm separating the axioms from their verifiable consequences has been bridged.

This makes a cycle. The knowledge of reality starts from experience, is processed through mathematical analysis and speculation, to end with experience again. But how often does the scientist have to predecide in this latter part? How often does he need to use the substantial and close interrelation which exists between mathematical models and the physical world?

The fact that simulation can be used as an important tool in science and technology is based on a simple observation. A complete scientific

---

[2] See definition in Chapter 2.

system is made up of fundamental laws which are supposed to be valid, if scientific conclusions are going to be reached by logical deduction. It is these conclusions which must correspond with the separate experiences. And it is this correspondence which tells much of the story of what goes on in experimentation concerning systems work.

Correspondences of this type do happen in a mathematical system, such as Euclidean geometry, except that there the fundamental laws are called axioms and there is no question of the conclusions having to correspond to any sort of experience. But in systems work the task of establishing the principles which are to serve as the starting point is not a trivial one. There exists no method which can be learned and systematically applied so that it leads to the goal. Neither does there exist much literature which could provide reference on this subject, since the whole field of problem formulation in systems studies is still in its infancy. The systems analyst has to develop these general principles by perceiving certain general features which permit of precise formulation amidst large complexes of empirical facts.

Once this formulation is successfully accomplished, inference follows on inference, often revealing relations which extend far beyond the province of the reality from which the principles were drawn. Here lies one of the major differences between the physicist and the systems engineer. As long as the principles capable of serving as starting points for the deduction remain undiscovered, the individual fact is of no use to the physical theorist. This is not true with regard to the systems work, for which every single fact is of potential importance. On these facts, often little ones by their own nature, the analyst will build a system complete, uniquely defined, and with no contradictions within itself.

Perhaps much of this difference is due to the nature of the particular universe to which each discipline appeals itself. One is concerned with the physical universe and the discovery of its internal laws, the other with man-made systems and their lifeblood, the information process. While the physicist cannot do anything with isolated empirical generalizations, the systems engineer may in cases work wonders with such generalizations since he is the generator of methods, theories, and procedures in the technological world.

Reversals in Long-Term Trends

Engineering came to form a distinct occupation early in the history of the Western World. It was the profession of the men who designed windmills and waterwheels, of those who devoted their lives to planning and supervising the extensive reclamation works executed early in the 17th century, those responsible for the construction of cathedrals, roads, bridges, aqueducts, and the many similar works (see Table I).

TABLE I

MAN-MADE POWER SYSTEMS

Century	Windmills	Steam	Electric	Nuclear
15th	Turret windmill			
17th	Extensive use of windmill pumps	Savery's steam pump	Earth as a magnet (Gilbert) Frictional generator (von Guericke)	
18th		Newcomen's engine Watt's engine Use of steam power as prime mover	Law of force between electric charges (Priestly) Law of force between magnetic poles (Coulomb)	
19th		Transatlantic steamship service Steam dredgers Steam turbine	Magnetic field due to current (Oersted) Ohm's law Faraday's law Electric motor Central power station (Edison) Transformer	Radioactivity (Becquerel)
20th			Tungsten lamp	Mass of electron (Millikan) Atomic bomb Industrial use of radio-isotopes Power generator through nuclear means

Engineering, as a separate profession comprised of a body of techno-logically trained individuals, is of fairly recent origin; recent, that is, if we except the military engineers. Here exactly lies one of the major points in the new trend. Now after centuries of distinction, we are talking of a total approach to the subject of applied science. We are talking of systems, be it military or industrial, which have common origins in research and many common characteristics in their application. We are talking of a continuation of the history of military applied science and of its current scientific and technological thinking, of a continuation of a history of immense developments in the art of war, developments which stemmed from and which created the melancholy and almost endless flux of armed conflicts and deliberate destructions since the time of the Assyrians.

> ... King Urzana of Musasir, whose life is described as one of sin and iniquity, who had broken the oath which he had sworn in the presence of the gods Ashur, Shamash, Nabu, and Marduk, had revolted against Sargon: he sent no gifts, he did not come to embrace the king's feet, nor did he send any messenger to bring him greetings. Such conduct deserved swift and condign punishment.

> ... The city of Musasir fell and Sargon ordered the inhabitants to be deported and the statue of the god Haldia, the tutelary deity of the city, to form part of the spoil. The wife, children and family of the king, who had himself fled, formed part of the total capture of some 6,110 inhabitants, twelve mules, 380 asses and unspecified live stock. Sargon himself took up residence in the royal palace, where he broke open the treasury and removed all the gold, silver, bronze, lead, cornelian, lapis-lazuli, ivory, rare woods, royal insignia, cermonial weapons and plate, which it contained.[3]

Weapons development and the project teams responsible for it have continued to grow since the end of World War II. Today, more than two-thirds of American scientists and engineers are engaged in this effort. Though in other countries the ratios might be smaller, trends point definitely in that direction. But what is a weapons system? Is it something so far apart, unhomogenious, and unrelated to, say, a process control ensemble? Is a computer designed for the military of no use to the civilian?

We have also to ask whether science and technology stand to profit from the contemplated merger of the two engineering disciplines. It is not difficult to answer this question. Whether real or imaginary, "terrible urgencies" confront all major powers. Vast social and technological energies throughout the world are focused, even in time of peace, on major scientific improvements in the art of war. These "needs" form the base on which rests the case of a "benefit." A case which impresses

---

[3] G. Contenau, "Everyday Life in Babylon and Assyria." Arnold, London, 1954.

a new role on engineering. We can speak of a double reversal in the transition from scientific theory to practice:

(i) the forementioned merger of the industrial and military research and engineering work in the realization that there can be enough fallout to help each other and both, and

(ii) a contemplated tendency in culture to broaden the scope of scientific endeavor and thus make the work of the scientist more challenging but also more speculative.

The 17th century and subsequent cultures narrowed the scope of knowledge to the mechanical arts. Scientific investigations were not allowed to trespass the established interests of the Church and the State. The Church condemned Copernicus' investigations, in that they moved the center of gravity, so to say, from the earth to the sun. Prejudice put its own boundaries on the scientific effort, even though there was nothing of a heretical nature in the physical sciences themselves and even though the pursuit of mechanics and hydrostatics infringed as little upon the holy dogmas as the invention of pumps and fountains.

For centuries, external pressures and man's own misbeliefs and prejudices succeeded in putting artificial boundaries to scientific investigation. This partition of interests, in turn, well suited the new practitioners of science, many of whom were merchants daily engrossed in the pursuit of pecuniary gain. The founders of the Royal Society, for instance, barred "all discourses of Divinity, of State affairs, and of News." The sciences were cut loose from the major provinces of human life at the very moment when physical discoveries and technological improvements were about to revolutionize both the material and the social basis of civilization. That proved to be a twofold misfortune. Not merely were these departments left without the benefits of the scientific rationale, but the sciences themselves, in perfecting the analytic method of dissection and dissociation, lost the sense of the whole and failed to develop a method of dealing with ensembles.

It is only recently that we have come to realize the great impact of studies on total systems and the importance of experimentation. Hence, the growing need for mathematical simulation. The urge for projecting into the future, of evaluating performance, of choosing among alternatives. The problems are many, they are urgent, and, most important, their implications are unknown to us.

> ... It is as if man had been suddenly appointed managing director of the biggest business of all, the business of evolution—appointed without being asked if he wanted it, and without proper warning and preparation. What is

more, he can't refuse the job. Whether he wants to or not, whether he is con-scious of what he is doing or not, he is in point of fact determining the future direction of evolution on this earth. That is his inescapable destiny, and the sooner he realizes it and starts believing in it, the better for all concerned.

What the job really boils down to is this—the fullest realization of man's possibilities, whether by the individual, by the community, or by the species, in the processional adventure along the corridors of time. . . .[4]

---

[4] J. Huxley, "New Bottles for New Wine." Chatto and Windus, London, 1957.

CHAPTER 2

Establishing the Nature of Simulation Studies

Simulation is essentially a working analogy. Analogy means similarity of properties or relations without identity. When we are able to construct analogous systems, measurements or other observations made on one of these systems may be used to predict the reaction of the others.

Simulation involves the construction of a working mathematical or physical model presenting similarity of properties or relationships with the natural or technological system under study. In this manner we can preoperate a system without actually having a physical device to work with, and we can predecide on the optimization of its characteristics. In most cases, simulation studies, to be properly done, require the making of new models able to fit, with the required precision, a specific situation. It is like developing a special kind of medicine to suit the needs of an individual patient.

A simulation study begins with the development of this custom-made model and continues with its processing or "operation" in order to determine the behavior of the system under examination. There is no practical restriction on what the system may be. However, for demonstration purposes in the subsequent discussion we will assume that the object of our study consists of technological works or equipment which can vary as to their nature from an oil refinery to a complex weapon system.

There is, of course, nothing new in all this. In petroleum manufacturing, for instance, when engineers design a fractionating column, this is precisely what they are doing. But when the designers wish to investigate the effect of varying conditions, especially if these conditions are beyond their control, the problem becomes much more complex. They need to preoperate whole sections of the factory, which may be of a completely new conception. To this interaction between mathematical experimentation and real systems we made reference in the preceding chapter when we talked about the impact of abstraction on man-made systems.

We have also made reference to the fact that in many problems with

15

which we are faced the variations are not only uncontrollable, but also unpredictable. This we have established as being one of the reasons why simple methods of solving problems often fail, and why we have to resort to more sophisticated methods such as mathematical simulation.

Step by Step

The first step in performing a simulation study is of course to investigate and establish all factors pertinent to the subsequent construction of the mathematical model. This will take the form of a description of the system under study and how it performs. It is essential to include in the model the variables which have a major effect on the performance of the real ensemble, but equally important to omit those details which have no material effect on the answer we are seeking. This is a matter of judgement, and experience will have a major impact in deciding which effects have a capital bearing on the solutions.

The foregoing may seem the obvious thing to do, but it is not always the easiest, if for no other reason than because the situations we are asked to study are more often than not unknown to us, at least in some of their crucial terms. This is why, in building up a mathematical model, we find it advantageous to visualize the behavior of unfamiliar systems on the basis of knowledge about the behavior of familiar systems, and of the expected resemblance of the former to the latter.

Unconsciously, this has been done since the beginning of civilization, only that bias has so often infiltrated into human thought that the distinction between scientific truth and pure imagination becomes impossible:

> . . . In accordance with the practice of trying to incorporate scientific principles as then known in narratives with a religious or an epic flavour, there was one version of the Creation epic which attempted to include the whole corpus of current astronomical knowledge by attributing to Marduk (the god of the gods, of its time) the creation of the heavenly bodies and of their movements . . .[1]

A basic practice of the research worker is to analyze past behavior of the system under study by considering historical data. From this analysis he may acquire enough background to build a tentative mathematical model. This is tested with actual data to see whether the obtained data are reasonable enough. The model, then, can be modified according-

---

[1] G. Contenau, "Everyday life in Babylon and Assyria." Arnold, London, 1954.

ly. This modified model needs to be tested again until a simulation close enough to reality results.

It must be appreciated that it is more often than not impossible to prove to one's own satisfaction that the performance of the model is a reasonable representation of the performance of the system being studied. The obvious check, of operating the model under conditions where the behavior of the actual equipment is known, is not very often the easy one to do. It can only be helpful under one set of conditions, certainly not when the equipment has not yet been built. We thus have to accept the hazard that the model may be in error. But this applies in every human action, particularly when we are planning for the future. It is a very familiar risk.

How close to reality a simulated model can be is subject to several constraints, among them time, cost, experience in this kind of study, knowledge of the workings of the simulated system, and the simplicity of the model itself. Another one of the obvious constraints concerning simulation studies has to do with the boundaries of its usage.

Models of mathematical simulation have been used to date

(i) *for purposes of experimentation or evaluation*, that is, in trying to predict the consequences of changes in policy, conditions, or methods without having to spend the money or take the risk of actually make the change in real life;

(ii) *as a means of learning about new systems* in order to redesign or refine them;

(iii) *as a tool in familiarizing personnel* with a system or a situation which may, as yet, not exist in real life;

(iv) *for the verification or demonstration* of a new idea, system, or approach; and

(v) *as a means for projecting into the future* and thus providing quantitative bases for planning and forecasting.

In all these areas, through the use of mathematical simulation, we can test plans, designs, or ideas and change them accordingly before putting a system into real terms. Through the use of electronic computers, the results of a year's operation, under different conditions and assumptions, can be obtained in a matter of hours. The operational ability of a certain plan, the efficiency of a design, or the impact of a certain course of action can be tested out. Simulation, therefore, is a powerful tool which cannot and should not be underestimated.

Classifying Simulators

One way of classifying simulators is by taking two dichotomies: data generation versus data reduction and guidance versus calculation. This is shown in Fig. 1.

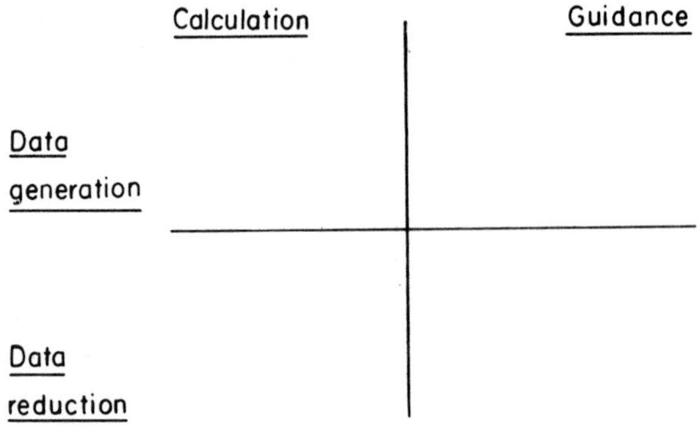

FIG. 1

In the "data generation–calculation" quarter-space lies much of the engineering usage of simulation, and its applicability in problems of physics. The data reduction–calculation quarter-space includes much of the statistical work and a great deal of abstracting procedures. Spaced flight simulators for study and research and mathematical models built for the control of real-time systems[2] can conveniently be placed in the data generation–guidance quarter-space. Finally, certain mathematical models, like the one developed for satellite tracking, belong to the guidance–data reduction domain.

A clarification is due at this point. In the beginning of this chapter, simulation was defined as a *working analogy*. Throughout this work, we will stick to this definition with particular emphasis on mathematical, digital, or numerical simulation. This has not always been the use of the word "simulation" though predominently it is the case today.

In the prewar period, the term "simulation" was uniquely associated with the analog means of calculation. This brings into perspective the distinction between analog and digital simulation. To understand the difference it suffices to make reference to the manner in which the Pythagorians reviewed mathematics. They considered a major division

---

[2] For instance such as the Westinghouse-TVA power production and distribution simulator, also known as the "economic load program." See chapter 23.

into "discrete" and "continued," each of these domains being further subdivided into the others (see Fig. 2).

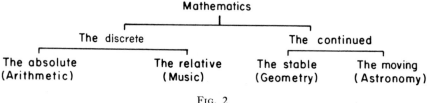

FIG. 2

Analog simulation[3] is based on continuous measurements made on a scale model of the system under study. Inversely, *digital simulation* involves discrete measurements obtained by processing a mathematical model on, say, a digital computer. Between these two situations there exist hybrids. General-purpose analog computers can be used to advantage for the analysis of equations or functions which represent physical systems. These physical systems can be anything from the flight of airplanes to the fission process in an atomic reactor.

The distinction between analog and digital simulation might be compared with the distinction we are accustomed to making between analog and digital computing devices. In general terms, existing computing machinery can be classified as digital computers, which deal with discrete entities (numbers), or analog computers, which deal with continuous physical variables. Both the analog and the digital machines can be subdivided.

In the digital-machines category we include both general- and special-purpose devices. These devices can be mechanical, electrical-electronic, or hybrid. A desk calculator is an example of a mechanical general-purpose piece of equipment. This distinction is shown in Fig. 3.

Within the class of analog machines we distinguish those working on the principle of direct analogy and those working by means of indirect analogy. Direct analogy is characterized by cases where problem variables and problem parameters are represented directly by variables and parameters on the machine. The mechanical direct analog computers are generally scale models such as wind-tunnel models, models of boats, hydroelectric works in miniature, and the like. Examples of electrical direct analogs are the network analyzer and equivalent circuits.

An example of mechanical indirect analog computer is the slide rule, where lengths on a stick are analogous to numbers. Nomograms belong

---

[3] See Part VII, Simulation by Analog Means.

also to this class. The electrical and electronic analog computer is the most common of the indirect type. It employs high gain amplifiers which, when applied in appropriate feedback loops, will perform mathe-

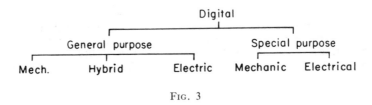

FIG. 3

matical operations. Analog computers as a class can be subdivided as shown in Fig. 4.

Simulation through analog computers is based on continuous measurement. The cost of analog computations, and for that matter simulation, increases in an almost logarithmic scale as the size of the problem or the

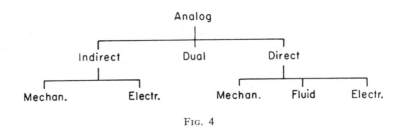

FIG. 4

required precision increases. Nevertheless, the researcher should not lose from perspective the fact that analog simulation has offered thus far a major service to the solution of technological and scientific problems.[4] The two approaches should be viewed as complementary rather than as strictly competitive.

Today, mostly because of the availability of high speed, high accuracy calculation media, digital computation may offer a larger potential for simulation studies than its analog counterpart. For this reason, our interest in the present work focuses primarily on digital processing, and the terms "mathematical simulation" and "digital simulation" are

---

[4] The writer has performed a major management research project on an analog computer. For reference see D. N. Chorafas, "Operations Research for Industrial Management." Reinhold, New York, 1958 and D. N. Chorafas, "Nouvelles Méthodes d'Analyse Économique," Edition Dunod, Paris, 1963.

used almost interchangably.[5] Furthermore, since the initial requirement in any such simulation problem is the derivation of the equations of the system, this will attract much of our attention.

Approaches to Simulation

One of the first realizations that comes to the mathematician, the physicist, or the engineer about to develop a simulation procedure is the lack of clear-cut approaches to simulation. This is both a challenge and a constraint. It is a constraint mostly in terms of time, effort, and expenditures, required because of the lack of well-established ways and means. It is a challenge because it opens to the researcher wide horizons for using his imagination. In simulation studies, the researcher is very much a discoverer of unknown domains and of new properties.

To start with, the researcher is faced with the need for making the appropriate abstractions when he characterizes an ensemble. The problem of mathematically describing a practical situation in precise and meaningful terms is often referred to as "model-making." Mathematical models describe the equilibrium conditions among significant system variables. They can be either static or dynamic. The variables themselves can be deterministic or probabilistic. Their choice and the establishment of the logical structure are of capital importance.

This leads us to the consideration of the first basic requirement of simulation studies, that of mathematical abstraction and its relation to physical reality. The impact of abstraction on the outcome of a certain simulation project is so great that we devoted to its treatment the whole first chapter of the present work. At this point it suffices to briefly consider the dangers which are present when the researcher fails to properly weigh factors and events.

Assume that the researcher is concerned with the definition of military response to a class of limited war situations. This definition must be made before military requirements (objectives and specifications) can be derived.[6] Hence the risks involved are deviations caused by unforeseen events. Furthermore, though the military requirements and the behavior

---

[5] The reader should also be aware of another distinction in the usage of the word "simulation." The term "Monte Carlo method" is sometimes used as a synonym for simulation. This is not a recommended practice. The Monte Carlo method, which was primarily a tool of the nuclear physicist, has today a much broader spectrum of applicabilities among operational research workers, and the mixing of terms may be, for him, confusing.

[6] Model-making for military systems is discussed in Chapter 17.

of the military system in specific situations can and will be treated quantitatively, the structure describing the interrelationship between political and military factors will be primarily logical. Their impact may be such as to reverse what a straight quantitative evaluation could prove. The process of abstraction would undoubtedly fail if all these possibilities were not given the proper weight.

If the first fundamental ingredient of mathematical simulation is that of abstraction, the second is the attitude of approximation. Classical mechanics has established in an excellent manner time-dependent processes. On the basis of its success, many deterministic models have been developed. Nevertheless, stochastic thinking has shown that natural and man-made systems are governed by probabilistic rather than by deterministic relationships. Researchers began to wonder how and to what degree the setting of certain parameters influences the value of other parameters in the system. If there is no influence, we say that independence exists. If there is an influence, we have a case of dependence, of stochastic liaison, of correlation.

Bernoulli had shown that through a mathematical study of samples we may succeed in knowing certain characteristics of the population from which the sample is drawn.[7] Sampling procedures, by their very nature, unsettle the foundations of the deterministic concept. Developments in the field of mathematical statistics help document this point. Scientists began to understand the shortcomings and insufficiencies of the deterministic approach. Even if, at a certain level, deterministic models represent an important part of the observed phenomena, the complexities of the "real" situation always add a stochastic part.

Simulators can be made of a basically stochastic or of a deterministic nature. There exist two dichotomies (Fig. 5). We can have a deterministic simulator of a probabilistic real system or vice versa. We can have a

Simulator

		Deterministic	Probabilistic
Real system	Deterministic		
	Probabilistic		

FIG. 5

---

[7] See D. N. Chorafas, "Statistical Processes and Reliability Engineering." Van Nostrand, Princeton, New Jersey, 1960.

deterministic model of a deterministic system or a probabilistic model of a probabilistic system.

An example of a deterministic–deterministic relationship is the study of a large number of variants, for example, of trajectories of missiles or of orbits of satellites. An example of a probabilistic–probabilistic relationship is the simulation of queues such as those created by road traffic, servicing, etc. In the domain deterministic (real)–probabilistic (model) belongs the use of Monte Carlo for the solution, say, of a complicated electrical network. This example gives one of the most powerful uses of stochastic models in deterministic real problems. Finally, in the probabilistic (real)–deterministic (model) domain belong the historical tables of statistics which (as is usually the case) present only the mean and not the variance of a distribution. Such is the case with mortality tables, failure statistics, and the like.

The use of deterministic models for probabilistic real situations or vice-versa involves a certain approximation. Even so, however, when approximations are under the control of the researcher and the user, model-making can be of major advantage in studies of natural and of man-made systems. The partial forecast, limited to a certain domain and to a certain level of precision, is within the realm of scientific thinking. Inversely, the absolute and total prevision, derived by dogmatic determinism, is contrary to the very basis of science. "Totality" by its own nature is too inflexible, and it overlooks the universal principle of change and of innovation.

Much of the misconception about the importance of probabilistic models stems from a misunderstanding of the words "random" and "randomness." When we say an event occurs at random we mean that to an outside observer, one not "in the know," the pattern of events is consistent with, and indistinguishable from, a truly random one. The point to emphasize is that an event may be planned, and known to those concerned, and yet it may appear quite a matter of chance to the outsider.

If the occurence of such an event is indistinguishable from a random one then it may be simulated by one really chosen at random. This is of course a matter of opinion, and not of fact, and one may well disagree. Not only does the successful application of stochastic principles depend upon the validity of this assumption, but so does the whole area of probabilistic studies.

The Process of Taking Risks

We have talked about certain basic characteristics concerning the nature of simulation studies. These studies can vary greatly as to nature and objective, but they do have one inherent fact in common: in order to experiment, the researcher, scientist, or designer must hypothesize.

Let's define *hypothesis* as a tentative statement or supposition made to explain certain facts or to lead to investigation by others. This definition leads us to the very fact that, while a certain mathematical model may be made to prove or disprove a hypothesis, that model itself, in its construction, may have required the making of a hypothesis which could very well be unproved.

> . . . Hypotheses are valuable and necessary instruments of the human mind for its dual task of adding to and organizing its knowledge. But they become dangerous when they are erected into absolute affirmations or dogmas, and pernicious when they claim immunity from constant testing against fact. . . .[8]

For instance, consider a mathematical simulator made to test the outcome of a Third World War. Say that the particular hypothesis to be tested is the effectiveness of the continental air defense system. A substantial number of other tentative statements have to be made before a simulator can be constructed, and that's where the trouble starts.

Some of the tentative statements in question have to do with the specific plan the enemy would choose to follow, and its variations. Nothing more uncertain than that! Other suppositions will be relative to the "product mix" the enemy would choose for his attacking force. Facts which are equally uncertain and very rarely predictable. Yet the value of the hypothesis concerning the defenses, which is closer to being under the control of the experimenter, may be no better. The efficiency of those defenses is in itself a matter of speculation and surely a function of the product mix and the strategy the enemy will follow. Add to this some wishful thinking and you have an idea of what can develop.

> . . . In this, there is a lesson for all other aspects of existence. The scientific method of the working hypothesis, as the only gateway to the erection of comprehensive theories, laws, and principles, to the establishment of firmer knowledge, and to the securing of more successful practice and better control of nature, can and should be utilized in other spheres—in morals, in politics, in social affairs, in religion.
>
> In other words, any new ideology must not be dogmatic, and must refrain from any claim to absoluteness or completeness; it must utilize scientific method, so as to be expansive, flexible, and unitive instead of rigid and eventually restrictive or divisive. Tolerance, respect for cultural and individual variety, acceptance of difference—these are some of the counterparts of the scientific method in other fields. However, they themselves should not be employed rigidly or in any absolute sense, but in the same sort of way that the principle of the working hypothesis is applied in the natural science.[8]

---

[8] J. Huxley, "New Bottles for New Wine." Chatto and Windus, London, 1957.

In any work, hypotheses are proved through experimentation, and this requires a careful collection, reduction, and evaluation of data. An observation has value only when it can provide a basis for interpretation. An interpretation can be done only on the basis of a hypothesis which is to be proved or disproved. We must predecide what comes in relation with the variables under study and how it affects them. Will the rains come because of a sacrifice to the gods?

In this framework of scientific research and evaluation the naked fact is only a sign as far as inference is concerned. Science works in large numbers. No single sign should ever be taken on its own merit as the weighting factor of a scientific decision. Data can only be considered in the cumulative. And this is not all. Facts are useless to science unless they are well understood and their relationships settled. An aspect of scientific research often overlooked is that the observed fact is a property not only of the system under observation but also of the coupling "system–measuring instrument." The researcher should be well aware of these fundamentals.

Uncertainty is not a characteristic peculiar to simulation work. In certain "established" sciences such as physics, proved hypotheses become laws and theories. With time we come to regard them as indisputable, confirmed by a substanial number of verifications. Yet how often theories are disproved, reversed by new evidence, and challenged by a completely different way of looking at the facts. Theories no longer represent the "maximum certitude" that might exist in scientific affairs. Theories are themselves subject to variance and change.

Nothing is terribly new in this approach, except the approach itself. There always existed enlightened scientists who had a deep doubt of everything around them. But there also existed others (a large majority) who favored the easy, dogmatic way; who preferred using a "legend" to formulating a hypothesis. Hence, when we say that the experimental method "develops" its own discipline we mean that, as a function of time, it is going from the metaphysical expectation to the hypothesis, from the single observation to the statistical treatment of experimental data, from the verbal theory to the theory which is mathematically formulated, and that this happens on a broadly accepted basis.

In all, the process of scientific investigation and experimentation can be visualized in a series of distinct well-established steps:

(i) Define the problem.

(ii) Locate the strategic variables.

(iii) Determine the relation of these variables to the parameters of the system.

  (iv) Formulate a hypothesis regarding the conditions being examined.
   (v) Form a mathematical or other model of analogy.
  (vi) Design and administer one or several experiments, as the situation demands.
 (vii) Test the hypothesis.
(viii) Evaluate the hypothesis according to the outcome of the experiment(s).
  (ix) Accept or reject the hypothesis and state the diagnosis.
   (x) Forecast future developments and systems interactions.
  (xi) Prescribe a course of action.
 (xii) Proceed with a follow-up phase, taking corrective action as necessary.

When the results of an experiment are on hand, the problem of scientific generalization arises. A decision is required on how widely applicable the obtained results are. Several factors can influence the possibility of generalizing. Their nature usually depends on the nature of the experimental approach. For instance, in statistical experimentation we are mostly concerned with four major factors:

  (a) the sample and how representative it is of a given population,
  (b) the task used in the experiment (what may be true in learning to count may not hold true in learning the analysis and synthesis of servomechanisms),
  (c) the specific conditions prevailing in the experiment,
  (d) the dimensional extremities (usually dimensional extremities "bring in" variables other than those under study).

The more the generalization exceeds the conditions and subjects on which the principle was derived, the larger will be the probable error in its wider application.

In most engineering and scientific work the limitations of the method can be overcome by an enlightened approach on the part of the experimenter. This is exactly why we so often stress that the systems analyst should be a wizard in his ability to design and administer experiments, to develop models, and to evaluate alternative designs. He should be a man willing to listen to every suggestion but determined to judge for himself. He should not be biased by appearance; have no favorite hypothesis; be of no school; and in doctrine have no master. Perhaps no man fits the words of George Bernard Shaw better than the researcher: "Never lend, never gamble, never marry, and never take anybody's advice."

CHAPTER 3

Developing and Using Models

In the first and second chapters of the present work, we established that the objective of simulation studies is the analysis of some real process (natural or technological) by mathematical means. This in turn requires the formulation of a mathematical model of the process being investigated. The model might be a mathematical expression in which the variables behave in a fashion similar to the actual system. It might contain elements of chance, weighting various probable actions of two or more "players," as in gaming; or it might represent the actual variables of the interdependent parts of a working ensemble.

In all, four points are of fundamental importance to the practice of any type of operational analysis:

   (i) the role of experimentation,

   (ii) the model,

   (iii) the measures of effectiveness, and

   (iv) the criteria for the decision.

These points need to be well established and their interrelation understood. They have a major bearing on system design and on operational planning in general. The criteria for decision would orientate the choice for the most efficient parameters. This is usually called *optimization*. It amounts to the selection of the best from among a number of possible situations or configurations.

The quantitative choice shapes up by expressing a performance quality function, a figure of merit, a utility function, or a payoff in terms of the appropriate variables. This becomes possible because of the very fact that the results of simulation studies are of a quantitative nature. They provide an opportunity for sound estimates of requirements, objectives, and goals and a basis for a more precise choice in design, planning, and decision making.

We said that there exist certain common characteristics among the problems suitable for operational analysis, such as an opportunity to decide among alternative courses of action and the possibility of quantitatively studing and measuring the system. To strengthen the payoff from

27

experimentation, we should add that it must be reasonably possible to collect data, and it should be feasible to evaluate results. These requirements have to do with the first and the third of the foregoing four basic points.

More precisely, the role mathematical experimentation can play is definitely a function of the problem at hand, of the skill of the experimenter, of the time and money to be invested, and of the model itself. The original problem should be continuously kept in mind. A very common fault is losing sight of the primary objective. Another fault is proceeding with insufficient data of the past behavior of the system. Human skill is needed mainly when questions that have to be weighted come up and when new factors, which may have to be introduced into the model, reveal themselves.

Evaluating Mathematical Media

While praising the many benefits to be derived from the experimental approach, we must also caution the reader as to its limitation. It is a limitation, for instance, that, although simulation studies are of a basically quantitative nature, in practice there exist qualitative factors that must also be taken into consideration. Equally, it is a limitation that while analytic techniques require unbiased reliable facts about the operations under study, very often only personal opinions are available to serve as the basis or sole source of information. Such is the case with certain mathematical media employed in simulation problems which make it necessary to oversimplify complex real life situations.

To these limitations might be added a certain human tendency to either overdetermine or underdetermine criteria. The criteria used in operational analysis must not be overdetermined (for instance asking maximum results for minimum cost) and should not be underdetermined or ambiguous (i.e., specifying "most efficient system" or "lowest cost system"). The criteria must not use implicit absurd evaluations of some inputs or parameters (i.e., treat valuable scarce inputs as free goods), and they should not ignore time (i.e., fail to consider how the attractiveness of alternatives changes with time).

The criteria to be used in experimentation must not ignore uncertainty, and they should take into account the effects of operations other than the one being studied. Yet, none of these limitations could be worse than the unchallenged use of certain prefabricated or "prototype" mathematical models.

We have defined a *model* as a simplified representation of an operation in the problem under study. Yet the word "simplified" does not necessarily mean simple and above all it does not mean an "all weather" formula. What we essentially mean is that, through the use of mathematical simulation, the experimenter is able to bring a complex problem into a proper perspective. He can then operate on this problem and optimize it, in the sense we have considered.

That is to say, instead of going straight from the original problem to its solution (Fig. 1), which may be tedious and unrevealing of basic

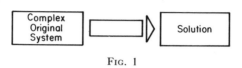

FIG. 1

facts, the experimenter uses the indirect approach of a mathematical model (Fig. 2). The idea behind this "transformation" is not new.

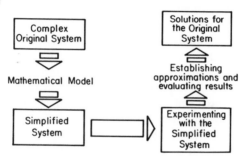

FIG. 2

The design engineer uses it in his everyday work from the analysis of servomechanism to the simple case of the logarithm and of its inverse, the antilogarithm. But, while the same mathematical tools are available to everybody, a great difference results from the ingenuity of the man who chooses and applies them. His method, skill, patience, and creative imagination all contribute to the final outcome.

In experimental work, there are no short-cuts or "tested universal approaches," unless one wishes to take the risk of failing blindly in his task. There exist no substitutes for the fundamental step-by-step approach we have mentioned:

(i) *Define the problem.*

(ii) *Collect operational data.* (Analyze possible failures in the data recording system, and in some cases devise a new recording system that will provide appropriate data.)

(iii) *Determine the dependence on operational parameters.* (Analyze the chance fluctuations of operations to give an insight into the statistical dependence of the results on the various pertinent operational parameters.)

(iv) *Devise an operational experiment.* (For instance, change parameters so as to learn actual effect on results.)

(v) *Narrow operational parameters* (to those to which the results are most sensitive).

(vi) *Be aware of the limitations of the method.*

And we have already said that mathematical experimentation also has its pitfalls and its dangers. One major danger lies in the tendency to distort a real situation; that is the situation present in a physical or technological system. Distortions are often made in order to fit a certain available model. The practice is unwise, even if expedient. As contrasted to the usage of prototype models, such as linear programming, simulation studies require rather tedious procedures, since it is necessary to develop custom-made mathematical equations able to fit the real system.

Another pitfall in mathematical experimentation lies in the human bias on linearities. This is particularly true when the proper hypothesis and assumptions have not bean clearly stated in advance.[1] Somehow, we have come to believe that linear relationships prevail in the world around us. Nothing could be more untrue. Yet, this false belief has conditioned our method of work to the extent that most of the analytic techniques which have been favored in the past were based on sets of linear equations. From this fact alone, mistakes and distortions have arisen.[2]

But the cautioning about the inadequacy of linearities and prototype models should not be interpreted as an urge to complexity. Quite contrary to this, the designer must remember that the over-all simplicity of the system is most important. It is this over-all simplicity which can bring into proper perspective the crucial factors underlying the system performance. It is this over-all simplicity which would allow the experimenter to determine the optimum among alternative designs. And it is again this over-all simplicity which will permit the study of details without losing the whole from view.

---

[1] The emphasis is placed particularly on the uncontrolled use of substitutes and approximations. At times the experimenter is free to develop the method he likes provided he clearly understands its limitations and the possibilities it offers to him.

[2] See, in Chapter 4, the discussion on linearities and nonlinearities.

Another pitfall quite common in experimentation is the belief that the making of a mathematical model completes the experimenter's task. This is not true. The development of a model does not complete the work of the researcher. After being developed, the model must be used with past data to see how closely it approximates the reproduction of such data. Only if and when this reproduction is close enough to the original information can the model be used for experimentation with some reasonable assurance of success.

Furthermore, even if the researcher believes he has made a "perfect model," follow-up is absolutely necessary. Follow-up is a never-ending activity. It has to do with the upkeep of a simulator, with both its accuracy and its economic utilization. We have put due emphasis on the required accuracy of a model. In what regards the particular detail in calculations, it is advisable to favor such detail only in reference to operations which are economically important. Accuracy of representation should be mostly stressed in the important operational areas, and this importance needs to be continuously evaluated in terms of financial or technological criteria.

But if the follow-up work to be done after a certain model is made seems important, other efforts following the development of a simulator can be even more voluminous. In the introduction to this chapter we talked about measures of effectiveness. More often than not these measures need to be established before the simulation begins. Yet, at times, a careful evaluation of the whole system after the first experimentations may reveal other criteria for optimization. It may be, for instance, that those conditions that provide a basis for minimum cost inhibit flexibility and thus harm the system's operational features in the long run. It may be that the criteria initially established are invalid, either because of lack of experience or because of changing conditions. Any such happening calls, simply, for rework.

Accuracy, flexibility, upkeep, and the desire never to lose from sight total systems characteristics and the final objective are the major reasons why we advised on a simplified approach to model-making. Basically, a mathematical model should be

(i) simple enough for manipulation and understanding by these who would use it,

(ii) representative enough, in the total range of the implications it may have, and

(iii) complex enough to accurately represent the system under study.

Transformations and Invariance

Perhaps no other case can better exemplify the power inherent in the use of mathematical models for study and research than the theory of algebraic invariantes. This theory, from which the concept of invariance has grown, originated from a relatively simple observation. The earliest instance of the idea appears in the work of Lagrange, and was later continued by Gauss. It is likely that neither Lagrange nor Gauss noticed that this simple but remarkable algebraic phenomenon was the basis of an important theory. Even Boole seems not to have fully realized the importance of what he found when he carried on and greatly extended the work of Lagrange.

This "simple observation" in question is as follows.

A necessary and sufficient condition that the equation

$$ax^2 + 2bx + c = 0$$

have two equal roots is that $b^2 - ac$ be equal to zero. Let us replace the variable x by its value in terms of y obtained by the transformation $y = (px + q)/(rx + s)$. This gives

$$x = (q - sy)/(ry - p).$$

Replacing x by its value in the original quadratic equation, we obtain a new equation:

$$Ay^2 + 2By + C = 0.$$

The coefficients A, B, C can be expressed in terms a, b, c:

$$A = as^2 - 2bsr + cr^2,$$
$$B = -aqs + b(qr + sp) - cpr,$$
$$C = aq^2 - 2bpq + cb^2.$$

It is then easy to show that

$$B^2 - AC = (ps - qr)^2(b^2 - ac)$$

where $b^2 - ac$ is the discriminant of the quadratic equation in x. Correspondingly, the discriminant of the quadratic equation in y is $B^2 - AC$. Thus the discriminant of the transformed equation is equal to the discriminant of the original equation times the factor $(ps - qr)^2$, which depends only upon the coefficients p, q, r, s, inherent in the transformation $y = (px + q)/(rx + s)$.

Boole was the first (in 1841) to observe that every algebraic equation has a discriminant, that is, a certain expression (such as $b^2 - ac$ for the quadratic) which is equal to zero if, and only if, two or more roots of the equation are equal. Boole first examined whether the discriminant of every equation, when its x is replaced by a related y (as was done for the quadratic), comes back unchanged except for a factor depending only on the coefficients of the transformation. He found that this was true. Next he examined whether there might not be expressions other than discriminants constructed from the coefficients having this same property of invariance under transformation. He found two such cases for the general equation of the fourth degree.

Eisenstein, following up a result of Boole's analysis, discovered, in 1844, that certain expressions involving both the coefficients and the x of the original equations exhibit the same sort of invariance, the original coefficients and the original x pass into the transformed coefficients and y (as for the quadratic). The expressions in question, which are constructed from the originals, differ from those expressions which are constructed from the transforms only by a factor depending solely on the coefficients of the transformation.

Neither Boole nor Eisenstein had any general method for finding such invariant expressions. Cayley, in 1845, set the problem of finding uniform methods which would give all the invariant expressions of the kind described.

For an illustration which does not involve any symbols or algebra, imagine any figure consisting of intersecting straight lines and curves drawn on a sheet of paper. Crumple the paper in any way you please without tearing it, and try to think what is the most obvious property of the figure that is the same before and after crumpling. Do the same for any figure drawn on a sheet of rubber, stretching but not tearing the rubber. It is obvious that sizes of areas and angles, and lengths of lines, have not remained invariant.

By suitably stretching the rubber the straight lines may be distorted into curves of almost any curvature one likes, and at the same time the original curves or at least some of them may be transformed into straight lines. Yet something about the whole figure has remained unchanged. Its very simplicity and obviousness might well cause it to be overlooked. In fact, what is unchanged is the order of the points on any one of the lines of the figure which mark the places where other lines intersect the given one. Thus, if moving the pencil along a given line from A to C we had to pass over the point B on the line before the figure was distorted, we shall have to pass over B in going from A to C after distortion. The order (as described) is an invariant under the particular transformations of the sheet of paper or of the sheet of rubber.

This illustration may seem trivial, but the intersections of world-lines in general relativity (where intersection of two such lines marks a physical point-event) is not much different in what regards the fundamental concepts. The mathematical approach powerful enough to handle such complicated transformations and to analyze the concepts of invariants was the contribution of many research workers, including Riemann, Christoffel, Ricci, Levi-Civita, Lie, and Einstein. The whole work was originated by the early workers in the theory of algebraic invariants, of which Cayley and Sylvester were the founders.

For a second example, imagine a knot to be looped in a string whose ends are then tied together. Pulling the knot, and running it along the string, we distort it into any number of "shapes." The question then is: What remains invariant?" In other words, "What is conserved under all these distortions which in the present case represent the transformations?" Obviously neither the shape nor the size of the knot is invariant. But the "style" of the knot itself is invariant; in a sense that need not be elaborated; it is the same sort of a knot whatever we do to the string provided we do not untie its ends. Again, in "past-day" physics, energy was "conserved"; the total amount of energy in the universe was assumed to be an invariant, the same under all transformations from one form, such as electrical energy, into others, such as heat and light.

Consider the following case: An observer fixes his position in space and time with reference to three mutually perpendicular axes and a standard timepiece. Another observer, moving relative to the first, wishes to describe the same physical event that the first describes. He also has the space-time reference system. His movement relative to the first observer can be expressed as a transformation of his own coordinates, or of the coordinates of the other observer.

The descriptions given by the two observers may or may not differ in mathematical form, according to the particular kind of transformation concerned. If their descriptions do differ, the difference is not, obviously, inherent in the physical event they are both observing, but in their reference systems and the transformation. The problem then is to formulate only those mathematical expressions of natural phenomena which shall be independent, mathematically, of any particular reference system, and therefore can be expressed by all observers in the same form. This is equivalent to finding the invariants of the transformation which express the most general shift in space-time of one reference system with respect to any other.

The analogies between the foregoing example and the case of mathematical simulation we are discussing are rather obvious. It suffices to repeat that this simple observation allows us to experiment with systems which, for the most part, may still be unborn or exist only in the creative imaginations of the designer.

The Dynamics of Model-Making

We said that whenever a working system is studied, either in part or in its totality, the interrelations and interaction among its subsystems and their components can be expressed in a mathematical form. To this expression we have given the name *model*, meaning a mathematical formula or set thereof. These formula(s), we explained, constitute a simplified representation of the system under study.

Consider, for instance, a simulation study for tool wear and tool replacement. The life of the tool between two subsequent breakdowns follows a negative exponential distribution, as shown by tests. After breaking down, a tool goes to the repair shop. The time the tool is away from the production department approximates a negative exponential distribution. A new product for order is given when the reorder level is reached for a specific tool.

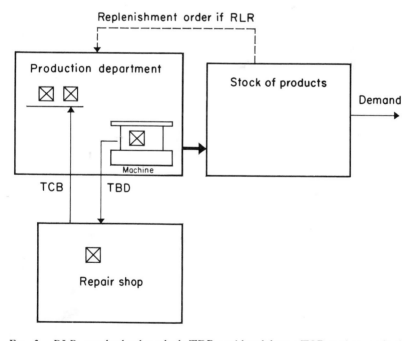

Fig. 3.   RLR, reorder level reached; TDB, tool breakdown; TCB, tool comes back.

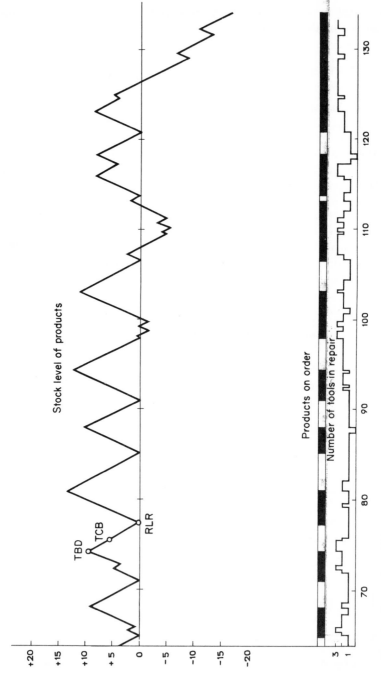

Fɪɢ. 4. Demand = 3200 products/day; toll life = 8000 products; time away = 8 shifts, 3 tools available, TBD = tool breaks down, TCB = tool comes back, RLR = reorder level reached.

The problem can be simply formulated as follows: "How many tools are necessary for uninterrupted operations?" The answer depends on four major factors, namely:

(i) number of machines available,

(ii) demand for tools,

(iii) the mean life of the tool,

(iv) the average time away of the tools in the repair shop.

Say that the production manager wants to find the answer to questions such as: "Does it pay to decrease time away by increasing the repair capacity of the shop?" or "How great is the influence of the life of a tool on the over-all operation of the production line?" Experimentation on a problem of this type has been accomplished by means of a computer-processed mathematical model. The machine program causes the computer to simulate what may happen on the production floor with respect to tool use, wear and tear, and the subsequent repair. This is done by taking data samples on tool demand and usage. A diagram of the work place is shown in Fig. 3.

To simplify the model, the experimenters assumed that the demand for tools on the production floor was constant and that the reaction time

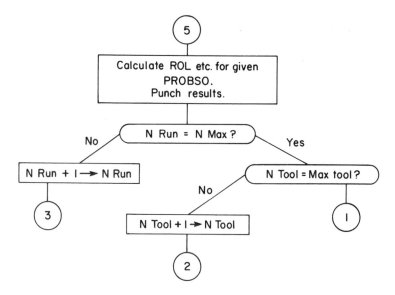

Fig. 5a. N TOOL is the number of tools available for a run; MIN TOOL, the minimum number of tools for which calculations have to be made; MAX TOOL, the maximum number of tools for which calculations have to be made; N RUN, serial number of this run.

was zero. Figure 4 shows a graphical representation of a part of a simulation run for an individual case. On the average, one year "real time" was simulated on a medium-size computer in two minutes. For this processing, the programming time was approximately one week. A flow chart of the computer program is given in Fig. 5.

The detailed data in Table I include an example of computer cal-

TABLE I

DATA COLLECTED FOR A SIMULATION STUDY OF TOOL WEAR AND TOOL REPLACEMENT[a]

Tools run	Reorder level (No. of units)	Reorder level (No. of days)	Proba-bility of a stock-out	Average negative stock of a stock-out (No. of units)	Average stock-out (No. of days)	Average period of time between two sub-sequent stock-outs (in days)
300001			.1580	10248	32	3125
300001	6400	2	.0730	12725	40	12500
300001	16000	5	.0460	7555	24	8333
300001	28800	9	.0052	1600	5	12500
300001	32000	10	.0002	1600	5	25000
300002			.0528	5527	17	8333
300002			.0528	5527	17	8333
300002	3200	1	.0340	4499	14	8333
300002	9600	3	.0080	3120	10	25000
300002	16000	5	.0002	1600	5	25000
300003			.2164	4359	14	1388
300003	6400	2	.0504	3873	12	3571
300003	9600	3	.0218	3655	11	8333
300003	12800	4	.0092	3269	10	8333
300003	19200	6	.0006	1600	5	25000
300004			.2082	18298	57	4166
300004	12800	4	.0972	19845	62	8333
300004	28800	9	.0488	15856	50	25000
300004	54400	17	.0080	2960	9	25000
300004	60800	19	.0002	1600	5	25000

[a] Production rate, 3500; rate of demand for new products per day, 3200; minimum lot size, 18 400; maximum lot size, 55 000; average tool life in units of products, 8000; time away of tools for repair, in number of shifts, 8; machines available for this particular product, 1; No. of shifts per day in the production department, 2; No. of shifts per day in the repair shop, 2; number of days the experiment was run, 250; first random number used, 4088977143.

TABLE I [*cont.*]

300005			.3296	11877	37	2083
300005	19200	6	.0818	6346	20	5000
300005	25600	8	.0334	4876	15	5000
300005	32000	10	.0090	3733	12	25000
300005	38400	12	.0008	1600	5	25000
400001			.0934	4348	14	5000
400001			.0934	4348	14	5000
400001	3200	1	.0492	3616	11	3125
400001	9600	3	.0074	2205	7	12500
400001	16000	5	.0002	1600	5	25000
400002			.0572	5740	18	5000
400002			.0572	5740	18	5000
400002	3200	1	.0332	5532	17	8333
400002	12800	4	.0086	2344	7	12500
400002	19200	6	.0002	1600	5	25000
400003			.1384	3477	11	2083
400003	3200	1	.0618	2604	8	2500
400003	6400	2	.0172	2009	6	6250
400003	9600	3	.0022	1600	5	25000
400003	12800	4	.0002	1600	5	25000
400004			.0168	2171	7	6250
400004			.0168	2171	7	6250
400004			.0168	2171	7	6250
400004	3200	1	.0030	1600	5	25000
400004	6400	2	.0002	1600	5	25000
400005			.1012	6362	20	4166
400005	3200	1	.0730	5002	16	5000
400005	6400	2	.0410	4456	14	4166
400005	16000	5	.0054	2074	6	12500
400005	19200	6	.0008	1600	5	25000

culations with ten runs. This information is graphically presented in Figs. 6 and 7. Table II indicates the resulting necessary number of tools, using as parameters *time away* (4 and 2 days) and *one-machine, many-machine* suppositions. With the available quantitative data on hand, the research workers concluded that it is financially advantageous to use a larger number of tools, correspondingly decreasing waiting times in the repair shop. They also concluded that the influence of special priority rules, in current use, should not be taken for granted but need to be investigated.

The subject experimentation provided data through which the influence of average life of a tool and the number of tools needed became quantitatively established. Nevertheless, the obtained solutions,

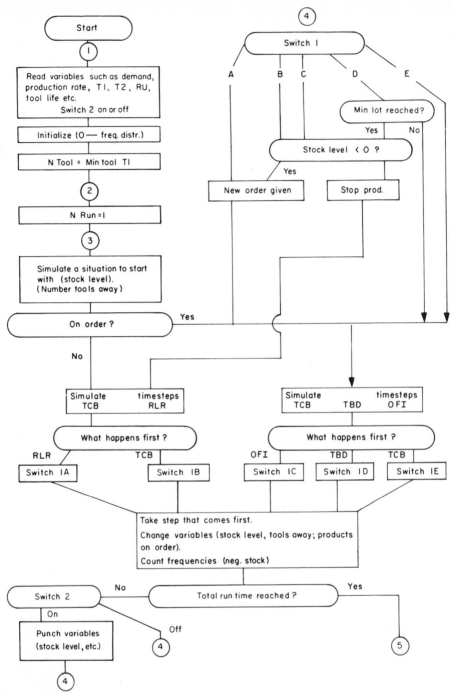

FIG. 5b. TCB, tool comes back; RLR, reorder level reached; OFI, order finished (because MAX LOT has been produced); TBD, tool breaks down.

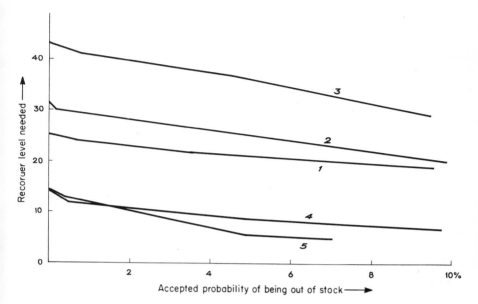

FIG. 6.   Relationship between accepted probability of being out of stock and the needed reorder level. Demand = 3200 products/day, tool life = 8000 products, time away = 8 shifts, 3 tools available.

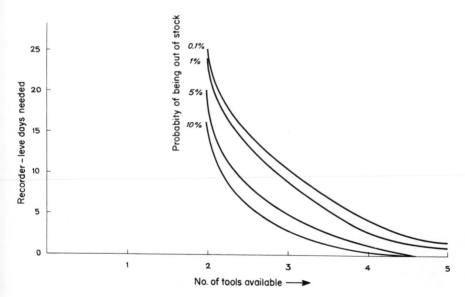

FIG. 7.   Inventory of products versus inventory of tools. Demand = 3200 products/day, tool life = 8000 products, time away = 8 shifts.

although valid at the moment of their calculation, were subject to obsolescence because of changing conditions in the production process.

TABLE II

NUMBER OF TOOLS NEEDED

Demand	No. of tools needed (one machine)			No. of tools needed (many machines)		
	Mean tool life in units of product			Mean tool life in units of product		
	40 000–10 000	10 000–4000	4000–2000	40 000–10 000	10 000–4000	4000–2000
Time away = 4 days						
6400–7200	7	10	10	5	8	12
5600–6400	6	9	14	5	7	11
4800–5600	5	8	12	4	7	10
4000–4800	5	7	10	3	6	9
3200–4000	4	6	9	3	5	8
2400–3200	3	5	8	2	5	6
1600–2400	3	4	6	2	4	5
800–1600	2	3	5	2	3	3
0–800	1	2	3	1	2	2
Time away = 2 days						
6400–7200	6	8	10	4	6	6
5600–6400	4	7	9	3	5	6
4800–5600	3	6	8	2	5	6
4000–4800	3	5	7	2	4	6
3200–4000	2	4	6	2	4	5
2400–3200	2	4	5	1	3	4
1600–2400	2	3	4	1	3	3
800–1600	1	2	3	1	2	2
0–800	1	1	2	1	1	1

This obsolescence of the computed data brings into proper perspective a very important point in experimentation. One of the major problems in the development of mathematical models for operational systems is that these systems are basically dynamic. New processes are added while others are abandoned. Alternate uses are found for existing units. New products are demanded and their production may completely change the nature of the existing facilities. New units are built to relieve existing units; bottlenecks are removed, thereby increasing the capacity of a certain process. As new data are obtained, the method of predicting the behavior of a system may change radically.

In production, for instance, a number of factors which are beyond the control of the experimenter can rot a simulator. The availability, cost, and quality of input commodities to a production process, such as skilled labor and raw materials, change. The demand, quality, and market value of products produced also vary. And we have already mentioned the changes in manufacturing facilities. All of these factors must be considered in the preparation of a simulator, and provisions must be made for the necessary alterations as a function of time.

As the changes in the industrial environment take place, the extent of information desired and required to define activity for any given period increases. This distinct requirement for data collection is relative to the diagnostic powers a certain simulator may have in order to assist its own upkeep. Equally important is that, when a model is prepared, provisions be made for omitting certain specific calculations, or adding others as the occasion demands.

The effective use of statistical data-sampling techniques can help in minimizing the volume of required information. It can also contribute to an increase in accuracy through a careful control of conditions in obtaining the experimental data. As for the calculation media, we will pay due attention to the role of a computer in simulation when we talk about handling and processing data and equations.

Pitfalls in Experimentation

We have made frequent reference to the fact that every single effort in simulation is not necessarily successful, that there exist many failures, mostly resulting from the experimenter's unawareness of or lack of care for the pitfalls he may encounter. The generic reasons behind pitfalls and failures in simulation vary widely. Of all reasons, one of the most dreadful is the misconception by the researcher of the nature of the problem itself. Many failures could be traced to this source. It exists because many researchers and consultants in this field have neither the background nor the patience to correctly analyze the situation they are faced with.

As an example of a fatal simulation let us look at a study made, not long ago, by a management consultant for one of his clients. The client, a medium size manufacturing firm, was a family-held company. Its Board of Directors was faced with the decision of whether or not the holding family should release control in order to get a major bank loan.

The need for this loan came about when the company laboratories developed a brand new product whose manufacture and distribution were, nevertheless, outside the main line of the enterprise. For reasons of identification, we will call this concern the Delta Industries.

With the money to be obtained from the bank loan, if this course were chosen, the Delta Industries could complete the developmental stage of the product, build a new factory of enough capacity to meet the anticipated demand, and set up the nation-wide distribution network management considered necessary. At least a minor portion of the loan would have been used for equipment renewal in the other two plants the company owned. The Board of Directors was divided on whether or not to take the bank loan. The consultant, presumably a mathematical analysis expert, who was called into the picture, set forth five alternative courses of action for the management:

(1) Take the loan at the expense of majority ownership, the holding family. With this, company management could proceed with the expansion plans.

(2) Do not take the loan. Continue as before and abandon the new product.

(3) Do not take the loan. Sell one of the two factories to raise enough capital and launch the distribution network. Subcontract the manufacturing of the new product.

(4) Do not take the loan. Convert one of the two factories, through internal financing, for the manufacture of the new product. Instead of developing a new distribution network, establish one in accordance with independent dealerships.

(5) Do not take the loan. Proceed with the new product through a subsidiary company established jointly with another manufacturing concern. (There was no indication of the source from which the money would come, nor if such interest was already expressed by another manufacturer.)

Having established these alternatives, the consultant directed his efforts to the construction of a mathematical model which would project the kind of benefits the company could derive from each of the courses of action. There is much to say about the incompleteness of the model itself, about its shaky mathematics, its failure to clearly state the assumptions made, and its omission of any consideration of the reasonableness of the various forecasts. But this is beyond the point, because this study was a failure even before the mathematics of the simulator were tackled.

To start with, it is superficial to mix generically different solutions.

The problem facing the Board of Directors was whether or not the family should release financial control of the Delta Industries. To the affirmative answer corresponded solution (1), to the negative solutions (2) to (5). These two distinct and well-defined possibilities should not have been mixed. Only after the directors decided whether or not they wished to release control could a simulation be done on the resulting alternative courses of action. Correspondingly, if the objective was to help the Board in making this decision, completely different course should have been taken.

The consultant, disregarding the basic indisputable fact of irrelevancy in the case of investigation, went ahead with a mathematical model which was expected to provide the experimental groundwork for all five alternatives. Leaving aside the relative merits of the uncertain simulator, the result of its superficial application could only be detrimental to the interests of Delta Industries.

But the consultant is not necessarily the only one to blame. Sometimes company management invites this kind of trouble on itself.

In another case, similar in nature to the preceding one, management insisted that a mathematician, whose services it required, proceed in his study with old, inadequate, and unreliable data. This was based on the opinion that just using mathematics was enough to counterbalance the inadequate and obsolescent character of the data and make the whole operation profitable. Poor company! And it is not an exclusive case. In industrial enterprises, in human societies, and, generally, in all organizational systems, the man-made gods of the time still reveal their commands and wishes through oracles and secret omens. It has been so since the antiquity:

> ... The whole of the royal family together with the families of the nobles were led into captivity during the destruction of Elam. This took more than a month, and over the ruins of the city Ashurbanipal ordered salt to be scattered and weeds to be sown. Silent for ever were the sounds of happy people, the cries of joy, the tread of houshold animals; the city site was the home of wild asses, gazelles and beasts of the plain. Ashurbanipal recovered the statue of the goddess Nana, who had remained in Elam for 1635 years, a place which he regarded as 'not fitting for her' and who was awaiting the coming of Ashurbanipal, which she had appointed, proclaiming that the king 'would lead her forth from this miserable Elam and would bring her to the temple E-anna', ...[3]

Today it is corporate management who interprets the wishes of "its Goddess Nana," deciding which place and time fits her best.

---

[3] G. Contenau, "Everyday Life in Babylon and Assyria." Arnold, London, 1954.

PART II

The Mathematics of the Simulator

CHAPTER 4

Writing and Testing Equations

Like most engineers, systems analysts have demonstrated a certain tendency to underestimate the problem of mathematical formulation. This has proved to be detrimental to the purpose of experimentation. Not only must the object of the investigation and the criteria to be used be well established, but also the mechanics of simulation must be carefully observed if one is to get any benefit at all.

The practice of following the development of mathematical equations and their subsequent testing with extreme care is one which can pay high dividends, and this is true not only for mathematical experimentation. In their professional practice, engineers are often confronted with the problem of formulating in mathematical terms the behavior of physical or technological systems. Consider, for instance, the case of a chemical engineer who has been asked to study a certain problem in process automation.

Superficially, the theoretical treatment of the automatic control for chemical processing could be taken in a cookbook approach. However, in actual practice it is not so much the instruments that determine the control as it is the process as a whole. To predict how the process will operate it is necessary to make not only ordinary heat and material balances but also dynamic balances, which essentially means being able to write differential equations for the plant.

A variety of technologically advanced subjects imply control of a dynamic situation rather than of steady-state phenomena. This in itself imposes the requirement that the systems engineer have a knowledge well beyond the basic principles of mathematics. As technological ensembles increase in complexity, more of a mathematical background is required rather than less, to face problems involving systems stability, the synthesis of multivariable complexes, predecision, optimization, data sampling, performance, evaluation, and inference through data reduction.

The man responsible for examining the behavior of complex systems should possess a profound knowledge of probabilistic and deterministic mathematical tools. Yet, this in itself, though very much desirable, isn't enough. The systems analyst should equally possess an acute synthetic ability, for in his profession it is often desirable to express in a set of mathematical equations the relationship between variables which come into interplay in a given ensemble. To this art, the present and subsequent chapters are mostly devoted.

Defining the "Most Likely" Equation

We call *empirical,* an equation whose development has been based on observed data and not on a theoretical derivation. An equation which has been theoretically derived is called *rational.* A major problem in deriving an empirical equation is to find the form which would truly represent the given data. Given that form, the processing procedure is no different than the one followed for the solution of rational equations.

Some of the difficulties in deriving empirical equations lie in the non-compatible characteristics we usually wish to give to them. For example, it is desirable to derive mathematical equations with as few as possible arbitrary constants. At the same time we wish these equations to be accurate in their representation of the data. Also, in a considerable number of practical cases a choice must be made among two or more functions which approach the ideal about equally. The following equations fall into this category:

(a) $y = x + 0.2x^2,$ (d) $y = x + 0.1x^2,$

(b) $y = 0.5\,\dfrac{1}{x^2},$ (e) $y = 0.5\left(\dfrac{1}{x} + \dfrac{1}{x^2}\right),$

(c) $y = \ln x,$ (f) $y = \dfrac{1}{x}\ln x.$

The curves for Eqs. (a) and (d) are shown in Fig. 1. The theoretical plot is indicated by the full line. The experimental data are indicated by dots. It is readily apparent that neither of the two rational curves fits perfectly the empirical data. Yet either curve can be used with about the same approximation for the description of the observed phenomena.

Had we not been given these equations to start with, we might as well have used the time-honored method for finding the most suitable form of a mathematical formula:

(i) Plot the experimental data in a graph.

(ii) Draw an approximate curve.

(iii) "Guess" the correct form of its equation.

This estimated form has obviously to be tested, and, if unsatisfactory, the whole process has to be repeated. In this iterative method for finding the true form of an equation, the optimum selection of the coordinate system plays a major role.

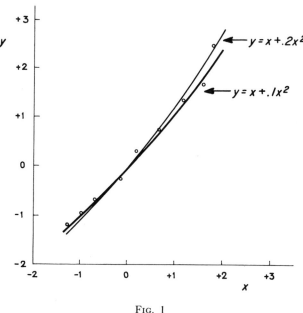

$$y = x + .2x^2$$

$$y = x + .1x^2$$

FIG. 1

As an example of equation formulation and usage consider the stochastic process $x(t, w)$ where w is a point in probability measure space and t is the time variable. The problem is the following: Given a set of values for $x(t, w)$ which is usually a relatively small finite number, we wish to determine the characteristics of this function which will be significant to us for future values of t.

Plotting, for example, *units produced* on the ordinate and *time* on the abscissa, we get a time versus production diagram. If we have a secular trend and a cyclical fluctuation with a given constant period superimposed on it, we may want to remove this periodic component from the available data. This can be done by applying a moving average with constant length equal to the period of the cycle. This method of moving averages is equivalent to approximating the true trend by a polynomial of the nth degree over the limited range of $m + 1$ points where $t - m$ to $t + m$ is the length of our period.

Considering the determination of $x(t, w)$ from a given set of measured points we first study a case which is essentially deterministic. Here the data points have or are assumed to have, for each t, a very small or no spread, as a function of w. This is frequently true in physical problems where the data measurements are made under well-controlled conditions.

The trend curve then is frequently taken to be the curve passing through each of the data points. Analytically this amounts to finding the particular function in a family of suitable simple functions (for instance, polynomials) which specifies the desired curve. This is essentially a matter of solving n linear equations with n unknowns. In many cases, when $x(t, w)$ as a function of w is not known, a normal distribution is assumed, and one has a problem in least-squares curve fitting. The type of simple curve or function to be used must again be established before any computing is done.

A number of technical, scientific, and other problems involve a least-squares linear relationship between two variables. This is nothing more than the familiar job of putting a best straight line through a scatter of points, done statistically to guarantee that the resulting line will be the best possible. The techniques of curve and surface fitting and multiple regression are extensions of this procedure.

Putting the best straight line through a series of points is a job of determining the values of two unknown coefficients in a linear equation which will best represent the points. In curve fitting, the problem is extended to finding three or more such unknown coefficients, still with the criterion of obtaining the best of all possible fits for the points in question. The method is not limited to the system having a single independent variable; systems of two, three, or more independent variables may also be treated in this fashion.

Curve fitting on a group of available data is an important subject in mathematical analysis. Consider as an example a system of x, y coordinates and two points I and II (Fig. 2). We draw an equidistant horizontal line A. The two vertical deviations from each point to the line have a common magnitude m. Any other line, as for instance B or C, gives a deviation of magnitude greater than m for one of the two points. Then, by definition, this line A represents the best fit to the given data. The equation for line A is simply $y = a$.

If we have more points, we will also have a corresponding number of deviations from the line of best fit. Figure 3 shows such a case with three points. The presented deviations are of equal magnitude from line A, and their signs alternate. The equation of A is $y = a + bx$. Any line other than A is not a line of best fit since any shift of A either parallel to itself or otherwise will result in an increase in one of the deviations.

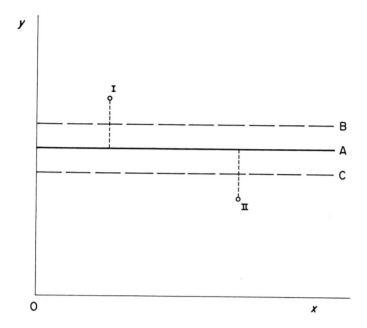

FIG. 2

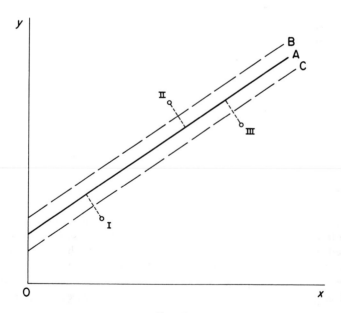

FIG. 3

To help avoid redundant effort in curve fitting over experimental
data it is advantageous to have available some curves and their respective
equations, which are in frequent usage, with their respective equations.

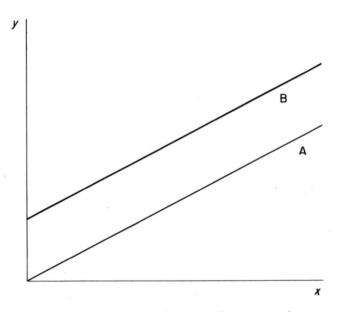

FIG. 4. Curve A, $y = bx$; curve B, $y = a + bx$.

Printed templates could greatly simplify the search job.

Linear and Nonlinear Equations

In Chapter 3 we made reference to our bias in favor of blind linearization of situations and processes which we have under study. We said
that, in order to make a linear method applicable, all activities must be
expressed in the form of linear relations. This is in itself a major constraint since very few real systems are linear by their own nature.

Linearization implies a deviation from reality which can range from
a controllable simplification to plain inadequacy. This is why we stressed
the need of a complete understanding of both the problem being
studied and the assumptions being made. There is no expected substitute
for careful study, observation, and analysis of the characteristics of the
natural or man-made systems we wish to investigate.

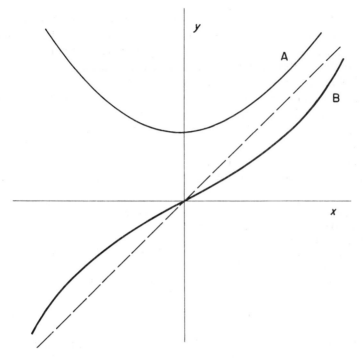

FIG. 5. $A = a_1 + a_2x^2$; $B = b_1 + b_2x^3$.

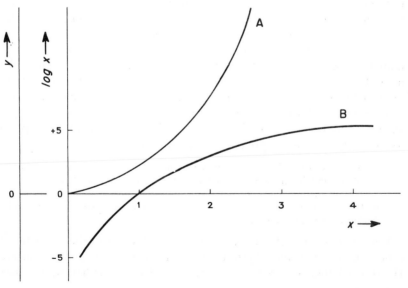

FIG. 6. Curve A, $y = cx^2$; Curve B, $y = \ln(1 + x) = x - \frac{1}{2}x^2 + \frac{1}{3}x^3 - \frac{1}{4}x^4 \ldots$

This "linear tendency" is found in several areas of mathematical effort, for example, the solution of differential equations, based on linear systems, although most of the physical parameters present in equations are actually nonlinear. Of course, one of the reasons for this preference is the fact that the most fundamental problems can be handled with linear approximations. More important yet, man comprehends linearity much better than nonlinearity, because the experimenter rarely takes care to state in advance his assumption and approximations. The result has invariably been a poor approximation to reality.

The fact that we are still loaded with bias in mathematics is, in itself, neither surprising nor uncommon. Evolution came just that way.

> . . . I am tempted to add another example—the evolution of those particular organizations of knowledge which we call concepts. This went hand-in-hand with the evolution of language—the invention of words as symbols for things, in place of sounds as signs for feelings, and was made possible by the expansion of the association areas in the cerebral cortex of the first ancestral men. 'In the beginning was the Word' is true of the development of human culture, for the evolution of verbal concepts opened the door to all further organizations and achievements of man's thought. . . .[1]

To illustrate the evolution in mathematical tools, it is enough to review a few important dates. The integral sign was first used by Gothfried Leibnitz in 1676, and as early as 1739 Euler had discovered the consistency of linear differential equations. Lagrange had formulated the general superposition theory of linear equations by 1760, but the date corresponding to Euler's linear discoveries for nonlinear equations was 1881 when Poincare published his works.

During the 1800's when mechanics was the favored subject of mathematicians, it was found that dissipative forces, such as friction, did not obey the linear laws. This was an upsetting discovery, since most mathematical theorists up to that time had concerned themselves with linear solutions only. With the discovery by Hertz in 1886 that electromagnetic waves could be propagated in space, it became even more important to find a formalized approach to nonlinear equations.

> . . . Newton clarified the whole of physical science and made the universe more comprehensible by introducing a few simple principles and postulates, such as the laws of motion, the postulate that matter consisted of uniform particles, the law of inverse squares governing their attraction; and then calculating and checking their implications. . . .[1]

For an example of the inconsistency which prevailed during this time, one may consider Ayrton's experiment with a negative resistance. He showed that an electromagnetic wave has a peculiar static charac-

---

[1] J. Huxley, "Evolution in Action." Chatto and Windus, London, 1953.

teristic (Fig. 7a). I is the current across an arc in the circuit shown in Fig. 7b. The voltage is $V = A + B/I$. Therefore, the incremental resistance becomes negative:

$$R_{\text{arc}} = \frac{dV}{dI} = \frac{-B}{I^2}.$$

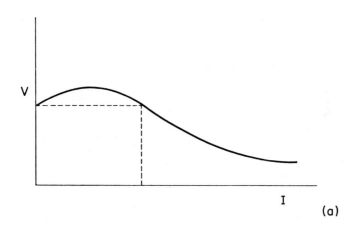

(a)

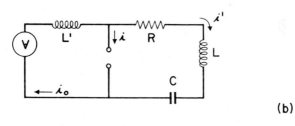

(b)

FIG. 7

Ayrton assumed that if L' is large t will remain nearly constant; $i_0 = i + i'$. Then

$$\frac{di_0}{dt} = 0 = \frac{di}{dt} + \frac{di'}{dt}$$

and

$$V = Ri' + L\frac{di}{dt} + \frac{1}{c}\int I \, dt,$$

by Kirchoff's law.

Differentiating with respect to time, we find $dV/dt = (dv/di)(di/dt)$. But, $di/dt = -di'/dt$. Substituting into Kirchoff's equation we get

$$\frac{d^2i'}{dt^2} + \frac{1}{L}\left(R + \frac{dV}{dt}\right)\frac{di}{dt} + \frac{1}{LC}i = 0.$$

dV/dt is the incremental arc resistance which is negative, so that the normal damping coefficient $R/2L$ of the *linear* circuit might become zero or even negative—i.e., the amplitudes of the oscillation might build up with time.

We see that a mistaken assumtion was made somewhere, for in reality dV/di decreases for very small and very large current values so that these self-contained oscillations become stabilized at certain definite amplitude values. The way this example goes, the result is that the actual amplitude of the nonlinear oscillatory response does not depend on the applied voltage V at all. Consequently we suspect that the superposition theorem does not hold in this nonlinear case.

A second assumption which we are prone to make with linear equations is that the uniqueness theorem is obeyed. To solve a linear system we may find two independent solutions, add them together by the superposition theorem, and make certain that the result is unique. This is not so with nonlinear equations, because in this case one component may very well affect and mask the contribution of another component. This masking introduces different beat harmonics into our solution over the same range, so that an infinite number of solutions is sometimes possible.

An example of what happens when the superposition hypothesis does not hold true was shown by Martienson, in 1910. Consider a voltage V of fixed frequency applied to a series combination of circuit elements (R, L, C). The inductance is caused by an iron core and is thus nonlinear (Fig. 8a). If we plot capacitance against current we find, by empirical methods, a curve which resembles the one in Fig. 8b. As we increase the variable capitance, the current takes the form of the solid portion of the curve to a point A. If we decrease the capacitance slowly the current takes the form of the dotted portion of the curve.

This hysteresis-type response gives a large region of instability (BADE), which contrasts markedly with the corresponding curve for a circuit with true linear components (Fig. 8c). However, had we used a large series resistance we might have decreased the instability region to almost nothing, and the nonlinear curve would have approached the general response of the linear case (Fig. 8d). With this, we are in effect masking the beat harmonics between pure "L harmonics" and pure "harmonics," thus showing the nature of the approximations made by using a linear approach.

The basic difference between linear and nonlinear equations is that in the case of linearity the dependent variable appears only in the first power and its derivatives. In the nonlinear case the dependent variable

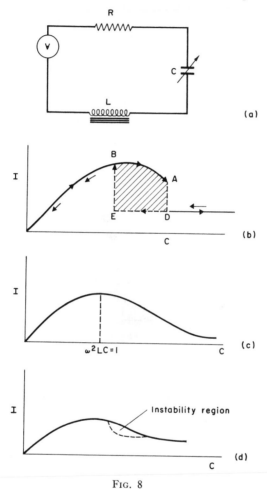

FIG. 8

may occur as a sinusoid or as a higher power than the first. These nonlinear components cause one of the most useful concepts of linear equations to be lost: the superposition theory. Furthermore, linear differential equations have unique solutions, which can be found from a general form containing the sum of its complementary and particular solutions. Nonlinear equations have no such general form, and harmonics and subharmonics of the functions may be present.

Physically a system described by a linear equation will contain only linear elements, i.e., those elements which have a characteristic curve that obeys a straight line. An example of a nonlinear element is a spring whose elasticity varies with its degree of compression or extension. Another example is the iron-core coil whose inductance varies with the current.

Nevertheless, it is often possible to describe nonlinear systems with linear equations. An example is the linear differential equation with varying coefficients, as would be the case if a spring constant, support length, etc., varied with time. The ideas of free and forced oscillation, free and forced frequency, and resonance are based on the principle of superposition and are therefore, strictly speaking, linear phenomena.

To follow the behavior of a nonlinear system, we will consider the case of free vibrations occurring in a mechanical system with nonlinear elasticity or damping. Here the natural frequency is no longer independent of the amplitude of vibration. Nonlinear elasticity or restoring forces have the most pronounced characteristic effect.

The example in Fig. 9 shows a system of springs and a mass with a

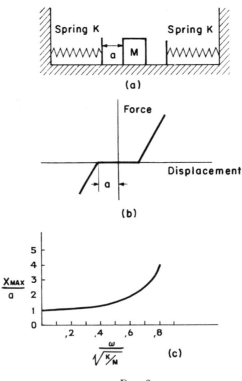

FIG. 9

normalized curve relating displacement and natural frequency. When a forcing function is applied to a system of nonlinear restoring forces, we find a resonant frequency, but it is somewhat different from an ordinary linear resonance. A spring system using "hard" springs (whose elasticity increases with increasing displacement) exhibits a practical resonance curve as in Fig. 10a.

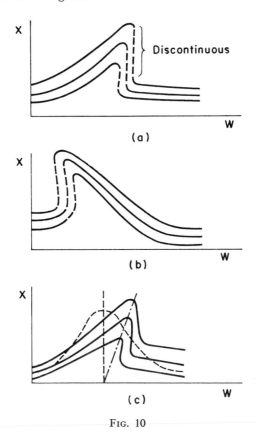

FIG. 10

Soft springs (elasticity decreasing with displacement) would give a curve as in Fig. 10b. In both cases, the family of curves present various magnitudes of the forcing function. The discontinuities are present as "jumps" in amplitude. Obviously there is no clear-cut resonant frequency; or rather, it is one of two unstable frequencies depending on whether it is approached from above or below.

Nonlinear damping is shown in Fig. 10c (plane curves); for comparison a linear resonance curve is also shown (dashed curve).

Considering Controlled Approximations

If the assumptions that a system has a single unique solution and that superposition can be used hold, the equation is linear. We may be interested in approximating the behavior of a system through linear equations because up to the present no consistent method for solving nonlinear equations has been discovered, as is the case with linear equations. Most of the work on nonlinear mathematical systems has resulted in solving specialized problems, and these solutions cannot be generalized.

> ... Today we can see life as a unitary process, made up of a number of smaller processes. The individual organism is a process within the species, the species a process within the radiation of a type, the radiation of a type a process within the succession of dominant groups, and this in turn a process within the overall process of realizing new possibilities of variety and organization. This point of view suggests questions of a new sort—questions about the nature and form of evolutionary processes, their definition and measurement, their limitations and restriction; questions about potentialities and their realization, about higher and lower, about improvement and progress. Above all, we have to ask how we can come to terms scientifically with a reality which combines both material and mental properties in its unitary pattern.[1]

It is mathematically feasible and, at times, experimentally acceptable to take a nonlinear equation and, either by using a limited region (so that the function remains linear) or by elimnating a nonlinear parameter (that is either small or of little importance), to proceed with a linear solution.

One example is the equation of the simple pendulum:

$$ML^2\ddot{x} + MGL \sin x = 0. \tag{1}$$

Since $\sin x$ is nonlinear, (1) is fundamentally a nonlinear equation. But if we consider only small angles, then we can approximate $\sin x = x$, and the linear equation

$$ML^2\ddot{x} + MGLx = 0$$

can be solved by the usual means.

To solve a nonlinear equation it is necessary, in general, to use one of the various solutions that apply to the particular problem. Some of the more common methods are Duffing's equation and solution, perturbation, van der Pol's method, etc. The Duffing equation and solution

$$\ddot{x} + c\dot{x} + f(x) = H(t)$$

---

[1] J. Huxley, "Evolution in Action", Chatto and Windus, London, 1953.

is applicable to problems where either $c\dot{x}$ or $f(x)$ is nonlinear, while the van der Pol method is useful for many forced equations. The method of perturbation develops the desired quantities in powers of some parameter which can be found by a series of linear relationships.

Many equations can be transformed into linear equations by a change in the variable. The so-called Bernoulli equation is useful in this respect. Consider the equation

$$\frac{dy}{dx} + py = Qy^n.$$

For its solution we divide by y^n, multiply by $(1 - n)$, and substitute $y^{1-n} = v$ in the result. Hence, we obtain

$$\frac{1 - n}{y^n} \frac{dy}{dx} + (1 - n)py^{1-n} = (1 - n)Q$$

or

$$\frac{dv}{dx} + (1 - n)pv = (1 - n)Q,$$

which is linear in v. The solution then follows:

$$v \, e^{(1-n)\int p \, dx} = (1 - n) \int Q \, e^{(1-n)\int p \, dx} \, dx + c$$

and therefore,

$$y^{1-n} \, e^{(1-n)\int p \, dx} = (1 - n) \int Q \, e^{(1-n)\int p \, dx} \, dx + c.$$

To iterate, a linear system is described by differential equations with first-order terms, the dependent variable, and its derivatives. For example,

$$\frac{dy}{dx} + y = 0$$

is the equation of a linear system;

$$\left(\frac{dy}{dx}\right)^2 + y = 0$$

is the equation of a nonlinear system,

$$y'' - K(1 - \cos y)y' + y = 0$$

is the equation of a nonlinear system since

$$1 - \cos y = 1 - \frac{y^2}{2} + \dots \, .$$

Furthermore, linearity assumes superposition. Consider the following examples of the difference between linear and nonlinear equations.

Linear:

$$\ddot{x} + A\dot{x} + Bx = H(t), \tag{2a}$$

A and B are either constant or variable coefficients. The solution will be superposition of free and of forced condition:

$$x = A_1 f(t) + A_2 f(t) + CH(t).$$

Nonlinear: several forms are possible such as

$$\ddot{x} + A\dot{x} + f(x) = H(t), \tag{2b}$$

where either $f(x)$ or $A\dot{x}$ may have a degree greater than one or a trigonometric expression such as $\sin x$. There is no general form of solution. The solution of this equation may consist of any number of terms containing harmonics, subharmonics, or nonperiodic functions.

In general, we may say that nonlinearities assert themselves through the damping term $\phi(x)$ or in the restoring force term $f(x)$ of an equation:

$$\ddot{x} + \phi(x) + f(x) = F(t).$$

If this equation is not time dependent, it may be converted to one of first order by using $\dot{x} = z$ as the independent variable.

In all, the process of solving nonlinear equations is both complex and time consuming. Yet, to bypass the fact that superposition and uniqueness theorems do not apply we simply attempt to approximate a physical picture to which they do apply, or take an infinite number of solutions on the hypothesis that the result will be unique. This is somewhat like the picture which physicists faced before the advent of quantum mechanics and wave analysis; the solution to our problem is similar, in that boundary conditions became the only possible limiting factor on what seemed to be a mass of random correlation. By using only portions of a nonlinear curve and restricting the applications to operate within these boundaries, we have been rather successful in solving nonlinear equations.[2]

The Testing Phase

Let's assume that the experimental data have been plotted on a graph. A hypothesis was made that a given curve fits these data. We are, hence,

---

[2] See also the discussion of the Monte Carlo method, in Chapter 8, p. 147.

confronted with the task of testing the suitability of this mathematical function. The objective is to establish whether or not this curve truly represents the experimental information.

We are particularly concerned with the equation of the curve and not with the value the arbitrary constants should take. Two methods are mostly used for curve testing. One is known as the *graphical* suitability test and the other as the *tabular* suitability test.

The graphical suitability test consists of two steps. First, rewrite the hypothesized function $\varphi(x, z, \alpha, \beta)$ in a linear form with respect to two selected functions f_1 and f_2. One of these functions usually involves the independent variable x and the other the dependent variable y:

$$f_1 = a + bf_2.$$

Neither of the f_i, $i = 1$, 2, includes the arbitrary constants. But the new constants a and b are functions of α and β.

An example might help towards a better understanding of the mechanics involved in this first step. Assume that the original equation is

$$z = \alpha e^{\beta + x}.$$

This equation can be rewritten in the form

$$\log z = \log \alpha + \beta \log e + x \log e.$$

In this case,

$$f_1 = \log z, \qquad f_2 = x, \qquad a = \log \alpha + \beta \log e, \qquad b = \log e.$$

A different transformation might have resulted by taking

$$\ln z = \ln \alpha + \beta + x.$$

In this case,

$$f_1 = \ln z, \qquad f_2 = x, \qquad a = \ln \alpha + \beta, \qquad \text{and } b = 1.$$

If the original equation were

$$z = (\alpha + x)^{\beta},$$

we could take

$$\log z = \beta \log \alpha + \beta \log x,$$

and then,

$$f_1 = \log z, \qquad f_2 = \log x, \qquad a = \beta \log \alpha, \qquad \text{and } b = \beta.$$

The second step in the graphical transformation consists of calculating f_1, $i = 1$, 2, with a few widely separated pairs of values for x and y. We must then plot f_1 as a function of f_2. As long as a straight line is obtained from this test we can consider this result as an indication that the hypothesized equation may be satisfactory.

Tabular suitability is a more convenient method for testing a hypothetical equation when more than two arbitrary constants are involved. Although there exist some variations in the approach to be taken, depending on the nature of the equation, four steps are generally followed:

(i) Make a plot of the experimental data.

(ii) From this plot develop a table of values.

(iii) Develop successive differences.

(iv) Examine the final set of differences with respect to constancy.

For an example, consider the equation

$$z = \alpha + \beta x + \gamma x^2 + \delta x^3 + \epsilon x^4.$$

We can write

$$z + \Delta z = \alpha + \beta(x + \Delta x) + \gamma(x + \Delta x)^2 + \delta(x + \Delta x)^3 + \epsilon(x + \Delta x)^4$$

or

$$\Delta z = (\beta \Delta x + \gamma \Delta x^2 + \delta \Delta x^3 + \epsilon \Delta x^4) + (3\gamma \Delta x^2 \ldots)x + (3\gamma \Delta x + 4\delta \Delta x^2 + \ldots)x^2 + \ldots . \quad (3)$$

By taking $\Delta x =$ constant, Eq. (3) can be rewritten in the form

$$\Delta z = a_1 + b_1 x + c_1 x^2 + d_1 x^3,$$

where a_1, b_1, c_1, and d_1 are constant. Repeating the preceding process we obtain

$$\Delta^2 z = a_2 + b_2 x + c_2 x^2,$$
$$\Delta^3 z = a_3 + b_3 x,$$
$$\Delta^4 z = a_4.$$

Hence, if the original equation of z holds and if Δx is kept constant throughout the test, the fourth-order tabular differences should be constant.

After the form of an equation has been accepted as truly representative of a given situation, there comes the problem of evaluating the arbitrary constants. The most accurate and possibly the best known means for this test is the method of least squares, but, because of the involved computational procedures it requires in many cases, we prefer to use approximate methods. One of them is known as the *method of the selected points*.

The method of the selected points calls for the following procedure. Plot z as a function of x and through the plotted points draw a smooth curve. From this curve choose a number of points equal to the number of arbitrary constants in the equation. The accuracy of the method will be improved if these points are at a considerable distance from each other, without being at the extremes of the curve.

By substituting these n pairs (x and z values for each point) into the selected equation, we obtain n equations with n unknowns. We then need to solve these equations for the desired arbitrary constants. This operation might be considerably simplified if the equation in question can be made linear with respect to its arbitrary constants.

For an example consider the equation

$$z = ax + bx^2 + cx^3,$$

which is linear with respect to its arbitrary constants. Selecting on the x axis the points 1, 2, and 3 we find on the z axis the corresponding coordinates 1, 2, and 3.5 (Fig. 11). From this set of equations we obtain the determinants

$$\begin{vmatrix} z & x & x^2 & x^3 \\ 1 & 1 & 1 & 1 \\ 2 & 2 & 4 & 8 \\ 3.5 & 3 & 9 & 27 \end{vmatrix} = 0$$

or

$$z\begin{vmatrix} 1 & 1 & 1 \\ 2 & 4 & 8 \\ 3 & 9 & 27 \end{vmatrix} - x\begin{vmatrix} 1 & 1 & 1 \\ 2 & 4 & 8 \\ 3.5 & 9 & 27 \end{vmatrix} + x^2\begin{vmatrix} 1 & 1 & 1 \\ 2 & 2 & 8 \\ 3.5 & 3 & 27 \end{vmatrix} - x^3\begin{vmatrix} 1 & 1 & 1 \\ 2 & 2 & 4 \\ 3.5 & 3 & 9 \end{vmatrix} = 0.$$
$$\quad\; D_1 \qquad\qquad\quad D_2 \qquad\qquad\quad D_3 \qquad\qquad\quad D_4$$

From this we derive the equations

$$D_1 = 108 - 72 - 54 + 24 + 18 - 12 = +12,$$
$$D_2 = 108 - 72 - 54 + 28 + 18 - 14 = +14,$$
$$D_3 = 54 \;\; - 24 - 54 + 28 + 6 \;\; - 7 \quad = +3,$$
$$D_4 = 18 \;\; - 12 - 18 + 14 + 6 \;\; - 7 \quad = +1.$$

Solving this system we have

$$12z - 14x + 3x^2 - x^3 = 0$$

or

$$z = \tfrac{7}{6}x - \tfrac{1}{4}x^2 + \tfrac{1}{12}x^3.$$

Hence,

$$a_1 = \tfrac{7}{6}, \qquad a_2 = -\tfrac{1}{4}, \qquad a_3 = \tfrac{1}{12}.$$

We have thus completed the evaluation of the arbitrary constants by one of the possible methods. However, it is necessary to test once again for goodness of fit of this equation to the experimental data. Obviously, using the x values 1, 2, 3 would only give an identity. Points other than the above should be used for this test, and the calculated z should be tested against the graphical value derived from Fig. 11.

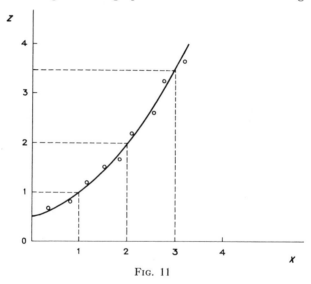

FIG. 11

Failure of the analytic data to conform to the graphical data, excluding computational errors, should be interpreted as evidence that possibly the equation in question does not represent, in a satisfactory manner, the experimentally obtained information.

Alternative Ways of Testing Equations

A simpler approach to this problem of testing equations is the so-called *straight line graphical method* with two and three arbitrary constants.

This is a continuation of the graphical tests for suitability described in the preceding section.

Suppose that we wish to find whether or not the arbitrary constants of a certain equation, which has been plotted, give a straight line. This evaluation can be done in an easy manner by testing for the constant slanting of the slope of this line, using the two-point formula $(z_2 - z_1)/(x_2 - x_1)$, where $z_i, x_i, i = 1, 2$, may be any two points on the line.

Suppose that the equation in question has already been written in the form $z = a + bx$, possibly through some transformation. The intercept a can be calculated by applying the formula

$$a = \frac{z_1 x_2 - z_2 x_1}{x_2 - x_1},$$

or it might be possible to read the value of a from the graph. When dealing with the straight line graphical method for equations with three arbitrary constants, it becomes necessary to eliminate one of the constants in order that the resultant equation can be treated in the described way. This can be accomplished through a transformation.

Another alternative method for evaluating the arbitrary constants is the *method of averages*. This is a particular case of the selected-points method, and it is applicable when the equation under study is linear with respect to its arbitrary constants.

Assume that the equation in question is of the form $z = \varphi(x)$, and that it contains n arbitrary constants. The method consists of dividing a number of m observed pairs of z, x values into n groups. Such groups should be approximately equal, and each group should contain only z, x values belonging to adjacent points. The values of z, x within each group should then be averaged, thus obtaining n values of means $\bar{z}$ and $\bar{x}$. Finally, the mean points $\bar{z}, \bar{x}$ should be used with the selected-points method as discussed in the preceding paragraphs.

The method of *moments* is also used for the evaluation of the arbitrary constants, but it is mostly favored in cases where the equation under study is an nth-degree polynomial. This method demands that the coordinates along the x axis of the points to which the equation is to be fitted differ by a constant Δx. Since this is a fundamental requirement, whenever the original data do not satisfy this condition it is necessary to start by plotting this data in graph form. We then fit on the data points a smooth curve, and on this curve choose a series of points with an equidistant projection on the x axis. Following this operation, we can define the different moments of z with respect to x:

(a) zero moment $$m_0 = \sum x^0 z \, \Delta x,$$

(b) first moment $\qquad m_1 = \sum xz \, \Delta x,$

(c) second moment $\qquad m_2 = \sum x^2 z \, \Delta x,$

(d) third moment $\qquad m_3 = \sum x^3 z \, \Delta x,$

(e) fourth moment $\qquad m_4 = \sum x^4 z \, \Delta x,$ etc.

Assuming m_i to exist for $i = 0, 1, \ldots n$, they are related to the desired curve in the following manner:

$$m_0 = \int_k^l f(x) \, dx$$

$$m_1 = \int_k^l xf(x) \, dx$$

$$m_2 = \int_k^l x^2 f(x) \, dx$$

$$m_3 = \int_k^l x^3 f(x) \, dx$$

$$m_4 = \int_k^l x^4 f(x) \, dx, \qquad \text{etc.}$$

Here, l represents the highest x value plus $\frac{1}{2}\Delta x$ and k represents the lowest x value less $\frac{1}{2}\Delta x$. The number of moments to be used depends on the degree of the equation under study. With a third-degree equation we need to use m_0, m_1, m_2, and m_3, while with the linear equation we will use only m_0 and m_1.

Assume the equation to be of the linear form:

$$z = \varphi(x) = a_0 + a_1 x.$$

Substituting for $\varphi(x)$ its equal and integrating we obtain

$$a_0(l - k) + \frac{a_1(l^2 - k^2)}{2} = \sum z \, \Delta x,$$

$$\frac{a_0(l^2 - k^2)}{2} + \frac{a_1(l^3 - k^3)}{3} = \sum xz \, \Delta x.$$

We can obtain the values of a_0 and a_1 by solving this system of two equations. For higher degree polynomials, manned computations using the method of moments become tedious, and it is advisable to use a computing facility. This method has its limitations. When a small number of points is considered, deviations in the calculated values of the constants from the values obtained through more accurate methods are rather important.

Working with equations which are linear as to their arbitrary constants, it is advisable to use the method of successive approximations in order to improve the estimated values of the constants obtained with one of the foregoing methods.

Briefly, the method of successive approximations consists of the following procedure. Let the polynomial in question be

$$z = a_0 + a_1x + a_2x^2 + a_3x^3 + \ldots + a_nx^n$$

and let z^1, $a_0{}^1$, $a_1{}^1$, $a_n{}^1$ be the values (first approximation) computed by one of the foregoing methods. The next step is to round off the $a_i{}^1$, $i = 0 \ldots n$, but not the z^1 which has been computed with their aid. Then, in order to obtain a second approximation we compute for the various given x values the corresponding differences $(z - z^1)$ and plot these points $[x, (z - z^1)]$.

Following this operation, a smooth curve should be drawn over these points. The distances from the plotted points to the curve represent deviations of the observed data from the second approximation which is to be derived at a later step. The distances of the points from the x axis represent deviations of the first approximation from the observed data.

The next step is to obtain the equation of the forementioned curve using any of the described methods. Then, by adding this correction equation to the equation of the first approximation we can obtain the equation of the second approximation. If a third approximation is necessary, the preceding steps can be repeated. The same is true for a fourth and other approximations if they are judged necessary. The best possible fit is reached when the obtained mth approximation curve, $m = 2, 3 \ldots -n$, coincides with the abscissa.

CHAPTER 5

Mathematical Functions and Curves

"Continuous type" problems constitute one of the important classes of problems in applied mathematics. This class includes problems with equations involving the operations of classical analysis, basically differentiation and integration, and any other operations in which limiting procedures play a role.

One of the characteristics that problems of this nature have in common is that none can be performed on a digital computer that does not deal with continuously varying quantities and hence is incapable of taking limits by finite numerical processes. We, therefore, proceed by solving not the original continuous problem but another one (descrete) which approximates the continuous in the sense that its discrete solution approximates the continuous solution of the continous problem.

We can think of the relationship between the corresponding problems as a mapping of the continuous into the discrete, and vice versa. Yet, we should also consider the fact that there exists a unique continuous problem corresponding to an infinite set of discrete problems. The mapping from discrete problem to continuous problem is many-to-one, which often times can lead to an ambiguity: we can write several difference equations corresponding to the same differential equation.[1]

Similarly, when we develop equations to fit experimental or other data we are always faced with the need of approximating the real situation, which is often unknown, in some appropriate sense. For this reason it is very desirable to find some principle or procedural guide that would enable us to develop characteristic equations without such a great ambiguity. We must set certain general requirements on the mathematical formulation.

A Classification of Functions

In Chapter 4, we spoke about curve plotting on the basis of statistical data. It is evident that in no way does it suffice to trace a curve through

---

[1] See the discussion on difference and differential equations in Chapter 6.

given points, to say that it represents a certain physical or other phenomenon. While making reference to this, we placed due emphasis on the
pitfalls which exist in the way, particularly when one accepts, without
testing, that a certain equation holds true because it seems to approximate
readily available data.

With due consideration to the foregoing, in the present chapter we
attempt to map and to exemplify certain classes of mathematical functions, paying particular attention to the mechanics involved in the
development of equations. It is always theoretically possible to represent
a "curve", described according to certain laws, by means of a definite
analytical equation in any system of coordinates. We will start the discussion in the present chapter by investigating the properties of a curve,
represented in Cartesian coordinates, by means of the equation
$f(x, y) = 0$.

In the past, functions were divided into two separate classes: *algebraic*
and *transcendental*. The curves presented by them were accordingly
divided into algebraic and transcendental curves. This classification is
chiefly based on the use of Cartesian coordinates; it is not valid when
other systems are used.

For functions whose both ranges are real numbers, a graphical representation was devised by Descartes. The older mathematicians held
that a function simply meant a single formula, at first usually a power
of the variable, but afterwards it was regarded as defined by any analytical
expression. This definition was extended by Euler to include the case
in which the function is given implicitly as a formal relation between
the two variables. Fourier, among others, recognized the arbitrary
nature of a function given by a graph. Today we accept that a function
can be completely defined by means of a graph arbitrarily drawn in the
finite and continuous domain of the independent variable.

The foregoing discussion brings into proper perspective the current
notion that a certain curve is indistinguishable by perception from a
sufficiently great number of discrete points. But a graph, arbitrarily
drawn, can be regarded only as an approximate representation of a
function, and all that is really given by the graph consists of more or less
arithmetically approximate values of the ordinates at those points of the
x axis at which we are able to measure them. Nevertheless, for a curve
to define a certain function, certain laws must be formulated by means
of which the values of the ordinates can be formally determined at all
points of the abscissa. Considerations of this nature led to the classification of functions depending on whether they possess properties such as
continuity, differentiability, and integrability, throughout the domain
of the independent variable or at special points in that domain.

It is fundamentally important to establish that the equation $f(x, y) = 0$ cannot in general represent a curve. This will be the case only if y can be expressed as a rational function $\varphi(x)$, where $\varphi(x)$ is a continuous, finite, differentiable, and separately monotone function. If $f(x, y)$ is a rational and integral function of the variables, then

$$f(x, y) = 0.$$

This is the equation of an algebraic curve, while the curve itself is the geometric representation of the function $f(x, y)$. In this way, a curve of the nth order can be defined as the geometric representation of a function which is of the nth degree in the variables. When $f(x, y)$ cannot be broken into two or more rational and integral factors of lower dimensions, the curve is called a *proper curve* of the nth order.[2] If $f(x, y)$ breaks up into two or more rational and integral factors of lower degrees, the curve is called *improper* or *degenerate*.
Let

$$v_0 + v_1 + v_2 + \ldots + v_n = 0$$

represent the expanded form of an $f(x, y) = 0$ equation, where

$$v_0 = a,$$
$$v_1 = b_1 x + b_2 y,$$
$$v_2 = c_1 x^2 + c_2 xy + c_3 y^2,$$
$$\cdots$$
$$\cdots$$
$$v_n = h_1 x^n + h_2 x^{n-1} y + \ldots + h_{n-1} xy^{n-1} + h_n y^n .$$

The subject equation may be made homogenous by introducing a third variable z. Then, the general equation of a curve of order n in homogeneous coordinates may be written in the form

$$v_0 z^n + v_1 z^{n-1} + v_2 z^{n-2} + \ldots + v_{n-1} z^{n-1} + v_n = 0.$$

It can be seen that the total number of terms in each of these equations is equal to $1 + 2 + 3 + \ldots + n + (n + 1)$, hence to $\frac{1}{2}(n + 1)(n + 2)$. The number of independent constants in each of these equations is equal to one less than the number of terms it contains. The general equation of the nth degree contains only $[\frac{1}{2}(n + 1)(n + 2) - 1]$, or $\frac{1}{2}n(n + 3)$, independent constants and can therefore be made to satisfy the same number of conditions and no more. By the same token, $\frac{1}{2}n(n + 3)$ conditions are required to determine a curve of order n.

---

[2] In this case, we call $f(x, y)$ an *irreducible* function.

A curve of order n is uniquely determined if $\frac{1}{2}n(n + 3)$ points on it are given.

The coordinates of each of the given points satisfy the equation under consideration and thus give a linear relation between the constants. We obtain $\frac{1}{2}n(n + 3)$ equations to determine the same number of unknown quantitites, in this case the equation's coefficients. But while $\frac{1}{2}n(n + 3)$ points will determine a curve of order n uniquely, these do not in all cases determine a proper curve. The necessary and sufficient condition for determining a proper curve uniquely is that the .points must all be "independent," that is, no group of them should lie on a curve of order lower than they can properly determine. If some of the points lie on one or more other curves of lower order, the curve of the nth order is not a proper curve, but consists of two or more curves of lower order.

Two curves of orders k and l, respectively, intersect in general at kl points. Let Q_k and Q_l be any two rational algebraic functions of x and y of degrees k and l, respectively. Then, if y is eliminated between the equations $Q_k = 0$ and $Q_l = 0$, the resulting equation in x will be of degree kl and will determine the abscissa of the points of intersection of the two corresponding curves. The intersection points are not all arbitrary. If $k < l$, then $\frac{1}{2}k(k + 3)$ of the points must be given which completely determine the curve of the kth degree. The remaining $kl - \frac{1}{2}k(k + 3)$ points can be so calculated.

Curve Fitting and Curve Tracing

Assume that we have postulated a linear relation between two given variables x and y:

$$y = a + bx.$$

Assume, also, that measurements on y, for different values of x, can be made with great precision. Then, the problem is basically one of statistical inference. On the basis of the sample values,

$$(x_1, y_1), \quad (x_2, y_2), \quad (x_3, y_3), \ ...,$$

we are required to estimate the parameters a and b of the subject equation.

Let us consider for a moment that x is fixed at x_1, and the corresponding y measurements are repeated. These y values will be normally distributed about a mean value given by $\mu_1 = b + ax_1$, and a variance of σ^2. Repeated measurements of y corresponding to fixing x at x_2 would result in a normal distribution about a mean value of $\mu_2 = b + ax_2$ with the same variance σ^2. It is then possible to show that the best estimates, a' and b', of a and b are given as solutions of the simultaneous equations

$$\sum_{i=1}^{n} y_i = nb + a \sum_{i=1}^{n} x_i,$$

$$\sum_{i=1}^{n} x_i y_i = b \sum_{i=1}^{n} x_i^2.$$

This procedure leads to the least-squares solutions. As such, the estimates a' and b' are unbiased. But what if $y = F(x)$ were the function of n x variables. For instance,

$$F(x) = a_0 + a_1 x_1 + a_2 x_2 + \ldots + a_n x_n .$$

We suppose that we have fixed variates x_1, x_2, ..., x_k, in which, for convenience of notation, we define x_1 to be identically equal to one. We need to make certain assumptions about normality of distribution of repeated measurements of y corresponding to fixed values of the x', on the basis of the sample of size n. The least-squares estimates a_1', a_2', ... a_k' of the parameters are then given as solutions of a' set of simultaneous equations. With this, we arrive at estimates for the parameters which are optimum in a certain sense, but these are "single" or "point" estimates. Besides, there exist types of curve-fitting problems, whose solutions require a more complicated procedure. An example is fitting an equation of the form

$$F(x) = a_1 e^{\lambda_1 x} + a_2 e^{\lambda_2 x} + \ldots + a_n e^{\lambda_n x}.$$

Hence, a method of successive approximations must be applied. This will lead to a set of linear equations whose solution provides the numbers by which to adjust our first estimates.

When the value of y is desired for an x outside the range of values covered by the data, we must resort to extrapolation. In Chapter 6 are discussed the basic methods of interpolation. Extrapolation and interpolation are alike in the sense that any of the interpolation procedures may be used for extrapolation. The chief differences lie in the accuracy of our results. Where the law stating the dependency of y upon x is known, no difficulty is experienced in either interpolation or extrapolation. All methods[3] may be used with equal safety if the range of extra-

---

[3] Except the simple proportional part method.

polation is not too great, but the Taylor series method is particularly applicable. Inversely, where nothing of the law of variation is known, beyond the range for which tabular values are given, extrapolations represent little more than guesses.

Say that we now wish to trace a curve for the equations that we have developed. We will consider Cartesian equations first, starting from the well-known procedure that if we give any value a to x, the resulting equation in y can be solved and will determine the points at which the line $x = a$ interesects the curve. Giving a set of values to x, we determine a corresponding set of values for y, and thereby obtain a number of points on the curve. Drawing a line freely through them, we can obtain a fairly good idea of the shape this curve will have.

To determine the points where the curve cuts the coordinates, we set $x = 0$ and $y = 0$ in the equation. If for any value of x, y the result of the equation is imaginary, we make the supposition that the curve is limited in some direction. The value of dy/dx at any point gives the direction of the tangent at that point; and by finding the points where dy/dx becomes zero or infinite, we can determine the points where the tangent, and consequently the direction of the curve, is parallel or perpendicular to the x axis. Whenever the nature of the equation we have on hand suggests simplifications, it is advisable to take advantage of these, so as to obtain more easily enough points to determine the approximate shape of the curve.

If the equation of a curve involves a variable parameter, we obtain a series of different curves by giving different values to the parameter. All these curves touch the "envelope" of the system. Each of the curves is intersected by its consecutive curve in points depending upon the parameter. The envelope is the locus of all these points of intersection.

Dynamic and Stochastic Analogies in Developing Equations

As an example on the development of equations, let us consider a couple of case studies from engineering. The first has to do with response characteristics and their corresponding deterministic and probabilistic interpretations. A substantial number of processes are characterized by a step response, monotonic and nondecreasing in time (Fig. 1a). The corresponding frequency response would have a nonincreasing amplitude and nondecreasing phase lag with increasing frequency (Fig. 1b). We call *monotone* processes the linear systems giving rise to such a response. Their behavior is manifested through *dead time* (delay) and *rise time* (dispersion).

The delay is usually associated with propagation or transport phenomena, as is measured by the ratio of travel distance to propagation or transport velocity. The dispersion in any physical process can ultimately be attributed to the law of increasing entropy, whereby the distributed resistances in any system cause an attenuation increasing with frequency.

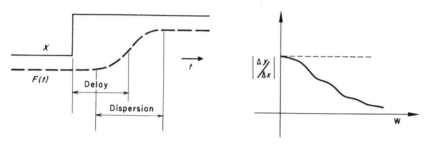

FIG. 1

Oscillatory processes, characterized by the presence of complementary energy-storage elements, have monotonic response whenever the energy dissipated per cycle becomes sufficiently large compared to the energy stored in each mode.

Let $\Phi(t)$ and $\varphi(t)$, respectively, denote the response of a linear process to unit step and unit impulse inputs. The general response $F(t)$ to an arbitrary disturbance $x(t)$ can be expressed in the form

$$F(t) = \int_{-\infty}^{t} x(t - t') \, d\Phi(t') = \int_{-\infty}^{t} x(t - t')\varphi(t') \, dt'. \tag{1}$$

Equation (1) expresses the convolution or superposition theorem. The plots for the step response (a) and the input response (b) are

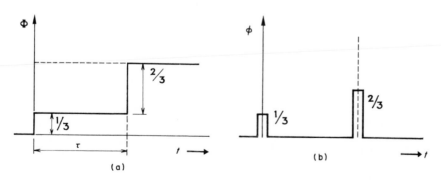

FIG. 2

presented in Fig. 2. It corresponds to a purely discrete process, for which the convolution integral becomes simply the series

$$F(t) = \sum_{i=1}^{\infty} x(t - \tau_i) \, \Delta\Phi(\tau_i),$$

where $\Delta\Phi(\tau_i)$ represent the jump magnitudes and τ_i are the corresponding occurrence times of the stepwise varying $\Phi(t)$. This response can be stated directly, since $\tau_1 = 0$, $\tau_2 = 1$. We can write

$$F(t) = \tfrac{1}{3}x(t) + \tfrac{2}{3}x(t - 1).$$

In Figs. 1 and 2, both the distribution graphs and the behavior of the combination laws lead one to suspect the existence of a strong analogy between certain deterministic dynamic processes and the probabilistic processes of mathematical statistics, in which behavior is governed by stochastic relationships. This becomes clearer if one considers that in stochastic processes the joint distribution results from independent random sampling of two distributions Φ_1 and Φ_2. Correspondingly, in dynamic processes the initial response results from the cascade of two linear elements, having step responses Φ_1 and Φ_2, as in the preceding case.

In either case the "distribution," or "response," is expressed by the commutative convolution integrals:

$$\Phi_n = \int_{-\infty}^{t} \Phi_1(t - t') \, d\Phi_2(t') = \int_{-\infty}^{t} \Phi_2(t - t') \, d\Phi_1(t').$$

Hence, it is independent of the order in which the operation is performed. It follows that each and every probability distribution in one dimension has a dynamic interpretation as a monotone process, while conversely the cascade of easily realized dynamic monotones offers a new means of containing joint sampling distributions. Also, many of the techniques and manipulations of statistical theory could have useful and important dynamic interpretations.

When information theory was developed by Claude Shannon in 1948, it was seen that there was a formal analogy to statistical mechanics, but it was not realized just how significant this relationship really was. In 1953, Leon Brillouin showed that the results of information theory were the same as those of statistical mechanics. Finally, in 1957, E. T. Jaynes, of Stanford University, showed that the methods of statistical mechanics are a special case of a general technique for guarding against bias . . .[4]

---

[4] M. Tribus, "Thermostatics and Thermodynamics." Van Nostrand, Princeton, New Jersey, 1961.

Quantum theory, as Tribus states, is physical theory—it tells us about the behavior of physical systems. Statistical mechanics, on the other hand, is a mathematical theory—it tells us about the combination and manipulation of properties. Their joined usage allows us, through relatively simple mathematical-statistical methods, to study and to influence the characteristics of large scale systems.

Example with the Wave Equation

Consider as the second case study, the development of the wave equation. We will be concerned first with the motion of a string of length *l*, stretched horizontally, fastened at each end, and set into vibration. it is assumed that the string vibrates in a vertical plane only, that the amplitude of vibration is so small as to make each point on the string move only vertically, and that the tension in the string does not change appreciably (Fig. 3).

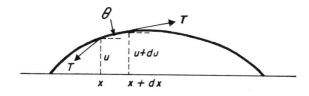

FIG. 3

To obtain an equation of motion for the string, we consider a segment of string of length dx between x and $x + dx$. If the density of the string per unit length is δ then the mass of this segment is $\delta\, dx$. The velocity of the string at any point is $\partial u/\partial t$, and its slope is $\partial u/\partial x$. The vertical component of tension exerted from right to left across any point in the string is

$$T_u = T \sin \theta,$$

where θ is the angle between the string and the horizontal. Assuming that θ is very small in this case,

$$T \sin \theta \doteq T \tan \theta = T \frac{\partial u}{\partial x}.$$

The net upward force dF, due to the tension on the segment dx of the string, is the difference in the vertical component T_k between the two ends of the segment

$$dF = T_u|_{x+dx} - T_u|_x \,,$$

$$dF \doteq \frac{\partial}{\partial x}\left(T\,\frac{\partial u}{\partial x}\right)dx.$$

If we do not limit ourselves to very small slopes $\partial u/\partial x$, then a segment of string may also have a net horizontal component of force due to tension, and the segment will move horizontally as well as vertically. If there is, in addition, a vertical force f per unit length acting along the string, the equation of motion of the segment dx will be

$$\delta\,dx\,\frac{\partial^2 u}{\partial t^2} = T\,\frac{\partial^2 u}{\partial x^2} + f.$$

For the horizontal string acted on by no horizontal forces except at the ends, and for small amplitudes of vibration, the tension is constant, and the equation may be rewritten

$$\delta\,\frac{\partial^2 u}{\partial t^2} = T\,\frac{\partial^2 u}{\partial t^2} + f.$$

The force f may be the gravitational force acting on the string, which is usually negligible. The force f may also represent an external force applied to the string to set it in motion. If f can be considered zero the equation can be rewritten

$$\frac{\partial^2 u}{\partial x^2} = \frac{1}{c^2}\,\frac{\partial^2 u}{\partial t^2}\,,$$

where

$$c = \left(\frac{T}{\delta}\right)^x.$$

The constant c has the dimension of velocity and it is the velocity with which the wave travels along the string.

LONGITUDINAL MOTION OF A ROD

This concerns the wave equation as developed for application to the longitudinal waves in a rod. It is possible for the particles of a straight rod to move in such a way that the only stress in the rod is a pure tension along its length. This tension will be different at different parts of its length. The main motion is longitudinal although there must be some lateral movement which is determined by Poisson's ratio.

If we write P for the tensional stress in the x direction then, using Newton's second law,

$$\frac{\partial P}{\partial x} = \frac{w}{g} \frac{\partial^2 u}{\partial t^2} , \tag{2a}$$

where u is the displacement of a particle in the x direction due to strain.

Before going further we have need for Young's modulus of elasticity. If a segment a of our bar is stressed in tension it will be of length $a + u$. The ratio of u/a is referred to as the strain. The ratio is denoted by α. Hooke's law gives $P = E\alpha$ or $\alpha = P/E$. E is a constant which is called Young's modulus of elasticity. Considering that under dynamic conditions strain will vary along the rod, we may write

$$\frac{\partial u}{\partial x} E = P. \tag{2b}$$

Differentiating Eq. (2b) we obtain

$$\frac{\partial P}{\partial x} = E \frac{\partial^2 u}{\partial x^2} . \tag{2c}$$

Equating Eqs. (2a) and (2c) we have

$$E \frac{\partial^2 u}{\partial x^2} = \frac{w}{g} \frac{\partial^2 u}{\partial t^2} \tag{2d}$$

or

$$c^2 \frac{\partial^2 u}{\partial x^2} = \frac{\partial^2 u}{\partial t^2} , \tag{3}$$

where

$$c^2 = \frac{g}{w} E.$$

Equation (3) determines the motion of the rod when the initial state of the rod and the conditions of the ends are known.

TORSIONAL MOTION OF A ROD

Let the x axis be taken along the longitudinal center of the rod. We are assuming pure torsion, that is, no tension, compression, or bending.

Let us assume that the section at a distance x from the origin is twisted through the angle θ relative to the section at the origin, and let ω denote the angular velocity of this section. The element of δx is twisted through the angle $\delta\theta$ and consequently the twist per unit length of this element is

$$\tau = \frac{\partial\theta}{\partial x}.$$

Let Q denote the torque in the element. Then

$$Q = Cn\tau = Cn\frac{\partial\theta}{\partial x},$$

where C is a constant which depends on the shape and size of the section of the rod and has the dimensions of the moment of inertia of an area.

Let I denote the moment of inertia of the cross section of the rod about the x axis. Then the moment of inertia of the element of the rod of length δx is $(w/g)I\,\delta x$ and the angular momentum of this element is $(w/g)I\omega\,\delta x$. The rate of increase of this angular momentum is equal to the total torque on the element, and this total torque is the excess of the torque at $(x + \delta x)$ over that at x, namely, $(\partial Q/\partial x)\,\delta x$. Therefore,

$$\frac{\partial}{\partial t}\left(\frac{w}{g}I\omega\,\delta x\right) = \frac{\partial Q}{\partial x}\,\delta x,$$

$$\frac{w}{g}I\,\delta x\,\frac{\partial\omega}{\partial t} = \frac{\partial Q}{\partial x}\,\delta x$$

$$= Cn\frac{\partial^2\theta}{\partial x^2}\,\delta x,$$

or

$$\frac{gn}{w}\frac{C}{I}\frac{\partial^2\theta}{\partial x^2} = \frac{\partial\omega}{\partial t}. \tag{4a}$$

If the section at the origin is at rest, or, say, is rotating with constant angular velocity, then the angular acceleration of the section at x relative to the section at the origin is the true acceleration of the section at x. That is,

$$\frac{\partial^2\theta}{\partial t^2} = \frac{\partial\omega}{\partial t}, \tag{4b}$$

in which case Eq. (4a) becomes

$$c^2\frac{\partial^2\theta}{\partial x^2} = \frac{\partial^2\theta}{\partial t^2}, \tag{4c}$$

where $c^2 = gnC/wI$.

Note that this equation is exactly like the equation for longitudinal oscillation of the rod except that θ is used instead of u.

Longitudinal Waves in Gases

When the air follows a simple pendular motion under the maintaining action of the source of sound, the ear hears a single tone, of which the number of complete oscillations per second is called the frequency of the source. If an instantaneous picture of the medium be imagined, the length of the unit of the "pattern," or the distance between successive compressions, is known as the *wavelength*.

The fractional decrease in volume, or the decrease in volume per unit of original volume, which a compressed body of gas may undergo, is known as the "condensation" s. We can write

$$s = -\frac{\delta v}{v}.$$

The compressibility may be defined as the fractional decrease of volume produced by unit change of pressure. The elasticity E is the inverse of this; the more compressible the gas the less elastic it is. The equation is

$$E = -\delta p\,\frac{v}{\delta v}, \tag{5}$$

where the negative sign shows that increase of pressure produces decrease of volume.

Let us consider a tube of gas of unit cross section, and two plane sections A and B of this tube, whose coordinates measured along the tube are, before the passage of the wave, x and $x + \delta x$, respectively. The initial volume of the slice so cut off is δx (Fig. 4).

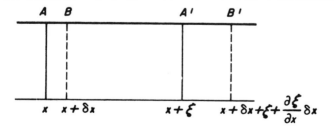

Fig. 4

At an instant of time δt later, let the arrival of the disturbance have displaced the end A of our slice by an amount ξ to A', so that its co-ordinate is now $x + \xi$. Other sections of the slice will have a different displacement, since the displacement will vary with x at a rate $\partial\xi/\partial x$. For instance, the displacement of the end B will be $\xi + (\partial\xi/\partial x)\,\delta x$, and this plane will now occupy a position B' given by

$$x + \delta x + \xi + \frac{\partial\xi}{\partial x}\,\delta x.$$

The new volume of the slice will be representing an increase of volume of $(\partial\xi/\partial x)\,\delta x$. The latter, divided by the original δx, is, by definition, the condensation $s = -\partial\xi/\partial x$.

The pressure on a section differs from the normal by an amount which varies with its position; so that, if that on the plane through A' is δp, that on B' is

$$\delta p + \frac{\partial(\delta p)}{\partial x}\,\delta x = Es + E\,\frac{\partial s}{\partial x}\,\delta x.$$

The total force on the slice equals the difference of pressure on the two ends:

$$-E\,\frac{\partial s}{\partial x}\,\delta x = E\,\frac{\partial^2\xi}{\partial x^2}\,\delta x.$$

Equating this to the mass x acceleration of the slice, the mass being $\rho\,\delta x$ where ρ is the density of the gas, we have

$$E\,\frac{\partial^2\xi}{\partial x^2}\,\delta x = \rho\delta x\,\frac{\partial^2\xi}{\partial t^2}$$

or

$$\frac{\partial^2\xi}{\partial t^2} = \frac{E}{\rho}\,\frac{\partial^2\xi}{\partial x^2}.$$

Putting

$$\frac{E}{\rho} = c^2,$$

we find that $\sqrt{E/\rho}$, i.e., c has the dimensions of a velocity.

THE PROPAGATION OF PERIODIC DISTURBANCES IN THE FORM OF WAVES

Let us consider a process that varies as either the real or imaginary part of the function:

$$u(x, t) = A\,e^{j\omega(t - x/v)}. \tag{6}$$

As t increases, the argument of the function changes. If, however, the coordinate x increases in such a way that the argument of the exponential function remains constant, that is, if

$$\left(t - \frac{x}{v}\right) = \text{constant},$$

then the phase of the function $u(x, t)$ is unaltered. We thus see that (6) represents a disturbance that travels along the x axis with a phase velocity of

$$\frac{dx}{dt} = v.$$

Let us consider a given instant of time t_0. For this value of t, we have

$$u(x, t_0) = A\, e^{j\omega(t_0 - x/v)}.$$

The value of the function at a given point x_1 is given at this instant by

$$u(x_1, t_0) = A\, e^{j\omega(t_0 - x_1/v)}.$$

If we now move along the x axis to a new point x_2 such that the function at x_2 resumes its value at x, we have

$$e^{j\omega(t_0 - x_1/v)} = e^{j\omega(t_0 - x_2/v)}$$

or

$$e^{-j\omega x_1/v} = e^{-j\omega x_2/v},$$

and hence

$$e^{j\omega(x_2 - x_1)/v} = 1$$

or

$$\frac{\omega}{v}(x_2 - x_1) = 2\pi$$

and hence

$$(x_2 - x_1) = \lambda = \frac{2\pi v}{\omega} = vT. \qquad (7)$$

The distance λ that gives the separation of the successive points of equal phase is called the wavelength. If f is the frequency of the oscillation, we have from (7)

$$\lambda f = v,$$

that is,

wavelength $\times$ frequency $=$ velocity of propagation of phase.

A process that varies in the form (6) is called a *plane wave* since u is constant in any plane perpendicular to the direction of propagation x. The simple plane wave (6) is a particular integral of a partial differential equation that is easily deduced. If u is differentiated twice with respect to t and twice with respect to x, we obtain

$$\frac{\partial^2 u}{\partial t^2} = -\omega^2 A \, e^{j\omega(t-x/v)}$$

and hence

$$\frac{\partial^2 u}{\partial x^2} = -\frac{\omega^2}{\sigma^2} A \, e^{j\omega(t-x/v)}$$

$$\frac{\partial^2 u}{\partial x^2} = \frac{1}{\sigma^2} \frac{\partial^2 u}{\partial t^2} .$$

This is called the wave equation in one dimension. It is fundamental in the study of many important physical phenomena.

Theoretical and Experimental Research for Supercritical Flow along Curved Walls[5]

As another example on the development of custom-made equations for the simulation of a physical process, let us consider a study concerning the supercritical flow of water. Progress in the theoretical development of high-velocity flow of water is due to the existence of extensively developed solutions in the supersonic flow of gases. That physical relationships must exist between high-velocity gas and liquid flow is immediately recognized from pictures showing, for example, the pressure-wave pattern created by a bullet in air and the wave disturbances of a similarly shaped bridge pier in water. The difference in the two cases is apparent only from the fact that the shock waves originating at the sharp tip of the bullet known as standing wave fronts, or hydraulic jumps, extend over a larger width.

The basic features of the analogy are obtained from the continuity, energy, and momentum relationships as commonly applied in hydrodynamics. The following assumptions are made: the flow in either medium is considered two-dimensional in the xy plane, the flow is

---

[5] A study by Dr. Ing. Th. Xanthopoulos of the Ecole Supérieur d'Hydraulique de Toulouse, directed by Professor E. Escande.

steady and frictionless, and the gas flow is considered adiabatic—no heat is added to or taken from the fluid. The energy equation then reads

$$h + \frac{V^2}{2g} = H_0 = \text{const},\tag{8a}$$

where V is the velocity of flow at any point and h and H_0 represent enthalpy and total heat content in foot-pounds per pound. The difference in enthalpy $(H_0 - h)$ can be expressed in accordance with the assumption of adiabatic conditions in terms of H_0 by the following expression:

$$\frac{V^2}{2gH_0} = \frac{H_0 - h}{H_0} = \frac{T_0 - T}{T_0},\tag{8b}$$

with T representing total absolute temperature. Considering the flow of water with a free surface on a horizontal xy plane, assuming hydrostatic pressure distribution and no friction losses, Bernoulli's theorem is written in exactly the same form as Eqs. (8a) and (8b). The term H_0 becomes the total heat H_0 with respect to the bottom, commonly known as specific energy, and h is simply the depth of flow since the enthalpy for gases under the conditions stated depends only on certain constants and the temperature T. The conclusion from Eq. (8b) is that

$$\left(\frac{h}{H_0}\right)_{\text{water}} = \left(\frac{T}{T_0}\right)_{\text{gas}}.$$

The continuity equations are written for gas and for water in the two-dimensional case as follows:

For gas

$$\frac{\partial(\rho V_x)}{\partial x} + \frac{\partial(\rho V_y)}{\partial y} = 0.\tag{9}$$

For water

$$\frac{\partial(h V_x)}{\partial x} + \frac{\partial(h V_y)}{\partial y} = 0.\tag{10}$$

The result is

$$\left(\frac{\rho}{\rho_0}\right)_{\text{gaz}} = \left(\frac{T}{T_0}\right)^{1/K-1} = \left(\frac{h}{H_0}\right)_{\text{water}}.\tag{11}$$

The ratio of the densities ρ/ρ_0 is found to correspond to the ratio of the water depths. Since the latter is also analogous to the ratio of temperatures in gas flow, as the result of Eq. (8b), a perfect correspondence

of the related quantitites is possible only for a hypothetical gas with
$K = c_p/c_v = 2$. However, many flow phenomena do not depend very
strongly on the value of K, so that actual gas flow (for air, $K = 1.4$)
shows satisfactory agreement with the corresponding flow of water in
numerous problems.

The pressure p in gas flow is not proportional to the depth h as one
might be inclined to expect. In accordance with the thermodynamic
principle, $p/p_0 = (\rho/\rho_0)_K$, and using $K = 2$ as derived before, the
comparison gives

$$\left(\frac{p}{p_0}\right)_{gas} = \left(\frac{\rho}{\rho_0}\right)^2_{water} = \left(\frac{h}{H_0}\right)^2_{water} = \left(\frac{p}{p_0}\right)_{water}. \qquad (12)$$

It remains to relate the velocity of sound or of pressure disturbances
in gases to the velocity of equivalent disturbances in water flowing in a
horizontal channel. (The channel may also be inclined so as to compensate for friction forces by a gravity component.) The velocity of
sound in gases is given by $a = \sqrt{K p/\rho}$ and the ratio of a to the velocity
of sound a_0 for an initial state H_0 would be given by

$$\frac{a}{a_0} = \sqrt{\frac{p}{p_0}\frac{\rho}{\rho_0}}. \qquad (13)$$

Using the analogies found so far from Eqs. (11) and (12), the equivalent ratio for water flow is $\sqrt{h/H_0}$ or, written in the final form,[6]

$$\frac{a}{a_0} = \sqrt{\frac{gh}{gH_0}}.$$

The quantity $\sqrt{gh}$ is recognized as the speed of propagation of small
waves or surges in shallow water, which is also often called the "celerity"
(c). Therefore, the quantity analogous to the velocity of sound in gases
is the wave velocity in open channels, provided the height of the wave
front remains small as compared to the depth of flow.

In gas dynamics as well as in hydraulics, use is made of the ratio of
the velocity of flow to the velocity of a pressure disturbance to indicate
the state and character of flow. The ratio of the velocity of gas flow to the
velocity of sound, V/a, is commonly known as the Mach number, which
has its equivalent in hydraulics in the Froude number $V/\sqrt{gh} = V/c$.

---

[6] We keep the equation in this form, to emphasize the ratio of small waves celerity
$\sqrt{gh}$ to the characteristic celerity $\sqrt{gH_o}$.

Equal values of these numbers therefore indicate comparable conditions of flow.

The following treatment takes up the standing hydraulic jump or the standing wave of the shock type.[7] Let Fig. 5 be the plan and elevation

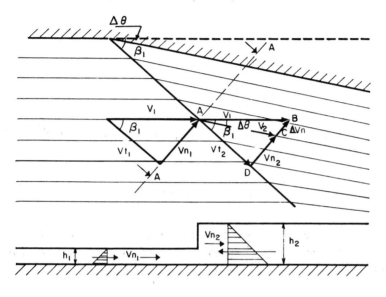

FIG. 5

of such a standing jump at right angles to the flow, and let the jump front be represented by a single line. Let the velocity of approach be V_{n1} and the exit velocity V_{n2}; the corresponding depths are h_1 and h_2. The stream lines are normal to the jump front and parallel to the vertical line, indicating a change in depth from h_1 to h_2 but with velocities V_{t1} and V_{t2} equal and parallel to the front. Since there is no flow across the front, it may be best thought of as a definite boundary, such as a thin plate separating the two streams.

The definition of the original quantities should be well remembered. The velocities V_1 and V_2 are composed of components normal and parallel to the wave front, and the place of the boundary in Fig. 5 is now taken by the jump front representing the regions (1) and (2). The normal component V_{n1} by definition is also the velocity of the jump or wave front, so that V_{n1}/V_1 is the sine of the angle β, properly termed

---

[7] The word "shock" is borrowed from the terminology of gas dynamics and indicates a rather sudden change of flow conditions.

the wave angle. The fact that V_{n1} changes to V_{n2} for flow across the jump line, while V_{t1} and V_{t2} remain the same, means, in effect, a change in direction by an angle θ for the velocity of flow from V_1 to V_2. The application of continuity and momentum relationships, combined with the geometry of the velocity vectors, results in Eqs. (14) to (19). Thus,

$$h_1 V_{n1} = h_2 V_{n2},\tag{14a}$$

$$h_1 V_1 \sin \beta_1 = h_2 V_2 \sin (\beta_1 - \theta),\tag{14b}$$

$$\frac{h_2{}^2 - h_1{}^2}{2h_1} = \frac{V_{n1}(V_{n1} - V_{n2})}{g}.\tag{15}$$

From Eq. (15) the jump celerity V_{n1} can be expressed solely in terms of h_1 and h_2,[8]

$$V_{n1} = V_1 \sin \beta_1 = c = \sqrt{gh_1 \frac{1}{2} \frac{h_2}{h_1} \left(1 + \frac{h_2}{h_1}\right)}.\tag{16}$$

The celerity becomes equal to the critical velocity only if the ratio h_2/h_1 approaches unity. Replacing $V_1/\sqrt{gh_1'}$ by the familiar Froude number F_1, Eq. (16) may also be written as

$$\sin \beta_1 = \frac{1}{F_1} \sqrt{\frac{1}{2} \frac{h_1}{h_2} \left(1 + \frac{h_2}{h_1}\right)}.\tag{17}$$

For $h_2/h_1 \approx 1$, Eq. (17) may also be written

$$\sin b_1 = \frac{1}{F_1}.\tag{18}$$

We can see the evident similitude with Mach number:

$$\sin a = \frac{1}{M}.$$

For a given relative height of jump the angle β_1 will depend only on the value of F_1—i.e., on the depth and velocity of approach. The minimum value of $\sin \beta$ for any given F can only be $\sin \beta = 1/F$, since h_2 would have to become smaller than h_1 to reduce $\sin \beta$ below this value.

---

[8] We express c and $\sin \beta_1$ in this form to keep in evidence the influence of the h_2/h_1 ratio.

A hydraulic jump is always accompanied by a certain energy loss ΔH, however small, which is given in terms of initial depth h_1:

$$\frac{\Delta H}{h_1} = \frac{(h_2/h_1 - 1)^3}{4h_2/h_1}.$$

It is easily seen that, for all ratios $h_2/h_1 < 2$, the energy loss is only a small fraction of the initial depth h_1, which in itself is small compared to the total head of energy in most supercritical flows of a practical nature. We may therefore meet shock waves, even as high as the initial depth, as jumps without energy dissipation. This is borne out by the physical appearance of such waves, which do not show the extremely turbulent surface-roller characteristic of higher jumps.

Theory of Front Waves

The law of sines applied to a triangle ABC gives

$$\frac{\Delta V_n}{V_1} = \frac{\sin \Delta\theta}{\sin (90° - \beta_1 + \Delta\theta)}$$

and, for infinitesimal changes of θ,

$$dV_n = \frac{V\,d\theta}{\cos \beta}, \tag{19}$$

in which the subscripts may now be omitted. Rewriting the momentum equation for infinitesimal changes in depth and velocity, a second differential expression for dV_n is obtained:

$$\gamma h\,dh = \frac{\gamma}{g} hV_n\,dV_n$$

or

$$dV_n = \frac{dh}{V_n}g.$$

Since V_n may be replaced by $V \sin \beta$, Eqs. (12) and (13) may be combined to give

$$\frac{V\,d\theta}{\cos \beta} = \frac{g\,dh}{V \sin \beta},$$

$$dh = \frac{V^2}{g}(\tan b)\,d\theta. \tag{20}$$

Equation (20) may be integrated to obtain the gradual change of depth with gradual angular deflections of the stream, if the basic assumption made in the beginning of this section is introduced to relate b and V to h.

The energy dissipation may be disregarded for such flow in accordance with the Bernoulli theorem.

Therefore

$$H = h + \frac{V^2}{2g} = \text{constant}$$

or

$$V = \sqrt{2g(H - h)}.$$

Since

$$\tan b = \frac{V_n}{V} = \frac{\sin b}{\sqrt{1 - \sin^2 b}} = \frac{\sqrt{gh}}{\sqrt{V^2 - gh}} = \frac{\sqrt{h}}{\sqrt{2H - 3h}},$$

Eq. (14) can be transformed finally into

$$\frac{dh}{d\theta} = \frac{2(H - h)\sqrt{h}}{\sqrt{2H - 3h}} = \frac{\sqrt{2h/H}(1 - h/H)H}{\sqrt{1 - 3h/2H}}. \qquad (21)$$

Integration of Eq. (21) gives

$$\theta = \sqrt{3}\tan^{-1}\sqrt{\frac{3h/2H}{1 - 3h/2H}} - \tan^{-1}\sqrt{\frac{1}{3}}\sqrt{\frac{3h/2H}{1 - 3h/2H}} - \theta_1, \qquad (22a)$$

in which θ_1 constitutes the constant of integration defined by the condition that for $\theta = 0$ the depth h is the initial depth h_1. Equation (22a) may also be written in an alternate form employing the Froude number to express

$$\frac{h}{2H/3} = \frac{3}{2 + F^2}.$$

Substitution of this equivalent results in

$$\theta = \sqrt{3}\tan^{-1}\frac{\sqrt{3}}{\sqrt{F^2 - 1}} - \tan^{-1}\frac{1}{\sqrt{F^2 - 1}} - \theta_1. \qquad (22b)$$

The graphical solution of Eq. (18b) is given in Fig. 6.

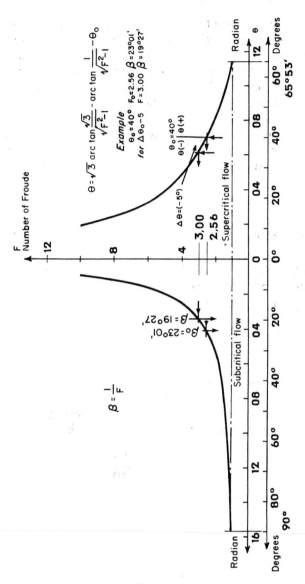

FIG. 6

The wave angle and the depth change Δh determine a change in the velocity normal to the wave front. Therefore, a definite change $\Delta\theta$ in the direction of flow must take place under each wave front. As the flow crosses successive wave fronts at arbitrary distances (the only requirement being that they be not too closely arranged to keep vertical accelerations small), the total change in direction may be related directly to the total change in velocity and depth between any two points along any stream line. Since any boundary of arbitrary curvature represents a stream line, the change of depth along such a boundary can be computed. Conversely, for any desirable changes in depth along a boundary the corresponding curvature may be determined.

Since a curved lateral boundary contains the origins of all disturbance lines, the characteristics of which are given by Eqs. (18) to (22), the entire surface configuration of the supercritical flow is determined by the family of disturbance lines emanating from that boundary or any combination of boundaries.

GRAPHICAL METHOD OF CHARACTERISTICS IN CURVED CHANNELS

To facilitate the analysis of wave systems due to continuous disturbances, such as those in curved channels or in channel contractions or expansions, a graphical method has been devised on the basis of the preceding theory with certain ingenious changes. This development was entirely the outcome of an early analysis of supersonic flow of gases by A. Busemann and is known as the "method of characteristics."

The basic equation for the graphical method of solving problems of supercritical flow of water is given by Eq. (21). For the purpose of obtaining the deflections of the stream lines as a function of the characteristics of the wave fronts, the ratio (h/H) appearing in that equation is replaced by its equivalent from the Bernoulli theorem:

$$1 = \frac{h}{H} + \frac{V^2}{2gH}$$

or, with $\bar{V} = V/\sqrt{2hH}$,

$$\frac{h}{H} = 1 - \bar{V}^2 \tag{23}$$

and

$$\frac{d(h/H)}{d\bar{V}} = -2\bar{V}.$$

Equation (21) is thus transposed into the form

$$\frac{1}{\bar{V}} \frac{d\bar{V}}{d\theta} = \frac{\sqrt{1 - \bar{V}^2}}{\sqrt{3\bar{V}^2 - 1}}. \tag{24}$$

Equation (24) represents the expression for an epicycloid between the circles of radii $1/\sqrt{3}$ and 1 as the limiting values of $\bar{V}$. Only for supercritical flow has Eq. (24) any physical meaning, since the denominator is zero for $\bar{V}^2 - V^2/(2gH) - \frac{1}{3}$ which corresponds to critical flow, whereas the numerator obviously can be zero only for zero depth or $V^2/(2g) = H$. The curve representing Eq. (24) may now be plotted between these limits noting that

$$\frac{d\bar{V}}{d\theta} = \infty \quad \text{for} \quad \bar{V} = \frac{1}{\sqrt{3}} = 0.577$$

and that

$$\frac{d\bar{V}}{d\theta} = 0 \quad \text{for} \quad \bar{V} = 1.$$

The corresponding values (h/H) are two-thirds and zero. For the drawing of the so-called "characteristics diagram" the curve is best transferred to a sheet of celluloid, which is then cut to serve as a templet between the two limiting circular arcs.

The subject diagram may be used as follows: In a rectangular coordinate system the space within a sector of, say, 46° on either side of the $\bar{V}_x$ axis is subdivided into sectors 2° or 4° in central angle, and the intervals are marked by radial lines between the inner and outer limiting circular arcs starting with 0° on the $\bar{V}_x$ axis. From each point on the inner circle the epicycloid may be drawn by the templet in both directions to the outer circle. In this fashion a dense network of intersecting epicycloids is obtained.

Since the radial distance between the limit circles comprises all possible values of between 0.577 and 1.00, a corresponding scale of conversion h/H may be added as shown in Fig. 7.

The physical meaning of the diagram may be demonstrated by first assuming a flow with initial values of V_1 and h_1 or F_1 for which V_1 can be computed. The diagram is next aligned with its $\bar{V}_x$ axis parallel to V_1 in the plane of flow, in which the design of the boundaries is laid out. If one of the boundaries is deflected through an angle $\Delta\theta$, the stream lines adjacent to the wall will turn through the same angle, and a disturbance line will originate at this point in the flow plane, beyond which the flow will be in a new direction and at a new value of $(h/H)_2$ or $\bar{V}_2$.

To find the latter, one must revert to the characteristics diagram. The initial value of $\bar{V}_1$ laid out along the $\bar{V}_x$ axis will be near an intersection of this axis with the two epicycloids. If the plane of flow indicates a positive disturbance, one of the branches leading inward is followed; in the opposite case one of branches going outward is followed from the origin until it intersects the radial line belonging to the angle of turn $\Delta\theta$. The radius vector to this point of intersection represents the new value of $\bar{V}$. Its direction is also the direction of the stream lines beyond the disturbance line in the flow plane, and its magnitude at once gives the hydraulic conditions of depth and velocity or F_2. One may thus

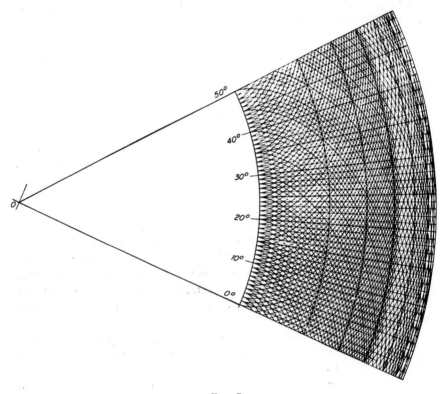

FIG. 7

conclude that every point in the characteristics diagram or in the velocity plane determines the hydraulic conditions in a section of the flow plane bounded by walls or disturbance lines. Before proceeding to extend the construction of stream-line patterns in the flow plane, a method of constructing the disturbance lines at the same time must be found. For this purpose another drafting device is utilized, which is based on the following theoretical considerations.

The component of the velocity normal to the wave fronts V_n was assumed to be given by $\sqrt{gh}$, therefore $(V_n)^2 = gh = gH - V^2/2$ and

$$V^2 = 2gH - 2(V_n)^2. \tag{25}$$

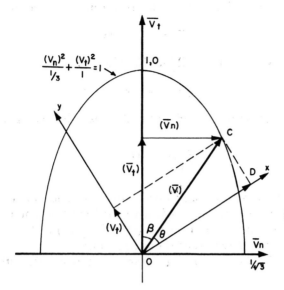

FIG. 8

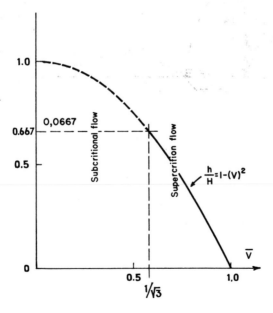

FIG. 9

In accordance with Fig. 5, the velocity V can be related to V_t and V_n by

$$V^2 = (V_t)^2 + (V_n)^2. \tag{26}$$

Introducing V^2 from Eq. (25) into Eq. (26) yields

$$2gH = 3(V_n)^2 + (V_t)^2. \tag{27}$$

Dividing Eq. (27) by $2gH$ gives the dimensionless components $\bar{V}_n$ and $\bar{V}_t$ in

$$\frac{(\bar{V}_n)^2}{1/3} + \frac{(\bar{V}_t)^2}{1} = 1. \tag{28}$$

Equation (28) represents an ellipse with major and minor axes of 1 and $1/\sqrt{3}$, respectively, and any radius vector from the center of the ellipse is equal to $\bar{V}$ since it is given by $\sqrt{(\bar{V}_n)^2 + (\bar{V}_t)^2}$.

Figures 8 and 9 represent these equations.

An example is shown in Fig. 10 in the manner just outlined.

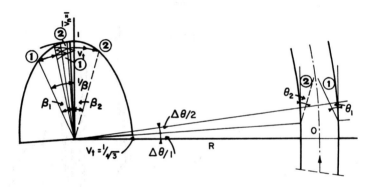

FIG. 10

CHAPTER 6

Considering Numerical Analysis

Thus far we have spoken about writing and testing mathematical equations. We also paid due attention to the pitfalls which exist, particularly those arising from attempts to use linear equations in situations where nonlinear conditions prevail. In the present chapter we will be concerned with certain aspects of numerical analysis. This discussion is not meant to be all-inclusive but rather to orient the reader to one fundamental aspect of numerical analysis: that of differential and difference equations.

The analysis of certain problems arising in mechanics, dynamics, statistics, probability, interpolation, theory of structures, wave filters, telephone lines, multistage amplifiers, and in general networks analysis can lead to the formulation of difference equations. Problems in nuclear physics, chemical reactions, heat flow, and ballistics are also subject to the application of difference equations, as long as they undergo finite changes.

Differential and Difference Equations

The development of solutions to linear differential equations started in 1675, when Leibnitz first employed the integral sign. Euler, in 1739, showed the consistency of linear equations. His discovery generated much interest among mathematicians. In 1760, Lagrange formulated the superposition theory—one of the most interesting results of the sustained attempt to categorize differential equations. From that point on, one "discovery" led to another. Laplace made a major contribution by introducing the transform which bears his name.

A *differential equation* is one involving one or more derivatives of a function. A *solution of a differential equation* is that expression for the dependent variable which does not involve any of its derivatives, and which, when substituted into the given equation, reduces it to an identity. An equation such as

$$\frac{dy}{dx} = f(x)$$

99

is a differential equation of first order and of first degree. Its solution is

$$y = \int f(x)\, dx + C.$$

The order of a differential equation is that of the derivative of highest order which occurs in it. For example, the equation

$$y = x\frac{dy}{dx} + \left(\frac{dy}{dx}\right)^2$$

is of first order. The equation

$$\frac{d^2y}{dx^2} + \frac{dy}{dx} + y = \varphi(x)$$

is of second order. The equation

$$\frac{d^n y}{dx^n} = \varphi(x)$$

is of nth order.

The differential equation $d^n y / dx^n = \varphi(x)$ is of the nth order and of first degree. Its solution can be found by n successive integrations. A function $y = \varphi(x)$ is said to satisfy a differential equation, or to be a solution of it, if, when the calculated values of $\varphi(x)$ and their derivatives are substituted into the equation, the result is correct for all values of x which are to be considered.

A differential equation like $dy/dx + 1 = 0$ has no unique[1] solution, while the equation $dy/dx + |y| = 0$ has the trivial solution $y = 0$. This last equation possesses no solution containing any arbitrary constants. If the solution of a differential equation of order n contains n independent arbitrary constants, we call it the *general solution* of the equation. The general solutions are classified as *complete* solutions or *singular* solutions. The singular solutions occur rarely and have the characteristic that they cannot be obtained from the general solution by specializing its arbitrary constants.

Differential and difference equations, though not alike, have many similarities. The usual difference is found in the ease or applicability with which the one or the other may be used from case to case. In the preceding paragraphs we defined an ordinary differential equation as involving only one independent variable, and including another variable (dependent) and its derivatives with respect to the independent. We said that the solution of this equation is essentially a relation between the dependent and the independent variables which is free of derivatives,

---

[1] For simulation purposes the equation: $y = -x \div C$ needs a complete and correct definition of boundary conditions in order to be of value — that is, additional data are necessary for a solution to become unique. We can fairly well state that an applied mathematical system means a well posed problem (physical or administrative) satisfying three criteria:

    1.— a solution exists

    2.— the solution is unique

    3.— the solution is stable for relatively small changes in data.

and which will satisfy the equality sign. The same is true of ordinary difference equations, only in lieu of derivatives we talk of finite differences.

Difference equations can be recognized by the presence of finite differences in the successive values of the independent variable. Their solutions involve discontinuities at equally spaced values of the independent variable. They arise in systems in which the variables change by finite amounts.

Difference equations may be used in general when there is a repetition of equal intervals of time, of switching cycles, or of equal units of structure. Some special cases of the differential equation fall into the category of a "difference equation." For example, any differential equation whose solution is attempted in terms of a power series, or of a McLaurent series, leads to a difference equation.

The general form of a linear difference equation with constant coefficients is

$$\Phi(x) = \sum_{n=0}^{\infty} d_n \, \Delta^n g(x),$$

where

$$\Delta g(x) = g(x + 1) - g(x).$$

A difference equation may be of the homogeneous or nonhomogeneous type, just as the differential equation. Its solution can be found by following the same rules used in the solution of the differential equation. However, the difference equation is usually simpler than the differential equation; therefore, it is easier to solve. For their solution, difference equations can be processed through electronic computers, hence, the particular interest they attract in numerical analysis.

The solution of difference equations involves discontinuities, i.e., jumps at equally spaced values of the independent variable. This type of change in variable is found in statistics, in interpolation, and in quantum theory. Difference equations are also applicable in physical systems where there is a recurrence of structure or where cyclic switching takes place. We mentioned that in electrical systems, for instance, these equations find applications in wave filters, in transmission lines, in multistage amplifiers, and in electronic switching devices.

The following is a brief comparison of linear difference and differential equations:

linear difference equation,

$$a_0 \, \Delta^n u(x) + a_1 \, \Delta^{n-1} u(x) + \dots a_{n-1} \, \Delta u(x) + a_n u(x) = \varphi(x);$$

linear differential equation,

$$a_0 \frac{d^n y}{dx^n} + a_1(x) \frac{d^{n-1} y}{dx^{n-1}} + \ldots a_{n-1}(x) \frac{dy}{dx} + a_n(x)y = f(x).$$

The finite differences Δ and the derivative d/dx are related by

$$\frac{dy}{dx} = \lim_{\Delta x \to 0} \frac{\Delta y}{\Delta x} = \lim_{\Delta x \to 0} \frac{f(x + \Delta x) - f(x)}{\Delta x}.$$

Differential and difference equations differ, basically, in respect to the assumed, or real, continuity of the function under consideration. Both equations have to do with changes. In the case of differential equations, the changes in the independent and dependent variables are gradual or incremental; whereas with difference equations we distinguish step changes which are of finite size.

As with differential equations, we use difference equations when a mathematical expression is known which relates the various parameters.

The Fundamental Operators

The calculus of finite differences uses certain fundamental operators. An operator is a symbol placed in front of a function to indicate the application of some process which will result in a new function. The following are the most important:

D = differentiation: $Df(x) = f'(x)$
E = translation to the right: $Ef(x) = f(x + h)$
Δ = difference: $\Delta f(x) = f(x + h) - f(x)$
k = constant: $kf(x) = kf(x).$

When several operators are applied to a function in a sequential manner, these are written in the form of a product. Each new operator is written to the left of those preceding it; however, with respect to the outcome, the order in which these several operators are written is immaterial. For instance,

$$E \Delta Df(x) = E\Delta f'(x) = E[f'(x + h) - f'(x)]$$
$$= f'(x + 2h) - f'(x + h),$$
$$\Delta DEf(x) = \Delta Df(x + h) = \Delta f'(x + h)$$
$$= f'(x + 2h) - f'(x + h),$$
$$DE \Delta f(x) = DE[f(x + h) - f(x)]$$
$$= D[f(x + 2h) - f(x + h)]$$
$$= Df(x + 2h) - Df(x + h)$$
$$= f'(x + 2h) - f'(x + h).$$

If an operator is to be repeated n times, it can be indicated in the corresponding power:

$$DDf(x) = D^2f(x),$$
$$\Delta^2\Delta\Delta f(x) = \Delta^4 f(x),$$
$$EE^3E^5Ef(x) = E^{10}f(x).$$

An operator with power zero produces no change to the function

$$\Delta^0 f(x) = f(x).$$

In practice we work mostly with powers of D and Δ integral and non-negative numbers—but all powers of E can be admitted. Let n and m be any two numbers. Then

$$E^m E^n f(x) = f[x + (n + m)h] = E^{m+n}f(x).$$

The rules of algebra hold true for operators. They are:

$$(\Delta + D)f(x) = \Delta f(x) + Df(x)$$
$$= f(x + h) - f(x) + f'(x),$$
$$(\Delta + E)f(x) = \Delta f(x) + Ef(x)$$
$$= f(x + h) - f(x) + f(x + h)$$
$$= 2f(x + h) - f(x),$$
$$(D + k)f(x) = Df(x) + kf(x)$$
$$= f'(x) + kf(x).$$

Two operators are called equal if, when they are applied to an arbitrary function, they produce the same results: $\Delta = (E - 1)$.

Consider the function $F(x)$, then

$$EF(x) = F(x + h),$$
$$EF(x) = \left(1 + hD + \frac{h^2D^2}{2} + \frac{h^3D^3}{3} + ...\right)F(x)$$
$$= e^{hD}F(x).$$

Thus,

$$E = e^{hD} \quad \text{and} \quad \Delta = (e^{hD} - 1).$$

Since the operators conform to the fundamental rules of algebra, we can write

$$E^\lambda\Delta = \Delta E^\lambda,$$
$$\Delta^n D = D\Delta^n,$$
$$(E^m D - \Delta)(E^m D + \Delta) = E^{2m}D^2 - \Delta^2,$$
$$(D - E)^2 = D^2 + E^2 - 2DE, \quad \text{etc.}$$

Consider the general form of a linear second-order difference equation with constant coefficients:

$$A_2 y(x + 2) + A_1 y(x + 1) + A_0 y(x) = f(x), \tag{1}$$

$y(x)$ is the unknown function, y being the dependent variable and x the independent variable. The coefficients and the driving function $f(x)$ are known. The equation states the relation among values of $y(x)$ for values of x separated by unity over a range of 2 units. There is no loss of generality by this choice of unit length because an equation in which increments of x are of length h can be converted into an equation in which the increments are of unit length by making the change of variable $x = hx'$.

The form of Eq. (1) can be changed to show more clearly its analogy to the differential equation. The first difference of the function $y(x)$ is

$$\Delta y(x) = y(x + 1) - y(x). \tag{2}$$

Applications of the operator Δ gives a higher-order differences:

$$\Delta^2 y(x) = \Delta[\Delta y(x)] = \Delta[y(x + 1) - y(x)] = y(x + 2) - 2y(x + 1) + y(x). \tag{3}$$

From Eq. (2),

$$y(x + 1) = (\Delta + 1)y(x); \tag{4}$$

from Eq. (3),

$$\begin{aligned} y(x + 2) &= (1 + \Delta)y(x + 1) = (1 + \Delta)^2 y(x), \\ y(x + 3) &= (1 + \Delta)y(x + 2) = (1 + \Delta)^3 y(x). \end{aligned} \tag{5}$$

Substituting (4) and (5) into Eq. (1) a second-order difference equation is obtained of the form

$$b_2 \, \Delta^2 y(x) + b_1 \, \Delta y(x) + b_0 y(x) = f(x), \tag{6}$$

where

$$b_2 = A_2, \qquad b_1 = A_1 + 2A_2, \qquad b_0 = A_0 + A_1 + A_2.$$

The analogy between second-order difference equations and a second-order differential equation is apparent from Eq. (6), where Δ^n is analogous to d^n/dx^n.

Since the basic dissimilarity between a difference equation and a differential equation is in the length of the increments of the independent variable, a differential equation can be obtained from a difference equation by dividing each term by the same power of h as the order of its difference and then let h approach zero.

Consider again a linear difference equation with constant coefficients as an equation of the form

$$a_0 \Delta^n \varphi(x) + a_1 \Delta^{n-1}\varphi(x) + \ldots + a_{n-1} \Delta\varphi(x) + a_n\varphi(x) = F(x). \qquad (7)$$

By using operator E, (7) can be written in the form

$$(b_0 E^n + b_1 E^{n-1} + b_2 E^{n-2} + \ldots + b_n)\varphi(x) = F(x). \qquad (8)$$

As with a linear differential equation, the solution of a difference equation consists of the sum of the complementary function and of the particular integral. The complementary function is the solution of the homogeneous equation

$$(b_0 E^n + b_1 E^{n-1} + \ldots + b_n)\varphi(x) = 0. \qquad (9)$$

Let $(x) = ke^{mx}$ be an exponential solution of the homogeneous equation. Also assume an increment $h = 1$: $E\varphi(x) = \varphi(x + 1)$. Then,

$$E\varphi(x) = Eke^{mx} = ke^{m(x+1)} = ke^{mx}e^m,$$

$$E^2\varphi(x) = Eke^{mx}e^m = ke^{mx}e^{2m}, \qquad (10)$$

$$\vdots$$

$$E^n\varphi(x) = ke^{mx}e^{nm}.$$

Substituting Eq. (10) into Eq. (3),

$$ke^{mx}(b_0 e^{nm} + b_1 e^{(n-1)m} + \ldots + b_n) = 0$$

or

$$kg^x(b_0 g^n + b_1 g^{(n-1)} + \ldots + b_{n-1}g + b_n) = 0$$

for $g = e^m$; and since $kg^x \neq 0$ it must follow that

$$b_0 g^n + b_1 g^{(n-1)} + \ldots + b_{n-1}g + b_n = 0,$$

which is an algebraic equation, and from which must be determined the possible values of g.

The following cases should be kept in mind in the solution of difference equations.

CASE 1. If $g_1, g_2, g_3, \ldots g_n$ are distinct real roots, then

$$\varphi(x) = k_1 g_1{}^x + k_2 g_2{}^x + \ldots + k_{n-1} g_{n-1}^x + k_n g_n{}^x$$

is the general solution of the homogeneous difference equations, where k_i, $i = 1, 2, \cdots n$, are arbitrary constants.

As an example, let the original equation be

$$(4E^2 + 7E + 1)\varphi(x) = 0,$$

then

$$4g^2 + 7g + 1 = 0$$

for

$$g = \frac{-7 \pm \sqrt{49 - 33}}{8} = \frac{-7 \pm 5.73}{8}.$$

The roots are $g = -12.73/8 = -1.59$, $g_2 = -1.27/8 = -.159$, and the required solution is

$$\varphi(x) = k_1(-1.59)^x + k_2(-0.159)^x,$$

where k_i are arbitrary constants.

CASE 2. If the algebraic equation has a pair of conjugate complex roots,

$$g_1 = \lambda e^{j\theta}, \qquad g_2 = \lambda e^{-j\theta},$$

then the solution will be of the form

$$k_1 g_1{}^x + k_2 g_2 = k_1 \lambda^x e^{j\theta x} + k_2 \lambda^x e^{-j\theta x}$$
$$= \lambda^x (A \cos \theta x + B \sin \theta x).$$

CASE 3. If the equation has x repeated real roots equal to y, then we assume the solution

$$\varphi(x) = y^x f(x),$$

and we locate a function of $f(x)$ which will satisfy the original difference equation.

Obviously when the difference equation is not of the linear homogeneous type, the particular integral must also be computed. The method of approach is similar to the one used with the linear differential equations.

The Derivative and the Integral of a Tabulated Function

We saw that

$$e^{hD} = (1 + \Delta)$$

or

$$D = \frac{1}{h} \ln (1 + \Delta),$$

$$D = \frac{1}{h}\left(\Delta - \frac{\Delta^2}{2} + \frac{\Delta^3}{3} - \frac{\Delta^4}{4} + \ldots\right).$$

Therefore,

$$Df(a) = f'(a) = \frac{1}{h}\Delta f(a) - \frac{1}{h}\Delta^2 f(a) + \frac{1}{h}\Delta^3 f(a) \ldots$$

gives the derivative of a function $f(x)$ at $x = a$. Higher derivatives can be obtained from

$$D^r = \frac{1}{h^r}\ln (1 + \Delta)^r,$$

where $r = 1, 2, 3 \ldots n$.

Introducing the operator $D^{-1} = 1/D$, such that $D^{-1}D = 1$ and $D^{-1}Df(a) = f(a)$, we obtain the integral of a tabulated function as

$$D^{-1}f(x) = \int f(x)\, dx + C.$$

The function would be

$$DD^{-1}f(x) = \frac{d}{dx}\int f(x)\, dx + \frac{d}{dx}C = f(x).$$

The following formulas are used for integration:

$$\int_a^{a+h} f(x)\, dx = h(1 + \frac{\Delta}{2} - \frac{\Delta^2}{12} + \frac{\Delta^3}{24} - \frac{19}{720}\Delta^4 + \ldots)f(a),$$

$$\int_a^{a+2h} f(x)\, dx = h(2 + 2\Delta + \frac{\Delta^2}{3} - \frac{\Delta^4}{90} + \ldots)f(a).$$

Simson's rule for approximate integration is

$$\int_a^{a+2h} f(x)\, dx = h\left(2 + 2\Delta + \frac{\Delta^2}{3}\right)f(a)$$

$$= \frac{h}{3}(1 + 4E + E^2)f(a).$$

The "three-eights" rule of Cotes is

$$\int_a^{a+2h} f(x)\, dx = \frac{3h}{8}\, [1 + 3E + 3E^2 + E^3]\, f(a).$$

The general formula is

$$\int_a^{a+nh} f(x)\, dx = nh \left[1 + \frac{n}{2} \varDelta + \frac{n(2n-3)}{12} \varDelta^2 + \frac{n(n-2)^2}{24} \varDelta^3 + \ldots \right] f(a).$$

The summation formula for polynomials, with the use of operators, is

$$\begin{aligned}
S_n &= f(a) + f(a + h) + \ldots + f(a + (n-1)h) \\
&= (1 + E + E^2 + \ldots + E^{n-1}) f(a) \\
&= \left(n + \frac{n(n-1)}{2} \varDelta + \frac{n(n-1)(n-2)}{6} \varDelta^2 + \ldots \right) f(a).
\end{aligned}$$

Examples of Difference Equations

The following is a number of examples on the application of difference equations.

EXAMPLE 1. Consider the transmission line shown in Fig. 1. It is given by the equation

$$E(x) - \left(2 + \frac{Z}{Z'} \right) E(x + 1) + E(x + 2) = 0,$$

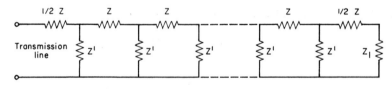

FIG. 1

and, for $Z = 12$ and $Z' = 3$, we have

$$E(x) - (2 + 4)E(x + 1) + E(x + 2) = 0$$

or

$$E(x) - 6E(x + 1) + E(x + 2) = 0. \tag{11}$$

By definition,

$$\Delta E(x) = E(x + 1) - E(x)$$

and

$$\Delta^2 E(x) = \Delta E(x + 1) - \Delta E(x)$$
$$= E(x + 2) - 2E(x + 1) + E(x);$$

therefore,

$$E(x + 2) = \Delta^2 E(x) + 2E(x + 1) - E(x)$$
$$= \Delta^2 E(x) + E(x + 1) + E(x + 1) - E(x).$$

But

$$E(x + 1) = \Delta E(x) + E(x)$$

and

$$\Delta E(x) = E(x + 1) - E(x).$$

Therefore,

$$E(x + 2) = \Delta^2 E(x) + \Delta E(x) + E(x) + \Delta E(x)$$

or

$$E(x + 2) = \Delta^2 E(x) + 2\,\Delta E(x) + E(x). \tag{12}$$

Also

$$E(x + 1) = \Delta E(x) + E(x). \tag{13}$$

Substituting Eqs. (12) and (13) into Eq. (11) gives

$$E(x) + 6\,\Delta E(x) + 6E(x) + \Delta^2 E(x) + 2\,\Delta E(x) + E(x) = 0$$

or

$$\Delta^2 E(x) + 8\,\Delta E(x) + 8E(x) = 0$$

and

$$g^2 + 8g + 8 = 0,$$

$$g = \frac{-8 \pm \sqrt{64 - 32}}{2} = -4 \pm \frac{\sqrt{32}}{2} = -4 \pm \sqrt{8},$$

$$g_1 = -6.83 \quad \text{and} \quad g_2 = -1.17.$$

EXAMPLE 2. Consider a second-order homogeneous difference equation

$$y(x + 2) - 5y(x + 1) + 6y(x) = 0. \tag{14}$$

This can be written as

$$\Delta^2 y(x) - 3 \Delta y(x) + 2y(x) = 0; \qquad (15)$$

or substituting $\Delta = E + 1$,

$$E^2 y(x) - E y(x) + 3y(x) = 0. \qquad (16)$$

The solution is of the form $y(x) = k e^{mx}$. The characteristic equation would be

$$e^{2m} - e^m + 3 = 0.$$

By letting $e^m = g$ we obtain $g^2 - g + 3 = 0$. Thus,

$$g_1 = 1.71 \, e^{j\phi}, \qquad g_2 = 1.71 \, e^{-j\phi},$$

$$y(x) = K_1 (1.71)^x \, e^{j\phi} + K_2 (1.71)^x \, e^{-j\phi}. \qquad (17)$$

K_1 and K_2 would be computed for any boundary conditions the problem might have.

Consider again Eq. (15), $\Delta^2 y(x) - 3 \Delta y(x) + 2y(x) = 0$. Instead of substituting $\Delta = E + 1$, let it be rewritten in the form $A^2 - 3A + 2 = 0$. Then the solution would be of the form $y(x) = K e^{mx}$, and for

$$A = \frac{3 \pm \sqrt{9 - 8}}{2},$$

$A_1 = 2, A_2 = 1$, it is

$$y(x) = K_1'(2)^x + K_2'(1)^x = K_1'(2)^x + K_2'. \qquad (18)$$

Equations (17) and (18) are both solutions to the original equation (14), but the shift along the axis when going from Δ to E must be taken into consideration.

EXAMPLE 3. Consider the oscillations of a chain of particles connected by strings. Say that there is a "weightless" string of length $(n + 1)$ stretched between two fixed points with tension T. This string is loaded at equal distances a with n equal masses M which are not under the influence of gravity. When the system is disturbed, it is required to determine its natural frequencies and the displacement of the Kth particle (Fig. 2).

It would be rather tedious to solve this and similar problems by writing the equations of motion of each particle. The solution is simplified by setting up a general difference equation which takes into account all of the moving parts of the system.

Let A and B be the fixed points and $(y_1, y_2, \ldots y_n)$ be the ordinates at time t of the n particles. By considering only small displacements, it is assumed that the tension of each section remains the constant value T. The restoring force on the Kth mass is given by

$$F_K = \frac{T}{a} [(y_{K-1} - y_K) + (y_{K+1} - y_K)]. \tag{19}$$

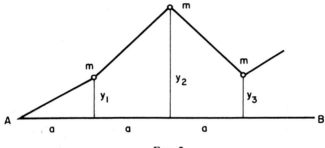

FIG. 2

From Newton's second law, the equation of motion is

$$M \frac{d^2 y_K}{dt^2} + \frac{T}{a} (-y_{K-1} + 2y_K - y_{K+1}) = 0. \tag{20}$$

Since each particle vibrates in a similar manner its motion may be described by

$$y_K = A_K \cos(\omega t + \Phi). \tag{21}$$

Substituting into Eq. (20) and canceling out the common cosine term yields

$$-\omega^2 M A_K + \frac{T}{a} (-A_{K-1} + 2A_K - A_{K+1}) = 0. \tag{22}$$

Then let

$$C = \left(2 - \frac{\omega^2 M a}{T} \right). \tag{23}$$

Equation (22) simplifies to

$$-A_{K+1} + C A_K - A_{K-1} = 0. \tag{24}$$

This is a homogeneous difference equation of the second order. The solution is similar to that of a differential equation. We start by assuming a solution of the form

$$A_K = B e^{\theta K}. \tag{25}$$

Here B is an arbitrary constant, and θ is to be determined. By substitution of this assumed solution into Eq. (6) we obtain

$$Be^{\theta K}(-e^{\theta} + C - e^{-\theta}) = 0. \tag{26}$$

For a nontrival solution we must equate the terms in parentheses to zero, then by solving for C and dividing by two, we have

$$\frac{C}{2} = \frac{e^{\theta} + e^{-\theta}}{2} = \cosh(\theta). \tag{27}$$

Since

$$\frac{C}{2} = \cosh(\theta) = \cosh(-\theta),$$

two values of θ are evident, and the solution is the sum of two terms such as $B_1 e^{\theta K}$ and $B_2 e^{-\theta K}$. However, it is more convenient to write the solution in terms of hyperbolic functions, which yields

$$A_K = P\sinh(\theta K) + Q\cosh(\theta K). \tag{28}$$

As with differential equations we must utilize the boundary conditions to determine the values of θ. If a particle is at the fixed end (A), then, in Eq. (28), A_K must equal zero. Therefore, Q must equal zero since $\sinh(0) = 0$ but $\cosh(0) = 1$. Thus the solution reduces to

$$A_K = P\sinh(\theta K). \tag{29}$$

Utilizing the fact that the amplitude at the fixed end (B) must also equal zero, $(n + 1)$ may be substituted for K which yields the requirement

$$\sinh[\theta(n + 1)] = 0.$$

This will be true when

$$\theta = \frac{r\pi j}{r + 1} \qquad \text{where} \quad r = 1, 2, 3, \ldots n.$$

With the values of θ known, it is now possible to determine the values of w by referring to Eqs. (23) and (27). Thus,

$$C = 2 - \frac{\omega^2 Ma}{T} = 2\cosh\frac{r\pi j}{n + 1} = 2\cos\frac{r\pi}{m + 1}.$$

Hence,

$$\omega^2 = \frac{2\tau}{Ma}\left[1 - \cos\left(\frac{r\pi}{n+1}\right)\right] = \frac{4\tau}{Ma}\sin^2\frac{r\pi}{2(n+1)}$$

and

$$\omega_r = 2\sqrt{\frac{\tau}{Ma}}\sin\frac{r\pi}{2(n+1)}$$

where $r = 1, 2, 3, \ldots n$.

In this manner, the natural frequencies are obtainable for each particle from 1 to n. For each of these values of θ_i, there corresponds a term for the amplitude of the Kth particle. Equation (29) can be rewritten as

$$A_K = P_r \sinh(\theta_r K) = P_r \sin\left(\frac{r\pi K}{n+1}\right).$$

According to Eq. (21) the displacement at time t of the Kth particle corresponding to a value θ_r is

$$y_K = P_r \sin\left(\frac{r\pi K}{n+1}\right)\cos(\omega_r t + \theta_r).$$

Here, P_r and θ_r are arbitrary constants depending on the initial conditions of the system.

EXAMPLE 4. Consider the case of a continuously loaded beam such as the one shown in Fig. 3. The moment equation is

$$M(x) + 4M(x+1) + M(x+2) = -\frac{\omega L^2}{2},$$

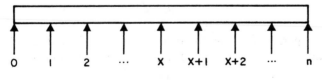

FIG. 3

which we can write in the form of a difference equation:

$$\Delta^2 M(x) + 6\,\Delta M(x) + 6M(x) = -\frac{\omega L^2}{2}.$$

This difference equation has two forms of solution, a complementary function and a particular integral. For the complementary function the equation is set equal to zero and solved as such:

$$\Delta^2 M(x) + 6 \, \Delta M(x) + 6M(x) = 0$$

or

$$g^2 + 6g + 6 = 0,$$

and $g_1 = -19.7$, $g_2 = -16.3$.

The particular integral is then solved in exactly the same manner as with differential equations. The following is a more extended treatment of a similar example.

EXAMPLE 5.[1] One of the methods most used in the analysis of a statically indeterminate structure, especially in continuous beams with different type of loading, is the so-called 'three-moments equation," which is derived in most standard texts on theory of structure. In special applications of the three-moments equation, it can be shown that it leads to a second-order linear difference equation with constant coefficients. It may be homogeneous or nonhomogeneous, depending upon the type of loading.

In any continuous beam such as shown in Fig. 4 and for any two

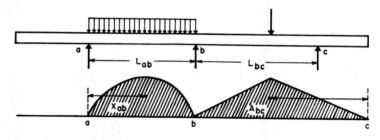

Fig. 4

successive spans defined by the three supports a, b, and c, with any type of loading on ab and bc, the three-moments equation is

$$I_{bc}L_{ab}M_a + 2(I_{bc}L_{ab} + I_{ab}L_{bc})M_b + I_{ab}L_{bc}M$$

$$= -6A_{ab}\frac{X_{ab}}{L_{bc}}I_{bc} - 6A_{bc}\frac{X_{bc}}{L_{bc}}I_{ab}, \quad (30)$$

---

[1] This example was worked by Mr. P. K. Georgies in a graduate course in applied mathematics which the writer was teaching during the Spring Semester, 1957, at the School of Engineering and Architecture, the Catholic University of America.

where

M_{abc} are the moments in the supports a, b, and c,

I_{ab} is the moment of inertia of ab,

I_{bc} is the moment of inertia of bc,

L_{ab} is the length of the span ab,

L_{bc} is the length of the span bc,

A_{ab} is the area of the moment diagram due to loading on span ab,

A_{bc} is the area of the moment diagram due to loading on span bc,

X_{ab} is the distance from the center of gravity of the area A to point a,

X_{bc} is the distance from the center of gravity of the area A to point c.

In the special case where the spans are equal, Eq. (30) becomes

$$M_a + 4M_b + M_c = -6A_{ab}\frac{X_{ab}}{L^2_{ab}} - 6A_{bc}\frac{X_{bc}}{L^2_{bc}}. \qquad (31)$$

Consider a continuous beam of equal spans, which on the left extends to infinity. If a moment M is applied to the left end, then a moment will be developed at each support, the value of which depends upon the value of M and upon distance from the point of application of M It is required to find the manner in which the effect of M is distributed

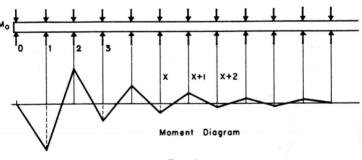

Moment Diagram

FIG. 5

In Fig. 5, the supports are numbered 0, 1, 2, 3 .... Let the support 0 represent the origin. Also consider x as being positive to the right, where x is an integer number of spans 0, 1, 2 ... . If M is the moment at any point x, then this moment is a function of x, therefore we can write

$$M_x = F(x). \qquad (32)$$

The moment at one span to the right of x is a function of $x + 1$:

$$M_{x+1} = F(x + 1), \qquad M_{x+2} = F(x + 2). \tag{33}$$

The operator E, by definition, gives

$$E^n F(x) = F(x + nh).$$

If we let $h = 1$, i.e., taking an increment of one span, the equation becomes

$$E^n F(x) = F(x + N),$$

and from Eqs. (32) and (33) it follows that

$$\begin{aligned} M_x &= F(x) = E^0 F(x), \\ M_{x+1} &= F(x + 1) = E F(x), \\ M_{x+2} &= F(x + 2) = E^2 F(x). \end{aligned} \tag{34}$$

The three-moment equation for the supports x, $x + 1$, and $x + 2$ is obtained by substituting for M_a, M_b, and M_c the M_x, M_{x+1}, and M_{x+2}, respectively, in Eq. (31):

$$M_x + 4M_{x+1} + M_{x+2}, = 0$$

Or, substituting the M_x, M_{x+1}, and M_{x+2} from (34),

$$(E^2 + 4E + 1)F(x) = 0. \tag{35}$$

This is a linear, homogeneous difference equation with constant coefficients. Its complete solution is given by the solution of the complementary function and the auxiliary equation. So start with

$$g^2 + 4g + 1 = 0,$$

with roots

$$g_1 = -2 + \sqrt{3} = -0.268, \qquad g_2 = -2 - \sqrt{3} = -3.732.$$

The complete solution of Eq. (35) will then be

$$\begin{aligned} F(x) &= C_1 g_1{}^x + C_2 g_2{}^x \\ &= C_1(-0.268)^x + C_2(-3.732)^x. \end{aligned} \tag{36}$$

But $F(x) = M_x$. Therefore,

$$M_x = C_1(-0.268)^x + C_2(-3.732)^x.$$

The constants C_1 and C_2 are found by referring to the physical boundary conditions, i.e., at $x = 0$, $M_x = M$; at $x = \infty$, $M_x = 0$. So

$$0 = C_1(-\infty) + C_2(-\infty),$$

and $C_2 = 0$ or ∞. Since, for $C_2 = \infty$, the value of M_x will be ∞, which is impossible, it follows that $C_2 = 0$. Therefore, $M_x = C_1 g_1{}^x$ or, substituting for the first boundary condition, $M_0 = C_1$. The final solution of (35) is

$$M_x = M_0(-0.268)^x.$$

The minus sign takes care of the sign of the moment. It gives negative moments for odd values of x and positive moments for even values of x.

Consider now a continuous beam of n equal spans loaded with a load of uniformly varying intensity from 0 to a maximum value of w, as shown in Fig. 6, and continuing to the right with uniform loading for one span.

The "three-moments equation" for any three successive supports is found by substitution into Eq. (31):

$$M_x + M_{x+1} + M_{x+2} = -\frac{\omega L^2}{2M}(x + 1). \tag{37}$$

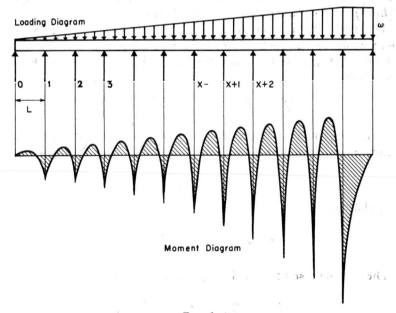

FIG. 6

By a method similar to the one followed in the previous case,

$$M_x = F(x) = E^0 F(x),$$
$$M_{x+1} = F(x + 1) = EF(x),$$
$$M_{x+2} = F(x + 2) = E^2 F(x).$$

Therefore, Eq. (37) becomes

$$(E^2 + 4E + 1)F(x) = -\frac{\omega L^2}{2M}(x + 1). \tag{38}$$

This is a nonhomogeneous linear difference equation with constant coefficients. Its complete solution is the sum of the solution of the complementary function and the particular integral. The solution of the complementary function is given by Eq. (36) and is

$$F(x)_{comp} = C_1 g_1{}^x + C_2 g_2{}^x,$$

where

$$g_1 = -2 + \sqrt{3} = -0.263, \qquad g_2 = -2 - \sqrt{3} = -3.732.$$

The particular integral is that of a nonhomogeneous equation $\Phi[EF(x)] = f(x)$, where $f(x) = -(\omega L^2/2m)(x + 1)$.

The particular integral of an equation of this form can be found more easily by the method of undetermined coefficients. Assuming a solution, $F(x)_{part} = Ax$, and substituting this equation into Eq. (38), we obtain

$$(E^2 + 4E + 1)Ax = -\frac{\omega L^2}{2m}(x + 1).$$

This is an identity in x, therefore it holds for any value of x. Then, setting $x = 1$, we obtain $3A + 8A + A = -(2\omega L^2/2m)$, or

$$A = -\frac{\omega L^2}{12m}$$

and, therefore,

$$F(x)_{part} = -\frac{\omega L^2}{12m} x.$$

The complete solution of Eq. (38) will then be

$$F(x) = C_1 g_1{}^x + C_2 g_2{}^x - \frac{\omega L^2}{12m} x$$

and

$$M_x = C_1 g_1{}^x + C_2 g_2{}^x - \frac{\omega L^2}{12m}\, x, \qquad (39)$$

since $F(x) = M_x$.

To find the constants C_1 and C_2, consider that at $x = 0$, $M = 0$, and, at $x = n$, $M = -\omega L^2/2$. Substituting the above boundary conditions into Eq. (39) we obtain

$$0 = C_1 + C_2 - 0 \qquad (40a)$$

and

$$-\frac{\omega L^2}{2} = C_1 g_1{}^n + C_2 g_2{}^n - \frac{\omega L^2}{12}. \qquad (40b)$$

Solving for C_1 and C_2, we have, from (40a), $C_1 = -C_2$ or

$$-\frac{\omega L^2}{2} + \frac{\omega L^2}{12} = C_1(g_1{}^n - g_2{}^n)$$

and

$$-\frac{5}{12}\omega L^2 = C_1(g_1{}^n - g_2{}^n).$$

Therefore,

$$C_1 = \frac{-5\omega L^2}{12(g_1{}^n - g_2{}^n)}$$

and

$$C_2 = \frac{5\omega L^2}{12(g_1{}^n - g_2{}^n)}.$$

Finally,

$$M_x = -\frac{5\omega L^2}{12(g_1{}^n - g_1{}^n)} g_1{}^x + \frac{5\omega L^2}{12(g_1{}^n - g_2{}^n)} + \frac{\omega L^2}{12n}\, x,$$

$$M_x = \frac{\omega L^2}{12}\left[\frac{5}{g_1{}^n - g_2{}^n}(g_2{}^x - g_1{}^x) - \frac{x}{n}\right],$$

$$M_x = \frac{\omega L^2}{12}\left[5\,\frac{-(-3.732)^x + (-0.263)^x}{(-3.732)^n - (-0.268)^n} + \frac{x}{n}\right].$$

CHAPTER 7

A Tool for Data Generation

In simulation studies, we are often required to generate data. The reason may be a need to test a certain set of equations, to supplement disperse information, or to complete data which have been made available only intermittently. This process may involve the development of special equations or the use of mathematical tools whereby intermediate values of a function may be established.

The data-generation problem is generic in a variety of fields. Literary data handling, for instance, is an example quite different in nature than mathematical interpolation theory. We talk about methods of establishing lists and patterns of keywords through the use of statistical tools. Information retrivial methods consist essentially of extracting from or interpolating to a given text significant words based on their frequency of occurence.[1] But though the means and the tools are different, the fundamental needs behind their use have striking similarities.

As an example of data generation, in the present chapter we are concerned with mathematical interpolation. Given a series of numerical values of a function, for equally spaced values of the argument, we search to find the value of the function for any intermediate value of the argument, independently of the analytical form of the function, which may or may not be given.

Introduction to Interpolation

Interpolation is defined as "the art of representing a function, known or unknown, in a form chosen in advance, with the aid of given values which this function takes for definite values of the independent variable." It is a method whereby intermediate values of a function may be found when the function is known at intervals over a range including the desired value.

---

[1] For reference see P. Tasman, "Indexing the Dead Sea Scrolls by Electronic Literary Data Processing Methods," IBM publication, November 1958 and L. D. Findley, C. C. Bolze, and R. A. Charpenter, "A Card Controlled Routine for Searching Chemical Compound Data," Midwest Research Institute, Kansas City, Missouri, 1958.

As an illustration, let $y = f(x)$ be a function given by the values $y_0, y_1, y_2 \dots y_n$ which it takes for the corresponding values, $x_0, x_1, x_2 \dots x_n$ of the independent variable x. Let $\Phi(x)$ denote an arbitrary simpler function so constructed that it takes the same values as $f(x)$ for $x_0, x_1, x_2 \dots x_n$. Then if $f(x)$ is replaced by $\Phi(x)$ over a given interval, the function $\Phi(x)$ is a formula of interpolation.

$\Phi(x)$ can take a variety of forms. We always choose the simplest form which will represent the given $f(x)$ over the interval in question. Since polynomials are the simplest functions, we usually take a polynomial for $\Phi(x)$. Most of the standard formulas of interpolation are polynomial formulas. In case the function $f(x)$ is known to be periodic, we prefer to represent it by a trigonometric series. The justification for replacing a given function by a polynomial or by a trigonometric series rests on two theorems proved by Weierstrass in 1885. They are as follows:

(1) Every function which is continuous in an interval (a, b) can be represented in that interval, to any desired degree of accuracy, by a polynomial. That is, it is possible to find a polynomial $P(x)$ such that $|f(x) - P(x)| < \epsilon$ for every value of x in the interval (a, b), where ϵ is any pre-assigned positive quantity.

(2) Every continuous function of period 2π can be represented by a finite trigonometric series of the form

$$g(x) = a_0 + a_1 \sin x + a_2 \sin 2x + \dots + a_n \sin nx$$
$$+ b_1 \cos x + b_2 \cos 2x + \dots + b_n \cos nx,$$

or such that $|f(x) - g(x)| < \delta$ for all values of x in the interval considered, where δ represents any pre-assigned positive quantity.

Since most functions can, within moderate intervals, be approximated by polynomials of a suitable degree, the interpolation formulas may be applied to a number of functions which are not polynomials. The only requirements for such application are that $f(x)$ be a real, single-valued function which is continuous in a certain closed interval and that, within this interval, it possess a continuous differential coefficient of the highest order.

Many of the applications of interpolation theory have been in the field of astronomy. The Nautical Almanac, for instance, gives the heliocentric longitude of Jupiter for every 4th day; but because of the slow, continuous, and systematic character of Jupiter's orbital motion, it is found sufficient to compute the longitude from the tables direct for every 40th day only. The intermediate places are then readily interpolated with an accuracy which equals, if indeed it does not exceed, that of direct computation. In the same Almanac, the moon's longitude is given for every twelve hours, for the moon's orbital motion is so rapid and complicated that it would prove inexpedient to attempt the interpolation of accurate values of the longitude from an ephermeris given for whole day intervals.

To render the problem of interpolation determinate, the tabular interval must be sufficiently small so that the nature or law of the function will be definitely shown by the tabular values in question. The condition thus imposed will be satisfied when, in a given table, the differences become constant at some particular order.

In a certain application, the control dial of an electronic metronome was marked off in equal parts while it actually operated according to an exponential function. It was desired to calibrate the dial in terms of pulses per minute produced by the metronome. Data were gathered, and the interpolation method was applied to determine intermediate values, thus affording a chance to see how closely Newton's formula would come to approximating an exponential function. The exponential in question is shown in Fig. 1. Both the actual and the interpolated number of pulses per minute are indicated for a setting equal to 65.

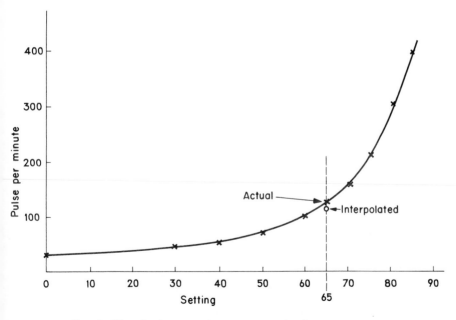

FIG. 1   Plot of pulses per minute versus setting for a metronome.

Similarly, Fig. 2 shows a comparison between actual and interpolated data from a study involving an exponential function in x, y.

In the majority of cases, the time is the argument of the tabulated function. This is particularly true of astronomical tables. But there

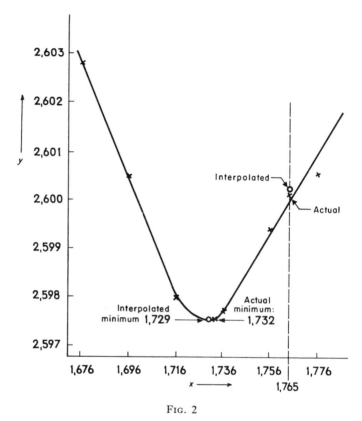

FIG. 2

exist tabular functions whose arguments are elements other than time, for example:

   (i) the force of gravity as a function of latitude,
  (ii) the atmospheric pressure as a function of the altitude,
 (iii) the angle of refraction in a particular substance, as a function of the angle of incidence.

The Mechanics of Interpolation

If we are given a series of quantities proceeding according to any law, and take the difference of every two consecutive terms, we obtain a series of values called the first order of differences, or briefly, the first differences. If we difference the first differences in the same manner, we form a new series called second differences. The process may be continued, if necessary, so long as any differences remain. The nth differences of any degree polynomial are constant, and any higher differences are zero. A *difference table* is constructed by arranging these values in a tabular form. This was discussed in Chapter 6, when considering the operator Δ.

Given that a difference table is the first basic step in this process, we shall start with an example involving two polynomials, differencing to the tabular values of functions, for equidistant values of the argument. These differences, for the function $\Phi(y) = y^2$, are listed in Table I.

TABLE I

DIFFERENCE TABLE FOR THE FUNCTION $\Phi(y) = y^2$

y	$\Phi(y)$	$\Delta\Phi(y)$	$\Delta^2\Phi(y)$	$\Delta^3\Phi(y)$
1	1	3	2	0
2	4	5	2	0
3	9	7	2	0
4	16	9	2	0
5	25	11	2	—
6	36	13	—	—
7	49	—	—	—

Consider the function $\Phi(y) = y^3 - y^2 - y$. For the corresponding difference table, see Table II. Notice that the resulting differences are

TABLE II

DIFFERENCE TABLE FOR THE FUNCTION $\Phi(y) = y^3 - y^2 - y$

y	$\Phi(y)$	$\Delta\Phi y$	$\Delta^2\Phi(y)$	$\Delta^3\Phi(y)$	$\Delta^4\Phi(y)$
1	—1	3	10	6	0
2	2	13	16	6	0
3	15	29	22	6	0
4	44	51	28	6	0
5	95	79	34	6	0
6	174	113	40	6	0
7	287	153	46	6	—
8	440	199	52	—	—
9	639	251	—	—	—
10	890	—	—	—	—

equal for all values of the argument, when the power of Δ is equal to the power of the polynomial. Hence, for the general case, let Y designate the argument; h, its interval; $F(y)$ or simply F, the function; y, $y + h$, $y + 2h$, ..., the given values of Y; F_0, F_1, F_2, ..., the corresponding values of $F(y)$; Δ^1, Δ^2, Δ^3, ..., the successive orders of differences. The argument, function, and differences for this general case appear in Table III.

TABLE III

DIFFERENCE TABLE FOR A POLYNOMIAL OF DEGREE i

Argument	Function	1st Diff.	2nd Diff.	3rd Diff.	...	ith Diff.
Y	$F(Y)$	Δ^1	Δ^2	Δ^3		Δ^i
y	F_0	a_0	b_0	c_0	...	l_0
$y + h$	F_1	a_1	b_1	c_1	...	l_0
$y + 2h$	F_2	a_2	b_2	c_2	...	l_0
.	.	.	.	.	...	l_0
.	.	.	.	.	...	
$y + ih$	.	.	.	c_i		
$y + (i + 1)h$	.	.	b_{i+1}			
$y + (i + 2)h$	F_{i+2}	a_{i+2}				
$y + (i + 3)h$	F_{i+3}					

Here $a_0 = F_1 - F_0$, $a_1 = F_2 - F_1$, ... ; $b_0 = a_1 - a_0$, ...; $c_0 = b_1 - b_0$, ... ; and so on.

One of the fundamental formulas of interpolation, Newton's formula, is

$$F_n = F(y + nh) = F_0 + na_0 + \frac{n(n-1)b_0}{2!} + \frac{n(n-1)(n-2)c_0}{3!} + ...$$
$$+ \frac{n(n-1)...(n-i+1)l_0}{i!} . \tag{1}$$

It holds for all values of n, fractional and negative, provided $\Delta^i = l_0$ = constant. The quantity n is called the interval of interpolation and, in practice is always less than unity. To obtain an expression for n, suppose that we are to interpolate the value of the function corresponding to the argument Y, whose value lies between y and $y + h$:

$$F_n = F(y + nh) = F(Y), \quad \text{or} \quad y + nh = Y,$$

and, therefore, $n = (Y - y)/h$, which determines the interval n.

However, in a large number of problems l_0 is not rigorously constant.

Newton's formula is approximately true for this more frequent case in which the differences of some order become approximately, but not absolutely, constant provided the value of n lies between 0 and $+1$.

Let there be a function $f(x)$ whose values at $x = a$, $x = a + h$, $x = a + 2h$, etc. are given. Then suppose the nth-order differences of the resulting difference table are constant. We want to compute the value of the function at some intermediate point, e.g, $x_j = a + k_j h$. We know that

$$E^n F(a) = F(a + nh),$$

also,

$$E^n = (1 + \varDelta)^n = 1 + n\varDelta + \frac{n(n-1)}{2} \varDelta^2 + \dots .$$

Thus,

$$F(a + nh) = F(a) + n\,\varDelta F(a) + \frac{n(n-1)}{2} \varDelta^2 F(a) + \dots . \qquad (2)$$

To compute the value of $F(x)$ corresponding to any intermediate point such as $(a + \frac{1}{3}h)$ we simply substitute $n = \frac{1}{3}$ into Eq. (2).

Another approach, known as the "equation method," consists in finding an empirical equation, $F = f(y)$, to fit certain selected tabulated values of y and F, substituting therein the given value for y and solving for the desired F. The particular type of equation selected will depend on the nature of the table. Ordinarily, the power series

$$F = A_0 + A_1 y + A_2 y^2 + A_3 y^3 + \dots \qquad (3)$$

suffices. For small ranges, only three terms are necessary. The A_i may be determined to yield an equation that will pass through any three selected points (y_1, F_1), (y_2, F_2), and (y_3, F_3). For such points, the three nearest the given y are usually chosen. The desired equation is

$$\begin{vmatrix} F & 1 & y & y^2 \\ F_1 & 1 & y_1 & y_1{}^2 \\ F_2 & 1 & y_2 & y_2{}^2 \\ F_3 & 1 & y_3 & y_3{}^2 \end{vmatrix} = 0. \qquad (4)$$

This determinant can be reduced to the form of Eq. (3) if values for the A_i are desired. Otherwise, we can substitute an appropriate value for y directly into this determinant and solve for the desired F. When the intervals $y_n - y_{n-1}$, $y_{n-1} - y_{n-2}$ have the same value $\varDelta y$, much time may be saved by changing the origin of the coordinates, as from

(0, 0) to, say, (y_k , F_k). Representing the new coordinates by y' and F', where

$$y' = \frac{y - y_k}{\Delta y},$$

$$F' = F - F_k ,$$

we obtain

$$y'_{k-1} = \frac{y_{k-1} - y_k}{\Delta y} = \frac{-\Delta y}{\Delta y} = -1,$$

$$y_k' = \frac{y_k - y_k}{\Delta y} = 0,$$

$$y'_{k+1} = \frac{y_{k+1} - y_k}{\Delta y} = 1,$$

$$F'_{k-1} = F_{k-1} - F_k ,$$

$$F_k' = F_k - F_k = 0,$$

$$F'_{k+1} = F_{k+1} - F_k .$$

In the new coordinate system, the determinant we originally considered becomes

$$\begin{vmatrix} F' & 1 & y' & y'^2 \\ F'_{k-1} & 1 & -1 & 1 \\ 0 & 1 & 0 & 0 \\ F'_{k+1} & 1 & 1 & 1 \end{vmatrix} = 0,$$

and it can be reduced to

$$\begin{vmatrix} F' & y' & y'^2 \\ F'_{k-1} & -1 & 1 \\ F'_{k+1} & 1 & 1 \end{vmatrix} = 0,$$

which can be easily solved for F', and $F = F' + F_k$.

An approach to interpolation of particular value is known as the the "Lagrange method." It can be used to find the corresponding F to a given y when instead of a formal table we have simply a group of corresponding y and F values not separated by the common difference Δy. The Lagrange formula assumes that F may be expressed as finite power series in y:

$$F = A_0 + A_1 y + A_2 y^2 + A_3 y^3 + \ldots .$$

This is the same as Eq. (3). Say the determinant of Eq. (4) is expanded to express F in terms of F_1 , F_2 , F_3 and the determinant minors, Z_i.

Expansion of the minors leads to the standard Lagrangian form of equation, namely,

$$F = F_1\left[\frac{(y - y_2)}{(y_1 - y_2)} \times \frac{(y - y_3)}{(y_1 - y_3)} \times \frac{(y - y_4)}{(y_1 - y_4)} \times \cdots\right]$$

$$+ F_2\left[\frac{(y - y_1)}{(y_2 - y_1)} \times \frac{(y - y_3)}{(y_2 - y_3)} \times \frac{(y - y_4)}{(y_2 - y_4)} \times \frac{(y - y_5)}{(y_2 - y_5)} \times \cdots\right]$$

$$+ F_3\left[\frac{(y - y_1)}{(y_3 - y_1)} \times \frac{(y - y_2)}{(y_3 - y_2)} \times \frac{(y - y_4)}{(y_3 - y_4)} \times \frac{(y - y_5)}{(y_3 - y_5)} \times \cdots\right] + \cdots .$$

In this equation there exist as many terms as there are points used in the interpolation.

An interpolation method whose usefulness is limited to tables based on a known transcendental equation is Taylor's series. The interpolation formula is

$$F = f(y) = f(y_0 + \Delta y)$$

$$= f(y_0) + f'(y_0)\frac{\Delta y}{1!} + f''(y_0)\frac{(\Delta y)^2}{2!} + f'''(y_0)\frac{(\Delta y)^3}{3!}$$

$$+ f''''(y_0)\frac{(\Delta y)^4}{4!} + \cdots + f^n(y_0)\frac{(\Delta y)^n}{n!} .$$

Here $\Delta y = y - y_0$ and the primes of the f function indicate differentiation with respect to y. To use this method, it suffices to

(i) select from the table an y_0 as near as possible to the given y;

(ii) form the $f'(y_0)$, $f''(y_0)$, etc. derivatives;

(iii) insert those values, together with the appropriate Δy, into the formula to obtain the desired F.

Finally, we should make reference to the "graphical" approach. It involves four basic steps:

(i) Select from the data table certain, convenient, corresponding values of y and F.

(ii) Plot these values on cross-section paper.

(iii) Draw the best curve to express $F = f(y)$.

(iv) Read the desired F from the curve.

The number of points plotted, the openness of the scales selected, and the care used in plotting and drawing the curve have obvious bearing on the accuracy of the result. The graphical method may be used as a substitute to analytical approaches with applications requiring frequent interpolations from a given table. Contrary to this, when interpolations are to be made from a given table only occasionally, simple numerical methods may be preferred. One such method assumes that between tabulated values of y, F varies linearly with y. The F value corresponding to a given y lying between two successive tabulated points, (y_k, F_k) and (y_{k+1}, F_{k+1}) is obtained from the equation

$$F = F_k + \frac{F_{k+1} - F_k}{y_{k+1} - y_k}(y - y_k).$$

The Computation of Derivatives

One is often required to find numerical values of the differential coefficients of functions either analytically unknown or complicated in expression. In the majority of such cases the function in question has been previously tabulated for particular values of the argument. The required derivatives are then readily computed from the differences of the tabular functions.

To compute derivatives of $F(y)$ at or near the beginning of a series, we use Newton's formula of interpolation:

$$F_n = F_0 + Aa_0 + Bb_0 + Cc_0 + Dd_0 + Ee_0 + \dots .$$

where

$$A = n, \qquad B = \frac{n(n-1)}{2!}, \qquad C = \frac{n(n-1)(n-2)}{3!},$$

$$D = \frac{n(n-1)(n-2)(n-3)}{4!}, \qquad E = \frac{n(n-1)\dots(n-4)}{5!}.$$

Differentiating these expressions successively with respect to n, and substituting the resulting values of B', B'', ...; C', C'', ...; etc. into the general formula, we obtain

$$F'(y+np) = \frac{1}{p}\left[a_0 + \left(n - \frac{1}{2}\right)b_0 + \left(\frac{n^2}{2} - n + \frac{1}{3}\right)c_0 \right.$$
$$+ \left(\frac{n^3}{6} - \frac{3}{4}\{n^2\} + \frac{11}{12}\{n\} - \frac{1}{4}\right)d_0$$
$$\left. + \left(\frac{n^4}{24} - \frac{n^3}{3} + \frac{7}{8}\{n^2\} - \frac{5}{6}\{n\} + \frac{1}{5}\right)e_0 + \dots\right],$$

$$F''(y+np) = \frac{1}{p^2}\left[b_0 + (n-1)c_0 + \left(\frac{n^2}{2} - \frac{3}{2}\{n\} + \frac{11}{12}\right)d_0 \right.$$
$$\left. + \left(\frac{n^3}{6} - n^2 + \frac{7}{4}\{n\} - \frac{5}{6}\right)e_0 + \dots\right],$$

$$F'''(y+np) = \frac{1}{p^3}\left[c_0 + \left(n - \frac{3}{2}\right)d_0 + \left(\frac{n^2}{2} - 2n + \frac{7}{4}\right)e_0 + \dots\right].$$

The values of B, C, D, E, for different values of n are listed in Table IV.

TABLE IV

NEWTON'S INTERPOLATION COEFFICIENTS[a]

n	B	C	D	E
0	0	0	0	0
0.05	—0.02375	0.01544	—0.01139	0.00899
0.10	—0.04500	0.02850	—0.02066	0.01612
0.15	—0.06375	0.03931	—0.02801	0.02157
0.20	—0.08000	0.04800	—0.03360	0.02554
0.25	—0.09375	0.05469	—0.03760	0.02820
0.30	—0.10500	0.05950	—0.04016	0.02972
0.35	—0.11375	0.06256	—0.04145	0.03026
0.40	—0.12000	0.06400	—0.04160	0.02995
0.45	—0.12375	0.06394	—0.04076	0.02894
0.50	—0.12500	0.06250	—0.03906	0.02734
0.55	—0.12375	0.05981	—0.03664	0.02528
0.60	—0.12000	0.05600	—0.03360	0.02285
0.65	—0.11375	0.05119	—0.03007	0.02015
0.70	—0.10500	0.04500	—0.02616	0.01727
0.75	—0.09375	0.03906	—0.02197	0.01428
0.80	—0.08000	0.03200	—0.01760	0.01126
0.85	—0.06375	0.02444	—0.01314	0.00828
0.90	—0.04500	0.01650	—0.00866	0.00537
0.95	—0.02375	0.00831	—0.00426	0.00260
1.00	0	0	0	0

[a] The maximum values are $B_{max} = 0.12500$ at $n = 0.50$, $C_{max} = 0.06415$ at $n = 0.42$, $D_{max} = 0.04167$ at $n = 0.38$, $E_{max} = 0.03260$ at $n = 0.35$.

Interpolating Data for Time Intervals

The following data are available on sunrise and sunset on a 31-day interval:

	Oct. 31	Dec. 1	Jan. 1	Feb. 1	
Sunrise	6:15	6:44	7:03	6:56	A.M.
Sunset	5:11	4:54	5:04	5:32	P.M.

It is required to compute

(i) the time of sunrise and sunset on December 15,

(ii) date and time of the latest sunrise,

(iii) date and time of the earliest sunset,

(iv) date of the shortest day $(t_{sunrise} - t_{sunset})$.

A sunrise time table is computed from the given data. The time is expressed in minutes after midnight:

Date	Time	Point
Oct. 31	375 min	A
Dec. 1	404 min	B
Jan. 1	423 min	C
Feb. 1	416 min	D

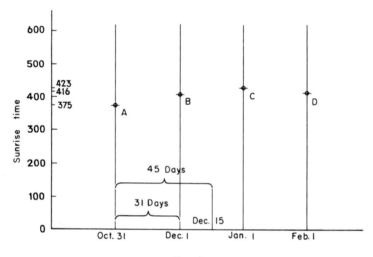

FIG. 3

Figure 3 presents a plot of the time of sunrise. We should write the equation of the curve connectings points *A*, *B*, *C*, and *D*. While the function $y = f(x)$ is unknown, we know the following corresponding values of *x*, *y*:

for   the function

x_0 $f_0(x_0) = y_0 = A$

x_1 $f_1(x_1) = y_1 = B$

x_2 $f_2(x_2) = y_2 = C$

x_3 $f_3(x_3) = y_3 = D$

In Chapter 6, we discussed E, the symbolic operator for increment. We said that $E = 1 + \varDelta$, $E^r = (1 + \varDelta)^r$ and, hence,

$$E^2 f(a) = E f(a + h) = f(a + 2h),$$

$$E^r f(a) = f(a + rh) = (1 + \varDelta)^r f(a)$$

$$= \sum_{k=0}^{r} C_{r,k}\, \varDelta^x f(a),$$

where $C_{i,k}$ is a multiplier. We can now write the corresponding difference table (see Table V).

TABLE V

Date, x	Time, $f(x)$	$\varDelta F(x)$	$\varDelta^2 f(x)$	$\varDelta^3 f(x)$
Oct. 31	375	29	−10	−16
Dec. 1	404	19	−26	—
Jan. 1	423	−7	—	—
Feb. 1	416	—	—	—

The time of sunrise on December 15 will be

$$t_{\text{Dec.15}} = t_{\text{Oct.31}} + C_1 \varDelta + C_2 \varDelta^2 + C_3 \varDelta^3,$$

where

$$C_1 = \frac{45}{31}, \qquad C_2 = \frac{C_1(C_1 - 1)}{2!}, \qquad C_3 = \frac{C_1(C_1 - 1)(C_1 - 2)}{3!}$$

and

$$t_{\text{Dec.15}} = 375 + \frac{45}{31}\cdot 29 + \frac{\frac{45}{31}\left(\frac{45}{31} - 1\right)}{2}(-10) + \frac{\frac{45}{31}\left(\frac{45}{31} - 1\right)\left(\frac{45}{21} - 2\right)}{6}(-16)$$

$$= 415 \text{ min} = 6{:}55 \text{ A.M.}$$

The sunset can be computed in the same manner.

   To compute the day and the time of the latest sunrise consider that this will happen at time t after the first available information—instead of the definite time interval of 45 days which we considered in the preceding case. Then the equation will be

$$F(t) = 375 + \frac{t}{31}\cdot 29 + \frac{\frac{t}{31}\left(\frac{t}{31} - 1\right)}{2}(-10) + \frac{\frac{t}{31}\left(\frac{t}{31} - 1\right)\left(\frac{t}{31} - 2\right)}{6}(-16),$$

which is a cubic equation in t. By simplifying we get

$$(3)31^3 F(t) = (11.35)31^3 + (86)31^2 t + 9.31 t^2 - 8t^3,$$

and $F(t)$ will be maximum when the derivative of the function is zero:

$$F'(t) = -(3)8t^2 + (2)(9)31t + (86)31 = 0.$$

Thus $t = 71$. The day of the latest sunrise is January 10.

In the same way the time of the latest sunrise (424 minutes or 7:04 A.M.) can be computed, also the day of the earliest sunset (December 23) and the corresponding time (4:54 P.M.). Finally from the given time data on four days of the year, we compute the length of the days for October 31, December 1, January 1, and February 1. Then making a similar table and applying the same procedure we find:

Shortest day: December 23,
Length of the shortest day: 9 hours, 59 minutes.

The foregoing computations involve an error. To compute that error one should derive the expression of the residue. It is:

$$f(x) = F(x) + R(x),$$
$$R(x) = (x - x_0)(x - x_1) \ldots (x - x_n)P(x),$$

where $f(x)$ is the actual function, $F(x)$ is the polynomial, and $R(x)$ is the residue.
For this derivation consider

$$\Phi(z) = f(z) - F(z) - (z - x_0) \ldots (z - x_n)P(x),$$

where z is a number which we may vary at will. While z is varying, x will be a constant. For $z = x$; and $x = x_0, x_1, x_2, \ldots, x_n$,

$$\Phi(z) = 0.$$

The $n + 1$ derivative is

$$\Phi^{(n+1)}(z) = 0,$$

where

$$\Phi^{(n+1)}(z) = f^{(n+1)}(z) - (n + 1)! \, P(x) = 0.$$

Therefore,

$$P(x) = \frac{f^{(n+1)}(z)}{(n + 1)!}$$

and

$$R(x) = (x - x_0)(x - x_1) \ldots (x - x_n) \frac{f^{(n+1)}(z)}{(n + 1)!} \, .$$

The Case of a Manufacturer

The director of a manufacturing plant wants to know when to expect peak demand for a certain product. He knows that the sales of this product are some function of the time of the year, but he does not know the function itself. The production manager provided the production records for every 30th day. That would have been as far as he could depend on his data, if it weren't for the fact that, although seasonal, the data gave a smooth curve, without upsetting peaks and valleys in-between. The information provided by the records is listed in Table VI.

TABLE VI

Date	Number of units produced	Date	Number of units produced
Jan. 1	1520	July 29	4680
Jan. 31	2020	Aug. 28	3920
Mar. 1	2830	Sept. 27	3120
Mar. 31	3680	Oct. 27	2250
Apr. 30	4510	Nov. 26	1620
May 30	5060	Dec. 26	1470
June 29	5130	—	—

Say that the director wishes to find out what the demand on his plant will be on April 15. We start by setting up the problem as shown in Table VII.[2] Δ^5 is the highest difference we will consider. The terms in Newton's formula will decrease in magnitude with higher order differences, since n is less than one, and there is a factorial term in the denominator. We will take March 31st as the start of the table. This is like saying that March 31st is taken to be the first data given, hence $y = 0$. Therefore,

$$y = 0, \quad h = 30, \quad a_0 = 83, \quad b_0 = -28, \quad c_0 = -20, \quad d_0 = 16, \quad e_0 = 9,$$

$$n = \frac{15 - y}{30} = \frac{15 - 0}{30} = 0.5.$$

---

[2] Data scaled down by a factor of 10.

By Newton's formula

$$F(\text{Apr. }15) = 368 + 0.5(83) - 0.125(-28)$$
$$+ 0.0625(-20) - 0.03906(16) + 0.02734(9) = 411.37.$$

On the basis of the available historical data we conclude that the number of units produced April 15th is equal to 4114. This number

TABLE VII

Y	F(Y)	Δ'	Δ^2	Δ^3	Δ^4	Δ^5
Jan. 1	152	50	31	—27	21	—41
Jan. 31	202	81	4	—6	—20	26
Mar. 1	283	85	—2	—26	6	10
Mar. 31	*368*	*83*	*—28*	*—20*	*16*	*9*
Apr. 30	451	55	—48	—4	25	—19
May 30	*506*	*7*	*—52*	*21*	*6*	*—36*
June 29	513	—45	—31	27	—30	64
July 29	468	—76	—4	—3	34	—41
Aug. 28	392	—80	—7	31	—7	—
Sep. 27	312	—87	24	24	—	—
Oct. 27	225	—63	48	—	—	—
Nov. 26	162	—15	—	—	—	—
Dec. 26	147	—	—	—	—	—

could be combined with current estimates on sales trends to establish the projected figure. If we wish to know when to expect maximum production, we need to find the derivative of the function and set it equal to zero:

$$F'(y + nh) = 0 = \frac{1}{P}\left[a_0 + \left(n - \frac{1}{2}\right)b_0 + \left(\frac{n^2}{2} - n + \frac{1}{3}\right)c_0 \right.$$
$$+ \left(\frac{n^3}{6} - \frac{3}{4}n^2 + \frac{11}{12}n - \frac{1}{4}\right)d_0$$
$$\left. + \left(\frac{n^4}{24} - \frac{n^3}{3} + \frac{7}{8}n^2 - \frac{5}{6}n + \frac{1}{5}\right)e_0 + \dots \right],$$

where n is unknown, and its value is desired. Rearranging terms, we have

$$0 = \left(a_0 - \frac{b_0}{2} + \frac{c_0}{3} - \frac{d_0}{4} + \frac{e_0}{5}\right) + n\left(b_0 - c_0 + \frac{11}{12}d_0 - \frac{5}{16}e_0\right)$$
$$+ n^2\left(\frac{c_0}{2} - \frac{3}{4}d_0 + \frac{7}{8}e_0\right) + n^3\left(\frac{d_0}{6} - \frac{e_0}{3}\right) + n^4\frac{e_0}{24}.$$

The peak will come somewhere between May 30 and July 29. Thus, for $F_0 = 506$, it is

$$a_0 = 7, \qquad b_0 = -52, \qquad c_0 = 21, \qquad d_0 = 6, \qquad e_0 = -36;$$

and

$$0 = 31.3 - 17.5n - 25.5n^2 + 13n^3 - 1.5n^4,$$

or $n = 0.57$, and therefore $(y + nh) =$ May 30 + 0.57(30) = June 16.[3] Hence, peak production will occur June 16th. We can easily find what this peak production will be, since we know the value of n. This comes out to be 5166 units.

Had we assumed that this peak was somewhere between June 29th and July 29th, the value for n would have come out to be negative. Negative values and values greater than one are allowed for n, provided the differences are carried out to a place where Δ^i is constant. In cases like the present, it is best to guess the approximate area and test for a solution. When Δ^i does not equal a constant, different areas should be tested until a value for n is found that is between 0 and + 1. This will give the most accurate solution to the problem.

A second division of this company had a problem with federal tax officials. The tax officials were trying to determine the number of television picture tubes manufactured at the plant. The accountant failed somewhere, and the investigators used data kept by a young industrial engineer. He had taken production line readings once a week during the months of June and July. The readings were taken every Wednesday at noon. The problem was to find the number of tubes manufactured on the 9th of July. The difference table is as follows:

	Date	No. of tubes	Δ^1	Δ^2	Δ^3	Δ^4	Δ^5	Δ^6	Δ^7
x_1	6 June	742	−33	9	60	−204	474	−923	1559
x_2	13 June	709	−24	69	−144	270	−449	636	—
x_3	20 June	685	+45	−75	126	−179	187	—	—
x_4	27 June	730	−30	51	−53	8	—	—	—
x_5	4 July	700	+21	−2	−45	—	—	—	—
x_6	11 July	721	+19	−47	—	—	—	—	—
x_7	18 July	740	−28	—	—	—	—	—	—
x_8	25 July	712	—	—	—	—	—	—	—

---

[3] For the sake of simplicity, the whole month is treated as if it were composed of working days only.

Let B equal the number of tubes manufactured on 9 July 1956. Then

$$B = 742 + \frac{33}{7}(-33) + \frac{\frac{33}{7}\left(\frac{33}{7} - 1\right)}{2!}(9) + \frac{\frac{33}{7}\left(\frac{33}{7} - 1\right)\left(\frac{33}{7} - 2\right)}{3!}(60)$$

$$+ \frac{\frac{33}{7}\left(\frac{33}{7} - 1\right)\left(\frac{33}{7} - 2\right)\left(\frac{33}{7} - 3\right)}{4!}(-204)$$

$$+ \frac{\frac{33}{7}\left(\frac{33}{7} - 1\right)\left(\frac{33}{7} - 2\right)\left(\frac{33}{7} - 3\right)\left(\frac{33}{7} - 4\right)}{5!}(474)$$

$$+ \frac{\frac{33}{7}\left(\frac{33}{7} - 1\right)\left(\frac{33}{7} - 2\right)\left(\frac{33}{7} - 3\right)\left(\frac{33}{7} - 4\right)\left(\frac{33}{7} - 5\right)}{6!}(-923)$$

$$+ \frac{\frac{33}{7}\left(\frac{33}{7} - 1\right)\left(\frac{33}{7} - 2\right)\left(\frac{33}{7} - 3\right)\left(\frac{33}{7} - 4\right)\left(\frac{33}{7} - 5\right)\left(\frac{33}{7} - 6\right)}{7!}(1559),$$

$$B = 742 - 156 + 79 + 477 - 697 + 233 + 21 - 7,$$
$$B = 692.$$

Using Interpolation with Engineering Problems

FIRST EXAMPLE. The transmission of high-frequency radio waves depends upon the reflection of these waves by the ionosphere. This reflection is due to a cloud of ions which varies in density throughout the day and night. The frequency of the wave which can be reflected depends upon this density; therefore, the highest, or "critical" frequency which can be used for transmission varies accordingly.

This problem is concerned with determining the critical frequency at a particular time of the day or night by using data taken at four equal intervals during a twenty-four hour period. We also wish to find the time at which the maximum critical frequency occurs. The data given are:

Time	Frequency
00	2.8
06	3.0
12	7.5
18	3.2

The time is measured in hours starting at midnight. The frequency is in megacycles. A table of differences is set up from this data (see Table VIII). Consider the equation

$$f_x = f_0 + C_1 \Delta + C_2 \Delta^2 + C_3 \Delta^3,$$

TABLE VIII

A DIFFERENCE TABLE BASED ON THE DATA OF EXAMPLE 1

y	$\Phi(y)$	$\Delta\Phi(y)$	$\Delta^2\Phi(y)$	$\Delta^3\Phi(y)$
00	2.8	0.2	4.3	—13.1
06	3.0	4.5	—8.8	—
12	7.5	—4.3	—	—
18	3.2	—	—	—

where f_x is the required frequency; f_0 the frequency at the initial reference point; C_1 is the time at which a frequency is required divided by the interval of measured data; $C_2 = C_1(C_1 - 1)/2!$;

$$C_3 = \frac{C_1(C_1 - 1)(C_1 - 2)}{3!} ;$$

and Δ^1, Δ^2, Δ^3 are the values from the difference table. We calculate the critical frequency at 8:00 A.M. :

$$f_{08} = 2.8 + \frac{4}{3}\left(\frac{2}{10}\right) + \frac{2}{9}(4.3) + \left(-\frac{4}{81}\right)(-13.1),$$

$$f_{08} = 4.68 \text{ megacycles,}$$

where $C_1 = 8/6 = 4/3$, $C_2 = 2/9$, $C_3 = -4/81$.

To find the time of the day at which the maximum critical frequency occurs, we express C_i in terms of t:

$$C_1 = \frac{t}{6}, \qquad C_2 = \frac{\frac{t}{6}\left(\frac{t}{6} - 1\right)}{2}, \qquad C_3 = \frac{\frac{t}{6}\left(\frac{t}{6} - 1\right)\left(\frac{t}{6} - 2\right)}{6}.$$

After substitution, this yields the following cubic equation:

$$\frac{-2.2}{(6)(36)}t^3 + \left(\frac{4.3}{(2)(36)} + \frac{2.2}{36} + \frac{2(2.2)}{36}\right)t^2$$

$$+ \left(\frac{1}{30} - \frac{4.3}{12} - \frac{2(2.2)}{6}\right)t + 2.8 = f_t .$$

By differentiating this equation with respect to time and setting the result equal to zero a maximum can be obtained. After simplification, this yields the following quadratic equation:

$$-0.0305(t^2) + 0.486(t) - 1.055 = 0$$

and $t_1 = 13.3$ hours or 1:18 P.M.

SECOND EXAMPLE. In engineering it is sometimes either necessary or convenient to solve problems by graphical methods instead of by strict mathematical approaches. Time and labor can be saved by looking for graphical solutions when the desired accuracy of the result allows the use of graphical methods.

Consider the following example: A magnetic solenoid is mounted vertically and has an iron plunger weighing 11 pounds that may be inserted in the center of the coil. The coil draws a constant direct current of 19 amperes. The length of both coil and plunger is 18 inches, and the coil resistance is 1.5 ohms. This arrangement is pictured in Fig. 4. The following data have been determined experimentally:

Distance plunger is inserted into coil, inches	0	6	8	10	12	14	16	18
Inductance, henries	0.050	0.065	0.080	0.113	0.154	0.193	0.220	0.225

Suppose it is desired to know

(a) the position at which the plunger will be drawn into the coil when inserted from the bottom,

(b) the maximum force the coil can support as it floats in the coil,

(c) the position the plunger will take under this condition.

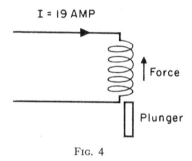

I = 19 AMP

Force

Plunger

FIG. 4

It might be desired to know the value of inductance at a particular point, as where the force on the plunger is a maximum. These values may not be obtained directly from the data, but as with the other examples, the given data can be used to obtain related values of other variables, from which we can obtain the desired information.

If we use the virtual displacement principle, $dE = F\,dx$, a new variable can be obtained from the given data; i.e., the force as a function of distance. Since the energy stored in the magnetic field of the coil is equal to $1/2LI^2$, the force F equals dE/dx, or $(1/2I^2)\,dL/dx$. If we take the change in inductance as a constant between intervals of known values, the calculation of force will apply at the point halfway between two values of x.

Since the energy will be in joules, a conversion factor must be used to change this unit into lb-inch, to be compatible with the data of the problem. Then the force will be calculated in pounds. The conversion factor is

$$\text{Force} = \frac{d}{dx}\left[\frac{LI^2}{2}\text{ joules }\frac{10^7\text{ dyne-cm}}{\text{joule}}\frac{\text{inch}}{2.54\text{ cm}}\frac{\text{newton}}{10^5\text{ dynes}}\frac{0.224\text{ lb}}{\text{newton}}\right]$$

$$= 1590\frac{dL}{dx}\text{ lb.}$$

The difference table for this example is given by Table IX. The values of x and $f(x)$ given in Table IX are plotted in Fig. 5. We see from this

TABLE IX

A Difference Table Based on the Original Data of Example 2

x (inches)	$f(x)$ inductance	Δ	Δ^2	Δ^3	Δ^4
0	0.050				
6	0.065				
		0.015			
8	0.080		0.018		
		0.033		—0.010	
10	0.113		0.008		0
		0.041		—0.010	
12	0.154		—0.002		0
		0.039		—0.010	
14	0.193		—0.012		0
		0.027		—0.010	
16	0.220		—0.022		
		0.005			
18	0.225				

plot the position at which the force on the plunger is equal to its weight as it is inserted into the bottom of the coil. This happens at a point 6.5 inches from the end. The point at which the plunger will float in the coil is at 16.25 inches. The maximum force on the coil is 33.2 lb, and occurs at 11.7 inches. Thus the maximum force the plunger can withstand when floating inside the coil is (33.2 — 11.0) lb, or 22.2 lb. The value of inductance at the maximum force point is 0.146 henry. These values can now be compared with those calculated using Newton's interpolation formula (see Table X). In calculations with the force

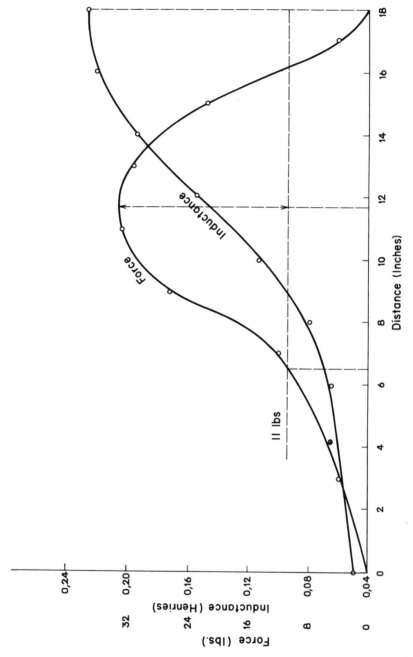

FIG. 5. Variation of inductance as the metal plunger is inserted and variation of force on the plunger when inserted from the bottom of the coil.

TABLE X

THIS DIFFERENCE TABLE IS BASED ON CALCULATED FORCE VALUES
(x VALUES MIDWAY BETWEEN KNOWN POINTS)

x	dL/dx	Force (lb)	Δ	Δ^2	Δ^3	Δ^4	Δ^5
3	0.0025	3.98		—		—	
			7.92		—		—
7	0.0075	11.90		6.43		—	
			14.35		—14.43		—
9	0.0165	26.25		—8.00		—14.38	
			6.35		—0.05		14.48
11	0.0205	32.60		—7.95		0.10	
			—1.60		0.05		—0.17
13	0.0195	31.00		—7.90		—0.07	
			—9.50		—0.12		—
15	0.0135	21.50		—8.02		—	
			—17.52		—		—
17	0.0025	3.95		—		—	

differences, we assume that error will be minimal when differences greater than Δ^3 are omitted. Using the Gregory-Newton interpolation formula, we find:

(1) For the location of the maximum force on the plunger,

$$f(x_{\text{max force}}) = f(x_7) + r\,\Delta f(x_7) + \frac{r(-1)}{2!}\,\Delta^2 f(x_7) + \frac{r(r-1)(r-2)}{3!}\,\Delta^3 f(x_7)$$

$$= 11.90 + 14.35r + \left(\frac{-8}{2}\right) r(r-1) + \left(\frac{-0.05}{6}\right) r(r-1)(r-2)$$

$$= -0.0083r^3 - 3.975r^2 + 18.284r + 11.90,$$

$$\frac{df}{dr} = -0.0249r^2 - 7.95r + 18.284 = 0,$$

$$r^2 + 319.0r - 734.0 = 0, \qquad r = +2.4,$$

$$f(x_7 + rh) = f(x_7 + 24.2) = f(11.8), \qquad x_{\text{max force}} = 11.8 \text{ inches.}$$

(2) For the maximum force,

$$F(11.8) = 11.90 + 14.35(2.4) + (-8.)\frac{2.4(1.4)}{2} + (-0.05)\frac{2.4(1.4)(0.4)}{6}$$

$$= 11.90 + 34.5 - 13.5 - 0.011$$

$$= 32.9 \text{ lb.}$$

(3) For the inductance at this location,

$$L(11.8) = L(10.0 + 1.8) = L(x_0 + rh), \qquad r = 0.9, \qquad h = 2,$$

$$L(11.8) = L(10) + r\,\Delta L(10) + \frac{r(r-1)}{2!}\Delta^2 L(10) + \frac{r(r-1)(r-2)}{3!}\Delta^3 L(10)$$

$$= 0.113 + 0.9(0.041) + \frac{0.9(-0.1)}{2}(-0.002) + \frac{0.9(-0.1)(-1.1)}{6}(-0.010)$$

$$= 0.113 + 0.0369 + 0.00009 - 0.00015,$$

$$L(11.8) = 0.149 \text{ henries.}$$

	Graph value	Calculated	% Difference
Maximum force	33.2 lb	32.9 lb	0.905
Location of maximum force	11.7 in.	11.8 in.	0.85
Inductance at this location	0.146 H	0.149 H	2.01

Hence, both methods offer equally good results. Where extreme accuracy is desired in calcuations, the solution of the Gregory-Newton formula which includes high orders of differences is good enough. It will be an exact solution if the differences turn out to be zero for some finite order, and if the resulting equations of high order can be solved.

THIRD EXAMPLE. A surveyor measured a plot of land on which a building was to be constructed. He used his steel tape which is accurate at 68°F. At 10 A.M. he measured an area 150 feet on one side. He neglected to record the temperature at the time the measurement was made, but later managed to get a table of temperatures for that day, which were recorded in the vicinity. The values were taken every 3 hours from midnight on throughout the day. There were readings for 9 A.M. and 12 noon, but he thought he could arrive at a more accurate answer by interpolating from midnight (see Table XI).

TABLE XI

DIFFERENCE TABLE

Time	Temp. (°F)	Δ^1	Δ^2	Δ^3	Δ^4	Δ^5	Δ^6
12 P.M.	60	—5	3	5	—12	12	6
3 A.M.	55	—2	8	—7	0	18	—
6 A.M.	53	6	1	—7	18	—	—
9 A.M.	59	7	—6	11	—	—	—
12 noon	66	1	—7	—	—	—	—
3 P.M.	67	—6	—	—	—	—	—
6 P.M.	61	—	—	—	—	—	—

$$\text{temp.}_{(10\ \text{A.M.})} = \text{temp.}_{(12\ \text{P.M.})} + C_1\,\varDelta^1 + C_2\,\varDelta^2 + C_3\,\varDelta^3 + C_4\,\varDelta^4 + C_5\,\varDelta^5\,,$$

$C_1 = \dfrac{10}{3} = 3.33,$ for hours from 12 : 00 P.M. to 10 : 00 P.M., increment distance,

$$C_2 = \frac{C_1(C_1 - 1)}{2!} = \frac{3.33(3.33 - 1)}{2} = 3.88,$$

$$C_3 = \frac{C_2(C_1 - 2)}{3} = \frac{3.88(3.33 - 2)}{3} = 1.72,$$

$$C_4 = \frac{C_3(C_1 - 3)}{4} = \frac{1.72(3.33 - 3)}{4} = 0.142,$$

$$C_5 = \frac{C_4(C_1 - 4)}{5} = \frac{0.142(3.33 - 4)}{5} = -0.0189,$$

$$C_1\,\varDelta^1 = 3.33 \cdot (-5) = -16.67,$$
$$C_2\,\varDelta^2 = 3.88 \cdot (+3) = 11.65,$$
$$C_3\,\varDelta^3 = 1.72 \cdot (+5) = 8.6,$$
$$C_4\,\varDelta^4 = 0.142 \cdot (-12) = -1.7,$$
$$C_5\,\varDelta^5 = -0.0189 \cdot (+12) = -0.227,$$
$$\text{temp.}_{(10\ \text{A.M.})} = 60 - 16.67 + 11.65 + 8.6 - 1.7 - 0.227$$
$$= 61.65°\text{F}.$$

The surveyor would have to correct for a difference of

$$68 - 61.65 = 6.35°\text{F}.$$

Pitfalls in Interpolation

The reader should also be aware of some pitfalls which exist in connection with the use or rather with the misuse of interpolation.

A traffic engineer, for instance, has available information from a survey of automobile accident deaths made by an insurance company. These data are grouped on a ten-year basis:

Year	Deaths
1915–1925	13 229
1925–1935	18 139
1935–1945	24 225
1945–1955	31 496

It is desired to find the number of fatalities in the period 1950–1955 and then the number of deaths in 1950. Is it possible to use interpolation theory? The answer is a straight "no." These data are grouped in a manner inhibiting the use of finite differences.

Consider the case of another traffic engineer attempting to interpolate the number of accidents on December 26 from the following information:

Date	Sept. 30	Oct. 31	Dec. 1	Jan. 1
Number of accidents	150	200	180	300

Again in this case the use of interpolation is not advisable. But for a different reason. It is a question of continuity in the distribution of the data. December 26 is very likely to be an "exceptional day," since people are returning home from Christmas vacation. As the highways are saturated with traffic, the accident rate increases. January 1 is also an exceptional day, but this does not say much as to how December 26 stands.

Consider the following case. Some data are available from the census of population for the year 1959 in a certain city:

	Feb.	May	Aug.	Nov.
No. of births	1606	1642	1886	1712
No. of deaths	701	710	665	759

From this information, the following questions are to be answered:

(i) the births and deaths in June,

(ii) the month and number of highest birth rate,

(iii) the month and number of lowest death rate,

(iv) month of greatest natural increase in population.

Could the analyst use interpolation?

CHAPTER 8

Solving Equations Through Statistical Methods

The knowledge of the relationship between probability problems and mathematical equations dates back to de Moivre, Lagrange, and Laplace. Their work was mostly connected with problems arising in games of chance. It wasn't until late in the last century that Lord Rayleigh proved that the solution of the "drunken walk problem"[1] yields an approximate solution to a parabolic-type partial differential equation in one variable.

The connection between probabilities and the differential equations of mathematical physics is also an old story to theoretical physicists. During the early years of the present century, it was studied particularly extensively by Einstein, Smoluchowski, Langevin, and many others. In 1928 Courant, Friedrichs, and Lewy, in an article on the use of difference equations for the solution of partial differential equations, included a treatment of the sampling technique to solve the difference equations corresponding to an elliptic differential equation. This work brought into perspective the existing relationship between random flights, that is, random walks in more than one dimension, and the first boundary value problem (or Dirichlet problem) for elliptic difference and differential equations.

Mathematical interest in the use of stochastic tools for equation solution was further stimulated by the publication, in 1931, of a paper by Kolmogorov dealing with the relationship between probabilistic processes of the Markoff type and certain integro-differential equations. Shortly afterwards, the book of Khintchine appeared, followed by papers by Feller and others.

Using the Monte Carlo Method

Random sampling, random walks, or, in more familiar terms, the Monte Carlo method, is basically applied to two varieties of problems.

---

[1] Where a random path is obtained by the simple rule that every step is as likely a step forward as a step backward.

One variety, which has received considerable attention, is the use of random samples for the solution of equations through the construction of an equivalent statistical system. The other is the exploration of a physical system whose properties are such that the prescription for random sampling describes the system about as well as it can be described. Using the Monte Carlo method, Von Neumann, Ulam, Metropolis, and others were able to solve problems that had previously been treated in only the most approximate fashion.[2]

In many cases approximations and truncations must be introduced into a certain process in order to keep the calculation time and expense within reasonable limits. This, in turn, limits the usefulness of the results obtained. To problems of this nature, simulation offers new frontiers, as can be shown, for instance, in the study of problems concerning multiple neutron scattering.

Elastic scattering of neutrons by atomic nuclei represents the usual type of nuclear physics experiment. A neutron beam of known intensity hits a scattering target. This target scatters neutrons in all directions producing a certain angular distribution. To investigate the distribution a neutron detector is employed, covering all scattering angles between 0 and 180°. To simplify the problem, we consider only two dimensions, and no attention is given to secondary effects.

After entering the scatterer, each neutron encounters along its path a certain number of nuclei belonging to the scattering material. Each such collision deviates the neutron by a certain amount. The length of path between two collisions and the amount of angular deviation varies from collision to collision according to the laws of statistics.

A mathematical treatment of this type of problem involves, in the first place, the formulation of the laws of free path length and angular deviation, which can be achieved by a mechanical or other model. The simplest model is an array of elastic balls. From this model, laws of free path length and angular deviation can be developed by the standard equations of basic mechanics. A suitable, all-inclusive model leads to the general formulation of a single scattering process. The second step then is to carry out the integration over all processes occurring within the scatterer.

Due to the complexity of the analytical solution, only particular cases of these calculations have been carried out. The multiple scattering of

[2] The Monte Carlo theory and certain of its applications in simulation studies (including its relation to queuing theory) have been treated by the writer in his book "Statistical Processes and Reliability Engineering." There would be no point in duplicating the same work. Instead, another powerful aspect of the Monte Carlo method will be discussed: its usage in the solution of mathematical equations.

charged particles, for instance, has been worked out on the assumption that the deflection caused by each collision is small. Another computation has been accomplished assuming that the scatterer is large in comparison to the mean free path between two collisions, so that many collisions occur before the particle escapes. In this case, diffusion theory can be used to estimate the multiple-scattering effect. Because of the limitations, the two solutions have no general validity.

Avoiding the work required by analytical integration of the general case, random sampling offers a solution where the number of comparatively simple computations can be tailored exactly to fit the accuracy of results that are required in a particular case. This is, in many applications, a most important advantage, not achievable by deterministic methods.

The outstanding property of the Monte Carlo approach lies in the suggestion that, where an equation arising in a nonprobabilistic context demands a numerical solution not easily obtained by standard analytical methods, there may exist a stochastic process with distributions or parameters which satisfy that equation.

The Monte Carlo method is based on the formulation of a game of chance or a stochastic process which produces a random variable. The expected value of the variable is the solution of the problem under study. An approximation to the expected value can be obtained by means of sampling from the resulting distribution. One of the early applications of the method was in solving the problem of neutrons penetrating a slab. This is basically a problem in integral equations of the Fredholm type.

When solving the multiple neutron scattering problem by Monte Carlo simulation, there is no difficulty in finding the stochastic process which yields the measured distribution, because it is a single collision process itself. The Monte Carlo method in this particular case is a step-by-step tracking of neutrons along their path through the scatterer. The behavior of the neutrons at each collision is selected in a random manner from existing possibilities. These choices are weighted according to the probabilities of their occurrence.

The incoming beam, which is supposed to be equally distributed over the front F of the scattering sample, is simulated by assigning a first random number R_1 between 0 and 1 to each one of the imaginary neutrons. The point of impact can then be computed by multiplying R_1 by the length F. After selecting a second random number R_2 the distance Δl_1 that each neutron penetrates into the sample before colliding for the first time can be computed as being equal to $\Delta l_1 - \lambda \log R_2$, where λ is the mean free path for scattering in the material of the sample.

By adding the components of Δl to the coordinates of the impact joint, it is now possible to compute the end coordinates of the initial path of the neutron before its first collision. To determine the new directions after scattering a third random number R_3 is assigned. For this step it is necessary to assume an initial curve for the angular-scattering distribution. To each scattering angle an interval in the range 0 to 1 is assigned which is proportional to the probability of its occurrence. The scattering angle after the collision is selected in such a way that it corresponds to the angular interval into which the third random number R_3 falls.

Another distance is selected following the foregoing computations, and the coordinates of the second-collision point are computed. If this point is outside the sample, the path is recorded for future reference. If the second-collision point is inside the sample, one more random number is assigned to find the new direction after the collision, the process continuing until the neutron leaves the sample.

After tracing the required number of neutrons through the sample, the angular distribution of the neutrons at the moment of exit from the scatterer should be the same as one would measure in the actual experiment. This will work under the condition that the input curve, assumed when assigning random numbers to scattering angles, has been the true angular distribution. By trial and error it is possible to choose an initial angular distribution that, when introduced into the Monte Carlo process, will give an angular distribution fitting experimental results.

Increasing the number of simulated neutrons will allow the experimenter to achieve results of any accuracy required, depending on statistical errors allowed. Nevertheless, as with almost all numerical processes, only an approximation to the correct answer is obtained. In this case, instead of the primary source of error being due to numerical roundoff, the "error" is due to the fact that only a finite sample can be taken.[3] The degree of accuracy depends on the sample size.

Monte Carlo Approximations

Simulation by the Monte Carlo method offers new approaches on pure mathematical problems. A typical case is the solution of the

---

[3] The word "error" has been used and misused in a variety of cases. Some of its uses have had contradictory meanings. In statistics and the information sciences in general, we view "error" not as an extraneous and misdirected event, but as an important, integral part of the process we are considering. Hence, its importance is fully comparable to the other "intended" and "normal" critical factors of an operating system, that is, provided we understand its bearing, we can set its implications, and we are able to keep it under control.

Laplace equation. Mathematical methods for solving this type of equation are known as series expansion, Gaussian elimination, and iterative methods. The Monte Carlo solution is particularly unconventional because it is more efficient to construct a stochastic process with parameters that satisfy the equation and compute the statistics of that process than to attempt to use the standard analytical methods.

For the Laplace equation, the region in which a solution is required is replaced by a mesh of $N_x N_y N_z$ points, as in the elimination method. Starting at a given mesh, we simulate a random walk from mesh point to mesh point. When the walk reaches the boundary, the corresponding value (from the boundary conditions) is noted. Random walks are repeated from the same mesh point, and the boundary values obtained are averaged over the number of walks. The limit of this average, as the number of walks tends to infinity, is the solution to the difference equation at the mesh point in question.

Consider a cube so that $N_x = N_y = N_z = N$ and a mesh point near the center of the cube. We would expect the order of N^2 steps to reach a boundary point. To reduce the statistical fluctuation in the average boundary value to less than say 0.1%, we would expect to trace 10^6 walks so that we have an order of $10^6 N^2$ operations for each mesh point near the center. There are in total N^3 mesh points. The complete Monte Carlo solution in a case like this requires too many operations to compete with iteration methods. It is, however, particularly useful where the value of the solution at only one point is required.

Understandably, not only the slow rate of convergence, but also the expected duration of a random trip must be considered. Formulas can be used for the calculation of the maximum expected duration of a random walk. The following makes reference to an n-dimensional sphere:

$$\text{E.D.} = K(d)V^{2/n}k^{-2}(1 + \mathscr{E}(d)),$$

where

$$
\begin{aligned}
\text{E.D.} &= \text{the expected duration,} \\
V &= \text{volume,} \\
d &= \text{dimension,} \\
k &= \text{mesh size,} \\
K(d) &= \text{constant depending upon } d,
\end{aligned}
$$

and where

$$\lim_{n \to 0} \mathscr{E}(d) = 0.$$

The interfering error has also to be considered. According to Kac[4] the error in a systematic method of obtaining a solution of a functional equation is of the order of $1/k^{1/d}$, while the error in a random technique is of the order of $1/k^{1/2}$ and, hence, independent of the dimension.

Let us suppose that a sequential game is being played by two players A and B. The probability that A wins a turn is α, the probability that B wins is $\beta = 1 - \alpha$. A price is at stake on each turn. The total sum of money involved is Z, with A having X, and B having $Y = Z - X$ monetary units initially.

We can graphically represent the $0 \to Z$ integral, dividing it into equidistant increments of length C. On the ordinate, a point starting at any intermediate site of the axis moves to the right a distance C with probability α and to the left with probability β. This represents the fortune of player A at any point of the game. Upon reaching Z, A wins all the money, and upon reaching 0, A loses all the money to B.

The probability $P(X)$ that A wins if he has X at any stage of the game is the solution of the difference equation:

$$\frac{P(X + C) + P(X - C) - 2P(X)}{C^2} + \frac{\alpha - \beta}{\beta C} \left(\frac{P(X + C) - P(X - C)}{C} \right) = 0.$$

The boundary conditions $P(0) = 0$ and $P(Z) = 1$ correspond to the hypothesis. If A begins with 0 monetary units he has probability 0 of winning, and if he begins with Z monetary units he is certain of winning.

The probability $P_N(X)$ of A winning in exactly N moves can be expressed in terms of $P_{N-1}(X + C)$ and $P_{N-1}(X - C)$. The sumation over N of both members of the resulting equation yields this expression. If the amount of money C involved in each move becomes smaller, and if α approaches β, then the finite-difference problem converges into a differential problem:

$$\frac{d^2 V}{dX} + 2k \frac{dV}{dX} = 0,$$

where the boundary conditions are

$$V(0) = 0 \quad \text{and} \quad V(Z) = 1.$$

The calculation of the integral $\int F(x)\ dx$, for $F(x) \geqslant 0$, between the limits R and S, is equivalent to finding the area L under the curve (Fig. 1). To start with, let's take a line $y = Q$ such that $Q > F(x)$ for all x

[4] Mark Kac, Applications of Statistical Methods to Differential and Integral Equations, November 1949 (notes on lectures delivered at M.I.T.).

in (R, S). Since $Q(R - S)$ is the area of the rectangle, $L < Q(R - S)$.

A set of points (x, y) can be chosen in the rectangle RQ_RQ_SS. Let the choice be made at random and with equal likelihood for every point. The number of times the point lies in the area under the curve can be tallied. We call "successes" the points falling in the area L. The ratio

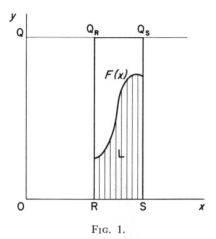

FIG. 1.

of these successes to the total number of tries h is a random variable. Its expected value is the ratio of the area under the curve to the total area of the rectangle.

Each point in the rectangle can be selected by choosing from two rectangular distributions in the x and y intervals. With the value of x chosen, the quantity y is compared with $F(x)$ to determine a "success" or a "failure." If

$$m = \text{the number of successes,}$$
$$L = \text{the area under the curve,}$$
$$u = \text{the total area of the rectangular,}$$
$$n = \text{the number of trials,}$$

then the distribution of successes has an expected value $E = nL/u$ and a standard deviation of

$$\sigma = \sqrt{n\frac{L}{u}\left(1 - \frac{L}{u}\right)}.$$

The standard deviation of m/n, the random variable of interest, is simply

$$\sigma_0 = \frac{\sigma}{\sqrt{n}}.$$

For large n the probable error decreases. Also, if Q is made small to increase the ratio L/u a greater accuracy can be attained with a smaller number of trials. As we have already stated, this is reflected in the accuracy of a Monte Carlo process. Third- and fourth-decimal accuracies are frequently difficult because of the foregoing relationship between accuracy and sample size.

Examples of Integration

With the advent of electronic digital computers the outlook in the use of stochastic methods for the solution of equations changed considerably. It suddenly became feasible to obtain large samples. When the method was first introduced in connection with computational media, in about 1947, statements were evoked attributing to it a panacean character; a supposition which has not been supported by the facts. Since then, it is generally agreed that, although many questions concerning the method remain unanswered, it should be regarded as another numerical tool especially suited for certain problems.

Let us consider first the simple problem of calculating the integral

$$F = \int_0^1 f(x)\, dx, \qquad 0 \leqslant f(x) \leqslant 1$$

by random sampling. In the preceding section we said that one Monte Carlo approach of evaluating this integral is to pick a number of points at random with a uniform density in the unit square and note which ones fall in the area between $f(x)$ and the x axis. The probability of any point falling in this area is just equal to F; therefore, if we compute the relative number of points that fall in the designated area, we will have an estimate of the integral.

In this calculation, the probable percent error depends only on the value of F and the number of points sampled, not on the character of $f(x)$. Since this is also true for a multiple integral of any order, the described process gives a method of evaluating integrals in which the number of points that have to be examined do not go up exponentially with the order of the integral or the accuracy required, provided that F is not small, for in that case the error would be large.

Now let

$$F = \int_0^1 f(x)\varphi(x)\, dx,$$

where $f(x)$ is a positive function and $\varphi(x)$ is a probability density function. The problem is to estimate the expected value of a function f

of a random variable when the probability of the random variable lying between x and $x + dx$ is $\varphi(x)\,dx$.

The standard sampling procedure would be to pick n values of x at random but according to the probability density $\varphi(x)$ and then take the arithmetic means of the $f(x_i)$. If we denote this arithmetic mean by $\bar{F}$ then

$$\bar{F} = \frac{1}{n}\sum_{i=1}^{n} f(x_i).$$

For large enough N the probable percent error is equal to

$$67.45\,\frac{\sigma}{\sqrt{n\bar{F}}},$$

where

$$\sigma^2 = \int_0^1 f^2(x)\varphi(x)\,dx - F^2.$$

The error formula does not depend on the dimensionality of the space or on the fine structure of $f(x)$ and $\varphi(x)$ but only on the size of the sample and the functional σ of $f(x)$ and $\varphi(x)$ as defined above.

In some cases, it is possible to have a distorted situation. This, for instance, is the case when $\varphi(x)$ is such that most of the sampled values of x lie close to 1 and, at the same time, because of the peak of $f(x)$, the important values of x lie close to 0. How important these values of x close to 0 actually are will depend on the proportion of the area that is located there. If most of the area is under the peak of $f(x)$, then the ordinary sampling technique will not give satisfactory results. For a remedy, the integrand of F can be transformed by dividing and multiplying by another distribution function $g(x)$. Thus,

$$\begin{aligned}
F &= \int_0^1 f(x)\varphi(x)\,dx \\
&= \int_0^1 \frac{f(x)\varphi(x)}{g(x)}\,g(x)\,dx \\
&= \int_0^1 h(x)g(x)\,dx.
\end{aligned}$$

We take

$$\bar{F} = \frac{1}{n}\sum_{i=1}^{n}\left[+f(x_i)\,\frac{\varphi(x_i)}{g(x_i)}\right],$$

where the x_i are picked out of the population described by $g(x)$ instead of $\varphi(x)$. The value of F cannot be changed by this sort of transformation, but the formula for σ^2 now becomes

$$\sigma^2 = \int_0^1 \left[\frac{f(x)\varphi(x)}{g(x)} \right]^2 g(x)\, dx - F^2.$$

It is possible to make σ as small as desired by choosing $g(x)$ appropriately. When φ becomes equal or almost equal to zero, the estimate $\bar{F}$ always comes out equal to F, independent of n or the x_1 we happened to pick.

But to carry out this optimum transformation we must know the value of F, which is the very thing we are looking for. In practice, therefore, we cannot hope to get this best $g(x)$ but can merely approximate it by the use of skill, preliminary analysis, and subsidiary calculations.

A sophisticated application of the Monte Carlo method is the problem of finding a probability model or game whose solution is related to the solution of a partial differential equation, and the determination of the least eigenvalue of a differential operator by means of a sampling process.

Solving Partial Differential Equations

An example using partial differential equations is the problem of establishing the numerical solution to the Laplace equation:

$$\left(\frac{\partial^2}{\partial x^2} + \frac{\partial^2}{\partial y^2} \right) Z = 0$$

or

$$\nabla^2 Z = 0,$$

where the function values have been stipulated around a boundary. Let's divide the region of interest into a square grid of mesh size d. We wish to obtain the solution of the finite-difference formulas at the node points of the grid. Such a formula at a node point K takes the form

$$\sum_{i=1}^{4} Z(K_i) - 4Z(K) = 0,$$

where K_i $(i = 1, \dots 4)$ are the four immediate neighbors of point K. The boundary conditions can be written

$$Z(Q) = \varphi(Q)$$

at points Q of the boundary, where φ is a known function.

We generate random paths starting from point K and ending at the boundary, using the rule that upon reaching any node point the probability of proceeding to each of the four neighboring points is equally likely. Upon reaching the boundary at the point Q the walk ends. The computed function is $\varphi(Q)$. The differential equation holds for points K interior to a region R and the boundary condition for points Q on the boundary of R. The validity of a random-walk procedure in solving the finite-difference equations corresponding to the boundary-value problem has given, thus far, valid proofs.

Elliptic partial differential equations can be solved numerically as a specialized system of linear algebraic equations. A process described by its transition probabilities runs on for m steps, or for a time t, where m or t are fixed in advance. When this process is suddenly terminated, it is required to find the probabilities of the various terminal states.

We can imagine placing traps, that is, absorbing barriers, along the way, which terminate the process automatically if it somehow falls into them. In the elliptic case, all possible terminal states consist of traps placed on the boundary of the region in question, and no time limit is set at all. The elliptic problem corresponds physically to the existence of a steady state.

In handling elliptic partial differential equations "local solutions" or solutions at a given point are possible. This makes possible the solution in certain restricted areas, or at certain points, without the necessity of treating the equations for all unknowns simultaneously as with the usual classical methods.

In several cases we can formulate the Monte Carlo approach from the physical process without first translating this process into a type of mathematical expression. This freedom in varying our approach is very important since it frequently happens that the mathematical formulation of the complete problem is not feasible, or if the formulation is feasible, the solution by standard techniques is not possible because of problem nonlinearities. For instance, consider the trajectory of a torpedo, or, more precisely, the impact point of the torpedo. The impact point is a random variable because of random variables in the guidance. In this case, sampling is done directly. Simulation of the trajectory can be performed on the basis of the character of the distribution of the random variables.

Random and Pseudo-Random Numbers

Mention should be made of the use of random numbers in all problems involving the Monte Carlo method. In some part of the process, the computitional media used for problem solution will require a source of "randomness."

It is possible to feed into the machine for reference a set of random numbers quoted from published tables, but this is not the most efficient approach. Where statistical experimentation is involved, we prefer to use a series of "pseudo-random numbers," each of which is obtained from the previous one by a simple arithmetical operation. The resulting numbers are determinate, and not stochastic, but have all the desired characteristics of random numbers. The wisdom of using them in place of those generated by a random process has long been debated, but the approach is generally taken as quite acceptable.

One of the first extensive projects in the generation of random sequences of numbers was undertaken by the RAND Corporation, in 1947. That work consisted of generating randon digits by counting electronically pulses from a random frequency pulse source and periodically printing out digits. Some one million random digits were thus obtained and tabulated.[5]

With the use of electronic computers, the favored method for obtaining sequences of pseudo-random numbers is based on calculating "modulo n" successive powers of a certain number A. On a computer, the module number n is usually taken to be a power of the base of the numeric system of the machine, for example 2 or 10, preferably, the largest power of 2 or 10 which can be accepted. The question then arises as to what number A will generate a nonrepeating sequence of maximal length.

There exists a number $a(n)$ such that no nonrepeating sequence generated by a number relatively prime to n may have length longer than $a(n)$. The length of any such sequence must be a divisor of $a(n)$ itself. We therefore look for the smallest number, here denoted by $S(n)$, which has the property possessed by $a(n)$.

In the pseudo-random number generation process, every sequence must repeat after $S(n)$ terms. Hence the sequence with precisely $S(n)$ terms is the best possible one which may be generated by A. Such a sequence does exist for every n, and methods are available for obtaining the generating number A.

With one of the current techniques in general use, a sequence of pseudo-random numbers is generated by the arithmetic process of performing successive multiplications and discarding many of the

---

[5] The RAND Corporation, "One Million Random Digits." The Free Press, Glencoe, Illinois, 1955.

"high" or the "high and low" order digits. The process can be described by the formula[6]:

$$x_i = 5^{2k+1}x_{i-1}(\text{mod } 2^m),$$ (1)
$$x_0 = 1,$$

for k a nonnegative integer and m the number of binary digits useful or desirable in the number produced. This method provides positive odd integers of m binary digits in length in the range $2^m > x_i \geqslant 0$. Sequences of such numbers are pseudo-random with uniform distribution if m is large.

A scheme of producing sequences of numbers which correspond to normal or Gaussian distributions consists in averaging subsequences of the numbers x_i, obtained from Eq. (1). If x has a distribution of mean μ and standard deviation σ, for which the moment generating function exists, then the random variable x formed by taking the average value $\bar{x}$ of N samples of x according to

$$y = (\bar{x} - \mu) \frac{\sqrt{N}}{\sigma}$$

approaches a standard distribution for large N.

For the generation of pseudo-random numbers, m is taken to be as large as possible, so that maximum periodicity is obtained. Its size is obviously limited by the binary size of the computer word. Usually k is chosen so that 5^{2k+1} is also as large as possible while still less than 2^m.

It is quite common to prepare a machine program which produces "normal random numbers." Multiplying these numbers by an arbitrary σ we then obtain deviates from the normal distribution. These would obviously have a standard deviation equal to σ. Such strings of numbers do pass the tests of randomness.

---

[6] See M. L. Juncosa, Random Number Generation on the BRL High Speed Computing Machines, Ballistic Research Laboratories, Report 855, Aberdeen Proving Ground, Maryland, 1953.

CHAPTER 9

Data Reduction and
Computational Media

In Chapter 8 we talked about statistical means in the solution of equations. In the preceding chapters we also made reference to the fact that, in mathematical experimentation, the researcher often uses statistical techniques. Mathematical statistics offers the possibility of conducting rationally designed and controlled experiments, of analyzing the resulting experimental data, and of simulating situations which could never be appropriately described by deterministic models.

Though statistical techniques are highly applicable in the study of both the natural and the man-made processes, we will not be concerned in the present work with their mechanics.[1] Instead, we will center our discussion on the use of statistical tools in data reduction, particularly those most applicable to the simulation studies with which we are concerned.

It suffices to say in the beginning that the nature of the tools we use determines the nature of the model we have available. In mathematical simulation we distinguish between "exact" or "deterministic" models (where chance plays a small role) and "probabilistic" models. Thus far, we have also mentioned another distinction, between "prototype" models and "custom-made" simulators. This gives rise to four possible combinations of mathematical tools and models, as shown in Fig. 1.

Prototype   Simulators

Deterministic

Probabilistic

FIG. 1

---

[1] For an all-inclusive discussion on statistical processes see D. N. Chorafas, "Statistical Processes and Reliability Engineering." Van Nostrand, Princeton, New Jersey, 1960.

To the fundamental difference which exists between deterministic and probabilistic models, we have often made implicit if not explicit reference. It would be useless to return to this subject. We have also stated that we only recently came to realize the extent of the stochastic nature prevailing in real processes, and that this realization constitutes a turning point in scientific thinking.

Outlining Certain Statistical Tools

In the beginning of Chapter 4 we said that, as technological ensembles increase in complexity, we need powerful mathematical tools to face problems involving systems stability, performance evaluation, data sampling, optimization, and inference through data reduction. Our tools for this job are regression, correlation, analysis of variance, sampling theory, and a whole range of other statistical techniques.

Let us consider briefly a practical example requiring correlation analysis. Basic components such as transistors, resistors, and capacitors are manufactured by many companies and have as many different characteristics. For a particular project some of the requirements of these components are quite critical, and call for an extensive evaluation of the various types available. Say that, for a certain type of transistor, the designer requires information on a certain characteristic which cannot be readily measured by the manufacturer. Statistical correlation can effectively give a good measure of this characteristic.

One of the basic and frequently encountered data-reduction problems is the determination of the parameters of a normal frequency distribution. For this problem the input data can be recorded as "raw score" or "raw score and frequency." Then they can be read into a computer together with the desired data-reduction program.[2] Let

$N =$ number of raw scores (or sum of the frequencies),

$\sum y =$ sum of the raw scores (or $\sum fy$),

$\sum y^2 =$ sum of the raw scores squared (or $\sum fy^2$),

$\sum y^3 =$ sum of the raw scores, third power (or $\sum fy^3$),

$\sum y^4 =$ sum of the raw scores, fourth power (or $\sum fy^4$).

We will use $\sum (y + 1)^4$ for checking purposes.

---

[2] Data-reduction practices can be better described with reference to digital or analog computing media for the manipulation and the storage of the input information. Hence, in the following we will make reference to "computing devices" as if they constituted an integral part of the mathematical procedure with which we are concerned.

From the values of $\sum y^3$ and $\sum y^4$, the machine will compute the measure of skewness, the measure of kyrtosis, and print the results. It will also check itself by comparing the appropriate sum of the summations with $\sum (y + 1)^4$. Simply,

$$\sum (y + 1)^4 = \sum y^4 + 4 \sum y^3 + 6 \sum y^2 + 4 \sum y + N.$$

For a case involving regression, say that we wish to determine the differences in life characteristics of certain components. Our primary interest concerns the failure rates. We have available a simplified plot of the cumulative failure distributions of two components A and B. Few failures occur initially, but the curves clearly indicate the wearing out (Fig. 2).

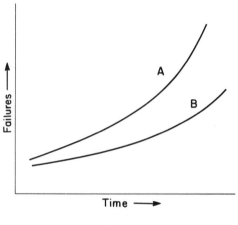

Fig. 2

A straight line fit to these data would be useless for comparative purposes since the "wear-out" distribution function usually is of the form

$$y = cb^x,$$

where x is the number of operations (usage or time) and y is the cumulative number of failures. However, this function can be handled through simple linear regression by fitting a straight line to the log function:

$$\log y = x \log b + \log c.$$

For data processing on a computer, the input data might, for instance, be given in (x, y) pairs. The machine will calculate $\log y$ and accumulate the required summations,

$$N, \quad \sum x, \quad \sum x^2, \quad \sum \log y, \quad \sum (\log y)^2, \quad \sum x \log y,$$

and for checking purposes,

$$\sum (x + \log y + 1)^2.$$

When this routine is followed by the linear regression analysis program, the machine can compute from these summations r, the coefficient of correlation; $\log b$, the regression coefficient (slope); $\log c$, the intercept; $\sigma_y{}^2$, the regression variance; $\sigma_b{}^2$, the variance of the slope; $o_c{}^2$, the variance of the intercept.

Say that one of the necessary criteria is that this curve must go through zero. Then the data must be fit to the line

$$\log y = x \log b.$$

To determine whether this is an acceptable fit, the machine can compare the sum of squares of the line forced through zero with the sum of squares of the least-squares line, by the variance ratio test.

In general, for a given data sample of n variables, the computational procedure is designed to determine that hyperplane in n space which approximates the sample observations of the dependent variable in a least squares sense. The approximation is regarded as suitable if, apart from what may reasonably be attributed to chance, the values predicted for the dependent variable by the hyperplane account for a large portion of this variable's sample variance.

As a tool, linear regression analysis is based on rather simple mathematics. The least-squares procedure was invented by Carl Friedrich Gauss in 1795. It can be equally applied if the data studied are birth rates and time, machine breakdowns and units of production, or parts requirements and sales volumes. A line derived by least squares will reflect any trend which may exist; "average values" do not show a true trend. It will also limit the effect of isolated radical values in a set of data.

Starting from the fundamentals, the basic formula for a straight line is

$$y = a + bx,$$

where b gives the slope of the line, that is, the rate at which y changes relative to x, and a is the point at which the line cuts the y axis. The formula for b is

$$b = \frac{\sum xy - [\sum (x)\sum (y)]/n}{\sum x^2 - (\sum x)^2/n},$$

where n represents the number of pairs of x and y values. With the values for a and b, the line of best fit can be drawn. This is the line which makes the summation of the squares of the distances of the dispute points (data) from itself a minimum.

With the use of machines to carry out the routine computational load, interest in the subject of multiple regression analysis has increased. Multiple regression and the analysis of variance are a part of what has been called "standard methods of analyzing data." Mathematically the two methods are closely related. The analysis of variance can be regarded as a special case of multiple regression in which the independent variables are arbitrary or dummy variantes. It is usual, however, to think of the analysis of variance as concerning itself with a single variable, while the purpose of multiple regression is to relate one or more dependent variables with two or more independent, or "causative," variables. In either case, it is conceptually easy to regard the approach as a breakdown of the "total variation" in a single variable into several component parts, regardless of how this breakdow is accomplished.

For an example of both the usage and the electronic computation of regression analysis, assume that it is necessary to compare the inherent (genetic) relationships between several of the characteristics of a variable under study with the observed correlations. For this we need the sums of squares and sums of products of all variables under consideration.

The observed correlations are equal to the product-moment correlations between the variables concerned.

The same quantities appear in a multiple regression analysis of a dependent variable y_i, on independent variables x_j, $j = 1 \ldots k$. For $k = 5$:

$$(y_i - \bar{y}) = b_1(x_{1i} - \bar{x}_1) + b_2(x_{2i} - \bar{x}_2)$$
$$+ b_2(x_{3i} - \bar{x}_3) + b_4(x_{4i} - \bar{x}_4)$$
$$+ b_5(x_{5i} - \bar{x}_5) + e_i$$

for $i = 1 \ldots n$, and where e_i is an estimate of the measurement errors involved.

Depending on the complexity of the problem it is often desirable to set up the entire group of variables in machine memory. Checks can automatically be performed since, say, $\Sigma x_j x_i = \Sigma x_i x_j$, and the two operations can be accomplished independently. There exist today many subroutines treating this problem, so that we do not need to elaborate further at this point.

Using Computational Media

To decide whether the objective of a suitable linear approximation has been obtained, not only do certain statistics need to be computed, but also significance tests must be made. Digital computers made possible the convenient handling of the considerable computation required in performing this type of analysis upon a substantial number of variables and observations. Presently available machine programs enable the computation and printing of:

(i) the means and standard deviations

(ii) the coefficients of simple and partial correlation, regression, and multiple correlation;

(iii) the standard error of estimate.

The input data are directly used only in the computation of the sums of squares and the sums of cross products for the variables, and from these three types of sums, the program developed the means, standard deviations, and simple correlation matrix. Many of these programs provide that the data are arranged by observation. Hence, the corresponding observations of all variables can be grouped together, so that all of the observations of a variable comprise one group.

With respect to machine usage, a certain approach usually has both advantages and disadvantages. Arrangement of the input data by observation will, for minimal machine time, require a large amount of high-speed memory to accommodate the double-precision partial sums accumulated in the formation of the matrix of cross products. For a given machine configuration, this imposes a restriction on the number of variables that can be handled efficiently. Yet, the calculation of the simple correlation matrix involves essentially a matrix multiplication to obtain the sums of cross products, and this input format enables direct formation of the premultiplier in such a way that the elements of the product matrix are conveniently generated serially rather than in parallel.

One least-squares polynomial routine performs the fitting of a polynomial of degree $k = 1, 2, 3, 4$ for a maximum total number of 500 datum points. The input required is in standard floating-point form, with the output available in the same format. With a small machine which has been used in this computation, the average speed for a total of 99 datum points for $k = 1$ was three to four minutes, for $k = 2$ it was five minutes, for $k = 3$ it was seven minutes.

In the abstract, these speeds may not seem to be so impressive, but anyone who has done data-reduction work can well understand their significance. The same can be said about questions of cost. At a data-processing center, large scale computer time costs upwards of $10 a minute. Yet comparative to the cost of manual computation this may be a very low price.[3]

Another routine, which handles input data in the fixed-decimal mode and provides the output in floating-point form, can fit polynomials up to the eleventh order with a maximum of 100 experimental points. In addition, four types of weighting factors are allowed: uniform weighting, weighting by the inverse first power of the dependent variable, and arbitrary weight factors at each point.

One of the methods for least-squares fitting, used with electronic computation, is an orthogonal polynomial fit to a set of m datum points. In producing the Nth-order approximation, all other approximating polynomials from order 1 to $N - 1$ and their respective residuals are calculated. The input, that is, the experimental measurements, must be provided in floating-point form, and the output is given in floating decimal.

A certain programming routine provides a least-squares fit to data obtained in a subcritical reactor. This routine calculates a hyperbolic sine fit when the absolute experimental uncertainty of the data is of the same magnitude at each point and a hyperbolic sine fit when the relative uncertainty is the same at each point. The average speed for a sine fit to 20 experimental points is three minutes.

Equally useful devices in data analysis are the correlation procedures used to obtain the interrelation of the stochastic variable or activity under study with other variables or activities which are thought to influence or resemble it. For a given stochastic process the analyst may want the autocorrelation for various lead or lag intervals or a serial-correlation with another process. An autocorrelation is often desired to find the presence of cycles within the data.

In the case where a given time series is interrelated with several other time series, recourse can be made to a multiple regression procedure. Most frequently, the dependence of the given series on the others is assumed to be linear as a first approximation. The steps involved in a multilinear regression program for an electronic digital computer can be divided into four parts:

(1) Transformation of initial variables into new variables, e.g., logarithms, or weighting of initial data.

---

[3] For example, in 1961, in Iran, the writer did a simulation study which needed a substantial amount of regression analysis with calculation of confidence intervals. Part of the work had to be done locally by two mathematicians equipped with desk calculators. The study was finished on a computer in Paris. The resulting cost ratio between manual and electronic processing was 10:1 in favor of the electronic processing.

(2) Calculations of the matrix of coefficients of the simultaneous linear equations to be solved for the least-squares estimates. This matrix, on inversion, readily yields the desired estimates and statistical constants. In addition to the matrix of simple correlation coefficients, the means and standard deviations are computed.

(3) Inversion of one or more positive-definite and symmetric matrices.

(4) Calculation from the inverse matrix of the required estimates and statistical constants such as regression coefficients, standard error of estimate, multiple correlation coefficient and its square, standard errors of regression coefficients, partial correlation coefficients and their standard errors, residuals.

Generally, following the computation of the partial correlation matrix the machine computes the specified dependent variable, the regression coefficients which determine the least-squares hyperplane, the multiple correlation coefficient, and the standard error of estimate. The square of the multiple correlation coefficient may be expressed as that fraction whose denominator is the dependent variable's sample variance and whose numerator is the variance of the corresponding values determined by the regression hyperplane. Consequently, the multiple correlation coefficient may be regarded as a measure of the goodness of fit of the regression hyperplane. The standard error of estimate is the square root of the average squared deviation of the observed values of the dependent variable from the values predicted by the hyperplane.

The standard errors of the regression coefficients can provide important additional information on interpretation of the results of the regression analysis, by enabling the determination of confidence intervals for the regression coefficients. For this reason, digital computer programs often offer as output confidence intervals, with several levels of significance determined for each regression coefficient from Student's t distribution. By referring to these intervals, the experimenter can test not only whether each regression coefficient is significantly different from zero but also the dependability with which this sample coefficient can be used to represent the corresponding population regression coefficient.

Computation with Random Sampling Problems

In Chapter 8 we spoke about the comeback of random walks in the broader and more inclusive form of Monte Carlo. Although the very substantial computational requirements of the method had, in essence, prohibited its use, this procedure has been made feasible thanks to electronic computation. The computer permits the everyday use of elaborate statistical procedures that had not been practical before. It makes possible the study of simultaneous effects from dozens of different variables, where, in manual media, it was quite difficult to study more than a few.

In the present section we will be briefly concerned with sampling problems as presented in studies which involve many contingencies or multidimensional spaces of a high order. As an example, let us consider the problem of calculating the probability of the transmission of neutrons through a shield. To work this analytically in a straight-forward probability fashion would involve the calculation of penetrating the shield in exactly n collisions. Since the calculation of the nth collision beam involves a multiple integration of an order of at least $3n$, the labor rapidly becomes fantastic.

Comparatively, it is much simpler to trace out typical life histories of neutrons and record the percent that succeed in penetrating this shield. The problem then reduces to a "success" or "failure" type of experiment. If we associate with each experiment a random variable x whose value is 1 if the experiment is a success and 0 if it fails, the expected value of x will be p, the probability of success. The random variable x has a binomial distribution.

One of the first problems to be treated by the Monte Carlo method was the attenuation of neutrons in a bounded or semi-infinite slab. Several researchers have been working on this problem with a variety of approaches. Some worked with a mass sample; that is, a thousand or so neutrons are taken simultaneously from impact to impact in the mass. In another approach, researchers have followed the path of each neutron until it is stopped or until it leaves the domain of the experiment. When such a history is terminated they restored the computer to the initial conditions, but continued the computing routine without change until the statistical information produced stable curves.

There exists a variety of physical arrangements for this problem and a corresponding variety of computing forms. In the following discussion we will confine ourselves to rectangular coordinate arrangements with neutrons arriving at a single energy. We have, at most, seven coordinates in the problem: E; x, y, z; a, b, c. These are energy, position coordinates, and direction cosines. Given the energy, the researcher can select a mean free path and a set of process probabilities. The mean free path length is multiplied by a number taken from a logarithmic distribution, representing the number of mean free path lengths traveled. This gives the path length. The path length is extended in turn by the direction cosines to give the x, y, z displacements and new position.

The process selection is made by comparing a random number with the process probabilities. The process may indicate termination, so too may the spatial position or energy. If termination is indicated the last result is printed and the machine restored to the initial energy and direction condition. When there is no termination, the process generally indicates a change in energy and direction, and the change is effected accordingly.

The direction change may be subject to a distribution dependent upon the process. In this case more than one set of randomly distributed transformations must be used, and which set depends upon the process. When the direction cosines have been transformed, the process is complete, the results are printed, and the routine starts over with the selection of mean free path and process probability.

Consider the problem of fluid flow through porous media, where the fluid is composed of several phases. It is not feasible to determine an analytic solution to the differential equations representing the flow, principally because the phases interreact. However, it is possible to determine particular numerical solutions for a given set of parameters. Thus practical study can be made although no general solution exists.

Similarly, electronically processed mathematical models have been used in the design of distillation equipment. In this application, heat and material balances around each plate, as well as the procedures for adjusting the operating parameters, are written in explicit mathematical and logical form. Data are entered concerning the geometry of the equipment and material composition of the products involved. The machine then evaluates the behavior of the tower under a given set of conditions. At each stage of the computation, the design can be re-evaluated against some set of criteria, adjusting parameters according to the procedure in such a way as to improve performance.

By adjusting the parameters under study, a system can be observed in operation under a wide variety of conditions. With this, the over-all design can be optimized. Simulation studies along with the use of electronic computers have been an invaluable tool in nuclear research and in many other fields. They have allowed for the solution of nonlinear hydrodynamic equations, problems in diffusion theory, and many similar problems. They made possible the combination of equations representative of all three types into one over-all calculation of reactor parameters, and thus they use the computer as a simulated complete reactor.

This is particularly valuable when the reactor geometry is complicated. Here, Monte Carlo methods can be employed to study the effect on criticality of cross section, energy-group variation, by-product poisoning, dimensional variation, and a host of additional variables. Notably, these calculations may be done in three-dimensional space and time. Thus the complete geometry of a reactor may be represented as it is, without the inaccuracies inherent in a two-dimensional approximation.

Computerizing Mathematical Models

It is questionnable whether, without the availability of high-speed data processors, mathematical models could be used to the extent they are in experimentation. Using computers, large, complex problems with many variable or statistical parameters can now be handled with a facility and speed never before possible.

Without computers, mathematical experimentation at a reasonably detailed level would have been too tedious, or even impossible to undertake. Mathematical experimentation would have had obvious shortcomings, as it would have necessitated over-simplification, thus decreasing its range of usefulness and the applicability of its results. In addition, lack of electronic data processing would have resulted in failure to reduce data-generation time to the level at which a mathematical model would attain its greatest degree of effectiveness.

High-speed computation is the key to obtaining either a few answers from a vast amount of data or a substantial number of answers from a limited amount of data. The former is known as data reduction, the latter as data generation. An example of data reduction is the earth satellite, which is constantly transmitting information on conditions in space as it meets them, second by second. A computer absorbs this tremendous amount of information, collates it, processes it, and finally reduces it to a meaningful pattern.

At the other extreme, consider the computer at the Cape Canaveral missile test center. It receives real-time data on the path of the fired missile, and on this basis forecasts the exact trajectory of the projectile. In other words, it generates data on the future behavior of the device, and if this behavior is forecasted to be getting out of control the computer can generate a signal which will either initiate the self-destruction of the missile in the air or inform the commanding officer, who will take the appropriate action.

Within this framework of data reduction and data generation, it is conceivable that in the years to come the electronic computer will become the core element in every industrial enterprise. Using mathematical models to solve industrial problems may be extended to the point where an electronic computer will be given the power to use its discretion as to which variables are to be controlled and within which range of variation. As the state of the art progresses, it may eventually become feasible that the computer will be informed through its own experimentation on the variables and the interactions which are to be considered, and on the limiting values on a certain program.

Even without this kind of machine sophistication, by using an elaborate simulator the researcher has a tool which permits him to make an exhaustive, detailed, and accurate evaluation of any case or set of operating conditions that he wishes to investigate. Using the computer, he is removing most limitations on the quality and thoroughness of the calculation itself. A more refined calculation procedure, which would be omitted from a hand method because it adds several hours to the evaluation time for a single case, might add only five minutes of processing to the computer program.

Yet, while electronic computation enables the analyst to eliminate many of the compromises that he must make with hand methods, computer usage itself imposes requirements. Preparing a mathematical simulator for data processing involves considerable planning. The allocation of the memory capacity of the machine is but one example.

A rule to remember, rather obvious to everybody involved in computer programming, is that fast memory, particularly if of limited size, should be reserved entirely for communication from one program block to another. A program block is a group of certain operations. The reason for distinguishing separate blocks within a given program is that, in this manner, we increase its flexibility with respect to program changes, additions, deletions, etc. Hence, a simulator program can be visualized as being composed of distinct blocks, each providing proper linkage to the next one in the line.

From the point of view of content, each block may consist of several memory loads normally referred to as "records." Data preserved on the fast memory, in spite of a block transfer, usually consist of available volumes, quantities, and any other information necessary to communicate. A certain area in the fast memory should be reserved for communication from one record to another. Fast-memory words should also be reserved for the over-all control program which coordinates the processing of blocks.

One of the program block's permanent store on the high speed memory might be used to advantage for "supervisory control" purposes.[4] For

---

[4] See also "Programming Systems for Electronic Computers." Butterworths, London, 1962.

instance, its functions might be conceived as those of simplifying additions or revisions to the remaining or "operating" program. The supervisory routine might accept as data a normal sequence of blocks to be used in a specific problem.

In running an operating plan, some of the data required by each block have been developed as a result of calculations in preceding blocks. Information communicated from block to block can be stored on the high speed memory. When reiteration is to occur, the contents of the memory must be saved at the reentry point so that the memory can be restored to the same condition upon reiteration to that block. Special control instructions can save the memory contents, then transfer operations to the first record of the called block.

The optimum utilization of the tape units is another matter of interest in planning the electronic processing of a simulator. If the simulator calls for other programs or more detailed models, then these are mounted on a separate "auxiliary program tape." A "dump tape" is usually reserved for preserving memory in the event that it is necessary. Finally, when the simulation study is completed, the preliminary print tape is edited and the entire output transferred to the "final output tape."

To simplify the upkeep of the simulator, it is advantageous to forecast technological and other changes of the system under study. This allows the programmer to anticipate a variety of changes and to make the necessary provisions for flexibility in his original program, for the incorporation of unanticipated changes might be costly in time, effort, and money.

In evaluating computer usage the first essential step is to attack the subject with a fresh mind. The second step is to get the facts:

  (i) Send individuals to orientation courses to learn what the equipment will do and will not do.

 (ii) Read pertinent books, articles, and reports on computer applications and principles.

(iii) Confer with people experienced in computer procedures and applications.

 (iv) Get in touch with computer manufacturers' research personnel.

  (v) Visit installations of electronic computers to see simulation work being actually performed.

The next step is to use vision and foresight in determining which operations can be performed by a computer: in establishing areas of decision-making where the computer can be of major assistance, in evaluating equipment requirements and cost, in planning the proposed computer runs, and in synthesizing savings and operating costs for future time periods.

During this study one should keep an open mind at all times. Often times benefits are hidden from the first analysis. The same is true for costs. Cost analysis for digital simulation is one of the areas where present-day accomplishments leave much to be desired.

The computer is an expensive device. It costs money whether it is used profitably or not. Often it costs much more money when it is not used profitably. A firm should neither commit itself to computers in a light manner nor take it for granted that such systems, when installed, are going to be used efficiently.[5]

---

[5] See D. N. Chorafas, " L'Influence des Ordinateurs sur la Structure des Entreprises " Les Editions de l'Entreprise Moderne, Paris, 1964; D. N. Chorafas, " Les Applications des Ordinateurs, dans l'Industrie, le Commerce et les Services Publiques. " Les Editions de L'Entreprise Moderne, Paris, 1961. D.N. Chorafas, " Die Aufgaben der Forschung in der modernen Unternehmung ", Oldenbourg Verlag, München und Wien, 1963.

CHAPTER 10

Putting Managerial Data in Mathematical Form

Companies have been using analytic techniques for such widely varied tasks as inventory control, transportation, plant or warehouse location, market forecasting, and management control. Fundamentally, the real power of mathematical analysis lies not so much in the solution of individual problems as in providing an increasingly clear vision of the enterprise as a whole. With competition getting tighter all the time in every domain of industrial activity, managers should realize that they can no longer "fly by the seat of their pants." They need an analytic navigator as much as a modern airliner needs an electronic navigational system.

Facts and Fiction in Using Mathematics

The analytic approach to managerial problems leans heavily on mathematics. This in itself, though necessary, is by no means a guarantee of success. The so-called "mathematical game"—e.g., the magic square—is an example of mathematical routines used in connection with problems other than those of science and technology. This routine consists of placing a set of integers in serial order, arranged in square formation, so that the totals of each row, column, and main diagonal are the same. Some notion of the fantastic lengths to which this largely frivolous topic was analyzed may be gained by noting that in 1838 a French work on the subject ran to three volumes.

The "order" of the magic square is the number of cells on one of its sides. There are no magic squares of order two. Magic squares grow quickly in complexity when we turn to order four. There are exactly 880 different types, ignoring rotations and mirror images, many of which are much more magical than required by the definition of a magic square. Fourth-order magic squares were linked to Jupiter by Renaissance astrologers and were believed to combat melancholy.

The theory of games of strategy is another example of mathematical model-making through gaming. Game theory is a means of dealing with competitive economic behavior. Work along this line is based on the fact that there exist several common factors in actual games and in economic situations, such as conflicting interests, incomplete information, and the interplay of free rational decision and chance. Hence, game theory is essentially an approach to simulation of competitive processes.

However, in terms of allowing the effective handling of management problems, game theory has proved to be a no greater contribution than the magic squares were. The sober outlook which prevails about the method is justified by the fact that game-theory models are restricted to two-person, zero-sum, finite strategy situations.[1] This is so far removed from reality that it is safe to say that game theory is not applicable to actual industrial situations.

If this, then, is the state of the art, why use mathematics in management in the first place? The answer should be found in the complexity prevailing in the modern enterprise, in the fierce competition it faces, and in the amplifying effects of managerial decisions. These are conditions which we have not known before. Such conditions make the relatively simple process of using one's own common sense"[2] in making decisions both an irrational and a dangerous practice.

But the use of mathematical analysis in managerial problems to be effective must be well planned and executed in a masterful way. There is no substitute for the use of the fundamentals:

   (i) Establish the problem.
   (ii) Observe first qualitatively then quantitatively.
   (iii) Formulate hypotheses about the unknown real situation.
   (iv) Experiment to test the hypothesis.
   (v) Decide on the hypothesis (accept—reject).
   (vi) Finally concertise the outcome in managerial terms.

In its simplest form a well-executed quantitative effort can assist management by putting into black and white alternative possibilities, risks, and expected returns. This is what was done by a certain American Company early in 1962, when the entry of Britain into the Common Market was still in the balance. This company, which had entered with manufacturing and marketing facilities both the Common Market

---

[1] See D. N. Chorafas, "Operations Research for Industrial Management." Reinhold New York, 1958.

[2] Defined by Einstein as "that layer of prejudice laid in the human mind before the age of fifteen."

and EFTA, had to decide about realigning facilities. But alternative courses, which were beyond its control, could upset any such arrangement.

The company's director of international operations gave a budget for investments according to his best judgement. His judgement was conditioned by the evolution in the different Common Market negotiations at that time. Other things equal, his return on investments was going to be dependent on the distinct expansion possibilities that could follow the negotiations. As of September 1962, the five following different courses the market structure could take might have had a distinct, and in some cases adverse, effect on the possible alternatives which were under his control:

Market Structure / Plans under control	Common Market of six	Enlarged Continental Common Market	Britain joins the E.C.M.	The U.S. get an associated status	Eastern Europe gets an associated status
Plan I. Factories in Britain					
Plan II Factories in Germany (including Berlin)					
Plan III. Factories in Britain/ France					
Plan IV. Lim. investments in Europe (depend on U.S. factories)					

Notice how an investment which for one market structure presents distinct advantages (e.g., establishing manufacturing facilities both in Britain and in France) turns into disadvantage if the market structure takes another course (e.g., the U.S. are given or assume an associated status). This turnabout alone might have been able to completely upset whatever a very careful study might have indicated as being the most profitable approach.

This example must not mislead the reader into believing that any mathematical analysis would be useless. In the contrary, tactical questions, such as the return on investments for different plant locations and manufacturing capacities, the calculation of the potential of a given market, and the like, could and should be treated in an analytical manner. But in trying to arrive at the strategic decision, which of the five market structures is most likely, the contribution of applied mathematics would be nil or negative. A luncheon with the Minister of Finance of one of the leading Common Market nations would be much more fruitful.

A European Common Market Simulator

The concept, the approach, and the fundamentals of a mathematical model which might be used in the making of a European Common Market simulator will be briefly described. For the purpose of our discussion, we will establish that the objective of this simulator is to represent, in a mathematical form, the structure of the European Common Market and its behavior with respect to changes in certain parameters relating to the producibility and marketability of industrial products.

The first decision in the development of this mathematical model has to do with its over-all structure. A division into two major parts was chosen: the one being a *data generator*, the other an *optimizer*. The data generator, given a set of input variables and for certain established values of the parameters of the model, should provide basic data on

(i) the national income for each participating country.

(ii) the gross market potential per country.

(iii) the specific sales potential per country and commodity.

(iv) the share of the market for each country-product combination.

(v) the cost of production.

The job of the optimizer is to process the information provided by the data generator. It should also have the ability to handle parameters relating to decisions made by policy-making bodies, such as the national governments. It should then optimize among alternative possibilities, subject to a given set of criteria. With a data generation-optimization ensemble made operational, we can effectively experiment with a number of different variables and parameters we wish to consider, and with the criteria we wish to see followed.

As with every problem in the study of natural or man-made systems, we must establish the variables and their boundaries. Among the variables to be established we must select those which we regard as the most critical and on whose study our effort will be mainly concentrated. When we talk of boundaries, we must distinguish between those implied by nature and those which are a result of the deliberate action of the researcher.

The following decisions were made to simplify the initial work:

(i) The simulator considers in detail only the action among the six countries of the Common Market, the rest of the world being considered in the cumulative as a trading area with both production and consumption capabilities. This assumption helps to simplify the model. A simplification which can be accomplished without much loss of generality as far as the internal workings of the market are concerned. Furthermore, the possibility is left open to proceed with the subdivision of the rest of the world market at a later date.

(ii) In the beginning only a limited number of products will be considered with their respective marketability. This is done in the belief that too much detail in the very first place may hurt rather than help the model.

(iii) Since the objective is to study the behavior of the national market and the effects of the national economy rather than those of a particular company operating with a certain national market, it is advisable to lump together, in a weighted average, homogeneous products made in a certain country, as for instance, automobiles.

While the forementioned assumptions average out—so to speak— certain specific fluctuations, it is also true that, on the whole, they help considerably in improving the accuracy of the simulator regarding the variables it is particularly intended to study.

In the light of the foregoing discussion, establishing the crucial variables of the system now becomes a more specific job:

(1) Since the objective is that of studying the reaction of the national market to the practices of the Common Market, it follows rather logically that the first crucial variable is that of *the tariff system.*

(2) A set of crucial variables is that of *the studied products*, from research and development to their production and marketing. The mathematical model should describe by means of equations the production capabilities and the market behavior for each product and country.

(3) To fill in the gap left by the established constraint of considering only a set of products available within each market, rather than their totality, another crucial variable would be the *compensating product*. This is conceived as a fictitious variable intended to take care of the gap left in the market by the nonconsideration of all products.

(4) *National productivity* (taking a projection into the future, but essentially based on historical information).

(5) *National industrial potential* (in the cumulative).

(6) *National employment history* (mellowed with the expected changes because of the evolution of the Common Market).

(7) *National income* (both in absolute and per capita figures).

(8) *Population changes* (including population transfers).

(9) *National currency* (both in relation to a certain reference currency and in relation to the other currencies of the Common Market).

(10) *Attractiveness of foreign-made products* within each country.

Considering the industrial structure of the Common Market countries, three basic products have been selected for the purpose of this study, namely: coal, steel, and chemicals, also three transformation products: automobiles, electromechanical appliances, and household electronics. Intercompany variations within each country and interproduct variations within a certain class can be leveled by considering weighting factors, which will take into account the specific business volumes of business for each product-country.

A basic banking system should be included in the simulator. One of the most difficult parts of this job is to account for money movements and decisions on, say, discount rates made by a banking system outside the Common Market structure. A banking system to be complete should include provisions for intercountry monetary transfers, for international Government loans, for loans to industry, and for loans to the public within a certain country. International monetary movements of a speculative nature may or may not be considered, but this decision would obviously affect the accuracy of the model.

Finally to eliminate variations due to transportation cost and other constraints within any given country, both production and consumption were (temporarily) taken for each product and country as concentrated on a given point. By this token, we distinguish "point sources" S_{ik} for product k and country i, and "sinking points" S_{jk} for product k and country j. Since this computation is based on weighted averages, for different k we may have different points. Even for the same k and for $i = j$, S_{ik} and S_{jk} may still be two different points. In this case, transportation cost should necessarily be charged even if that product is produced and consumed in the same country.

The following equations were considered of importance for the simulation of the productive system (within each of the Common Market countries) and for the respective consumption markets.

1. THE NATIONAL INCOME EQUATION

In econometrics the national income Y is expressed in the form of one of the alternative equations

$$Y = C + G - I + E - P, \tag{1a}$$

$$Y = \pi X = \sum_k \pi_k x_k, \tag{1b}$$

$$Y = Mv. \tag{1c}$$

In Eq. (1a), C is the total consumption by the public (both consumer and capital goods), I the investments made by industry (mostly in capital goods), G the Government expenditures, E the exports, and P the imports. In Eq. (1b), π and X represent price and quantity of goods, respectively, hence the form $\pi_k x_k$, for the ith item. This expresses the national income as the sum total of the produced real goods. Finally, in Eq. (1c) the national income is expressed as the money supply M times the velocity of circulation of money v.

The interplay of these equations offers a good possibility for the inclusion and representation of the forementioned variables in the simulator.

2. GROSS SALES POTENTIAL

The gross sales potential equation must include all items k made in any country i and consumed in a given country j. (It may be $i = j$.) Hence, GSP is expressed as a function of the following variables:

$a_1 = $ minimum price for product k
$a_2 = $ national support
$a_3 = $ foreign attraction

a_4 = general economic conditions in this country
a_5 = general level of employment
a_6 = investment habits of the public
a_7 = savings by the public
a_8 = marketing expenditures
a_9 = tax structure
a_{10} = salary level within each country;
K = available capital in the country
N = employment level
$\sum_j \psi_{jk}$ = innovation factor for k

$$A = F\left(\frac{\text{const}}{\min \pi_i}, \frac{1}{a_2}, a_3, a_4, a_5, a_6, a_7, Y, N, K, \sum_j \psi_{jk}, \sum a_8, \frac{1}{a_9}, a_{10}\right).$$

The reason for differentiating between K and a_7 is that the available capital in a country does not necessarily come from the savings made by the public. International capital movement, for instance, could be a major factor.

3. Specific Sales Potential

The specific sales potential is calculated for a certain item k made in any country i and consumed in country j, where possibly $i = j$. This is computed as the product

$$B = b_0 mT,$$

where b_0 is the extrapolated level on 10-year data computed through a simple linear regression line or through a weighted equation, as, for instance,

$$\frac{(X_1 + X_2) + 1.5(X_3 + X_4) + 2(X_5 + X_6) + 2.5(X_7 + X_8) + 3(X_9 + X_{10})}{20},$$

m is a multiplier taken equal, greater to, or less than 1 for

$$\pi_{ijk,n} \lessgtr \pi_{ijk,n-1}.$$

$T = et + \epsilon$, where t is the time period n, e is a constant multiplier, and ϵ a random fluctuation. In this form, the time factor can be used to represent business cycles.

As defined $\sum B < A$. This would become an equality only if a "plug item" is used to compensate for the products and services available in an economy and not being represented by the simulator under discussion.

The reason for differentiating between "gross" and "specific" sales potential is that a certain market may show a preference in consuming item x versus item y. This may be a function of custom, of short trend, of fashion, or simply a random event. Performing a step-by-step calculation using two equations would present interesting possibilities for studying the interaction among different items.

4. Share of the Market

Share of the market by a producer country i, on a certain item k, consumed in country j can be expressed by the function

$$D = f\left(\frac{\pi_{jk}}{\pi_{ijk}}, \psi_{ijk}, a_2, a_3, \frac{a_8}{\bar{a}_8}, d_1, d_2, d_3, H\right),$$

where

π_{ijk} = price for item k, in country j, made by country i
π_{jk} = mean price for item k in country j
ψ_{ijk} = innovation factor, expressed as a function of research and development
a_2, a_3 = as in GSP. Notice that the share of the market is analogous to a_2 while GSP is inverse.
a_8 = marketing expenditures
d_1 = factor for serviceability and marketability
d_2 = sales organization factor (classification in great, average, low)
d_3 = capital investment of the producer (a multiplier)
H = sales of ijk at the $n-1$ period.

5. Cost Equation

This considers the cost of production plus overhead and profit. Production costs can either be calculated by extrapolation or be presented in the form of a mathematical equation (taking into account factors such as labor cost, depreciation, overhead, etc.). In either case, allowances should be made for expansion and innovation. Overhead can be added on a % basis over the production costs based on actual data for each nation.

Finally, regarding the equations of the optimizer, let i indicate the producing country, j the consuming country, and k the type of product. If x_i indicates production in country i, c_j consumption in country j, and x_{ij} the item produced in country i and consumed in country j, then

$$x_i = \sum_i x_{ij},$$

$$c_j = \sum_j x_{ji}.$$

The price of the kth item at a certain consumption point can be expressed as a function of the price of this item at its point of origin, of the necessary transportation expenses τ_{ij}, and of the added customs duties and special taxations ρ_{ij}. Hence, with reference to Eq. (1b), we can write

$$\pi = f(\pi_{ijk}, \tau_{ijk} + \rho_{ijk}).$$

With reference to this equation, government decision-making is mostly concerned with variations in custom duties and special taxation.

A Mathematical Model of Civilian Air Carrier Traffic

We will now turn to the specific problem of developing a mathematical model for forecasting purposes. To plan ahead for an industry as young and rapidly growing as the air transport, forecasts for short-, middle-, and long-range periods are needed for both the commercial operators and the various governmental units charged with providing airports, traffic control, and regulatory functions. Short-range predictions are necessary for the assignment of aircraft to routes and schedules. Middle- and long-range forecasts are most useful for facilities planning, for aircraft procurement, and for control-system planning. For the users of forecasts, over-all statistics and individual route statistics are essential.

Historical data arranged in histograms cannot tell the whole story. Planners must have at their disposition experimental means much more powerful than a pie chart or a statistical table. It is not the simple event but its correlation to other events which can lead to a decision. No matter how able the planner is, his memory is rather limited as to the amount of information it can hold at any given time. Human calculating ability is also restricted. These limitations work to the detriment of the executive's capability to forecast and control.

A model for use in air-transport planning should forecast over-all activity, average passenger loads between any given city, and size and timing of peak loads between cities. The air-transport simulator to be described has exactly the foregoing objectives. Certain restrictions were intentionally established in the beginning of the study in order to increase its approximation to reality and, hence, its usefulness over a more limited area. Some more restrictions were inherent in the nature of the problem, and therefore they were unavoidable.

To demonstrate a work method and also keep this example to a manageable size, only the problem of forecasting over-all activity for air transport was selected, analyzed, and mathematically formulated.[3] As it will be seen, with data generated from the simulator, a high degree of correlation is obtained between total passenger miles and the independent variables of population, gross national product, and the available seat miles.

Before proceeding with the mechanics of the mathematical model, we need to consider the factors influencing the level of air travel in the United States, measured in total annual passenger miles, and the manner in which the factors interact with each other.

TABLE I

Basic Data

Year	TPM[1] (millions)	ASM[1] (millions)	P[2] (millions)	GNP[3] (billions)
1938	457	908	129.7	85.2
1946	5910	7508	140.0	209.2
1948	5910	10 304	146.2	257.3
1950	7955	12 984	150.4	258.1
1952	12 461	18 973	156.4	345.4
1953	14 668	23 128	158.8	363.2
1954	16 696	26 717	161.5	360.6
1955	19 741	31 163	164.4	390.8
1956	22 276	35 138	167.5	414.7
1957	25 250	41 491	170.0	433.9
1965			195.04	570.04

Table I shows the basic data used in this study. Throughout this study, a continuation of the 1958 economic climate was assumed, with no major catastrophies, war upsets, or extended depressions. Also, the market was taken as elastic; this assumption was based on the rationale that with the prevailing conditions in the development of the air-transport industry there are reasons to believe in background growth factors which exist in contrast to other transportation markets.

Indeed, this assumption, made in 1958, has been fully documented. As seen in Fig. 1, international air travel has joined international trade and investment in helping to shrink the size of the globe. It can be

---

[3] The utilized data on the air-transport industry were obtained from the Air Transport Association. Population and gross national product are based on United States Department of Commerce information. The population figures are the midyear estimates for each respective year. This study was made in 1958, and the subject information is taken with reference to that time.

shown that, in the United States, the air transport industry has not only taken a major share of the growth in passenger miles but also has expanded at the expence of other transport media, such as the railway and the ship.

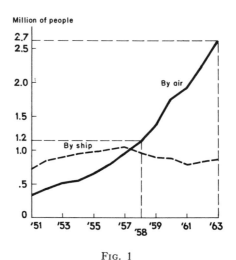

FIG. 1

Still, the full potential of air travel has not been exploited. At present only about 35% of the entire adult United States population has ever been in an aircraft, and about one-half of all commercial flying is done by one-tenth of one percent of the population. Background reasons of this kind support the hypothesis of elasticity in this particular market.

In the course of the data analysis, the demand for air travel on the part of the public appeared best measurable by population increase and by the growth of the gross national product. Increased movement of people is the direct result of rising income levels, greater leisure time, and ease of travel. Growth of either populations or GNP tends to increase the demand for air transportation; used together, a more complex relationship must be expected as these two factors are not fully independent of each other.

In the study in question, supply was measured by the total available seat miles flown. While this is a rather imperfect measure, as it does not take flight scheduling into considerations, it was the only measure of supply readily available (see Table I).[4]

---

[4] The reader should notice the upset this factor may suffer as a result of change in the generation of the aircraft. With the span of a few years, the jets have more than doubled the passenger-carrying capacity of the airlines.

In the course of the data analysis it was found that simple plotting of the independent variables (discussed in the preceding paragraphs) against total passenger miles as the dependent variable showed a non-excessive scatter. Simple correlation might have been considered; nevertheless, on the basis of the obtained experimental results it was decided that multiple linear correlation would offer the best approach. The mathematical model chosen by the experimenters has the form

$$X_1 = a + b_2 X_2 + b_3 X_3 + b_4 X_4 , \tag{1}$$

for

$X_1 =$ *Total passenger miles* by the Air Transport Association, Facts and Figures 19th Edition, 1958,

$X_2 =$ *U.S. population*, by the Department of Commerce, Bureau of Census, Census of Manufacturing, 1954,

$X_3 =$ *Gross national product* as project by the Department of Commerce, Office of Business Economics,

$X_4 =$ *Available seat miles*, by the Department of commerce, Bureau of Census, Midyear Estimates.

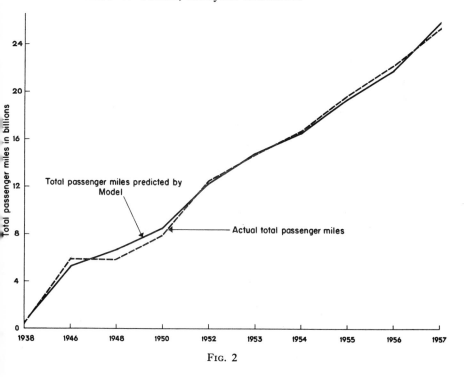

FIG. 2

The data-processing phase involved testing each independent variable in itself, as well as in groups of two and three versus the dependent variable. The best results were achieved with a multiple correlation using all three independent variables. The obtained correlation coefficient between real and simulated data was 0.997. A pretty high figure indeed. The plot is shown in Fig. 2.

Actual computational data are presented in Table II. Equation (1) was subjected to a variety of tests in order to establish the proper values

TABLE II

X_2 P	X_3 GNP	X_4 ASM	X_1 TPM	TPM (regression)
129 70000000	85 20000000	908 000000	457 000000	473 599000
140 00000000	209 20000000	7508 000000	5910 000000	5254 406000
146 20000000	257 30000000	10304 000000	5910 000000	6794 805000
150 40000000	285 10000000	12984 000000	7955 000000	8248 753000
156 40000000	345 40000000	18973 000000	12461 000000	12177 568000
158 80000000	363 20000000	23128 000000	14688 000000	14762 063000
161 50000000	360 60000000	26717 000000	16696 000000	16475 916000
164 40000000	390 80000000	31163 000000	19741 000000	19410 136000
167 50000000	414 70000000	35138 000000	22276 000000	21859 332000
170 00000000	433 90000000	41491 000000	25250 000000	25887 429000
x154.490000	314.540000	20831.4000	13134.4000	
s 12.863980	107.172011	13031.8870	8037.9823	
1489349	12308284	14628775	9027216	
12308284	103372564	118185952	73188838	
14628775	118185952	152847079	94065644	
9027216	73188838	94065644	58148245	

$b_2 = 212.3030,$ $b_3 = 21.4450,$ $b_4 = 0.652780$

$a\ \ = 25589.4600$

$\beta_2 = 0.339769,$ $\beta_3 = 0.285930,$ $\beta_4 = 1.058344$

(where β indicates influence variables P, GNP, ASM)

$r^2 = 0.994500,$ $r = 0.997246$

for a and b_i, $i = 2, 3, 4$. This mathematical model took the following form after a shift of decimal points to allow the most convenient scaling of variables:

$$\text{TPM} = 25\,590 + 212.3(\text{P}) + 21.44(\text{GNP}) + 0.6528(\text{ASM}),$$

where

TPM = Total Passenger Miles in millions,

P = Population in millions,

GNP = Gross National Product in billions,

ASM = Available Seat Miles in millions.

An example of the use of this model is illustrated in Fig. 3. The Commerce Department predictions for population and gross national product in 1955[5] were combined with available seat miles ranging from 20 000 to 200 000 million miles to compute total passenger miles for each assumption of ASM. In addition, TPM/ASM × 100, the "percent

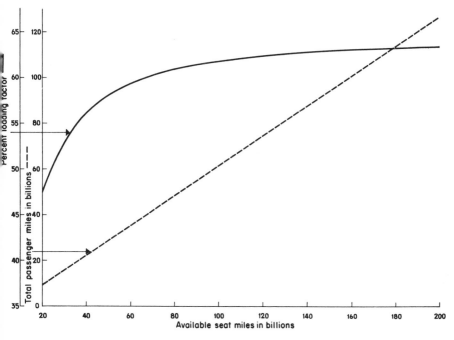

FIG. 3.   1965 estimate of airline activity based on seat miles available.

loading factor" was computed. The results of these computations have been plotted. The graph shows the influence of the available seat miles offered on the actual passenger miles flown. Studies of this nature can help in deciding how many seat miles should be made available to the public to operate at an economical load factor.

The obtained correlation coefficient of 0.997 would indicate that this model fits the historical data almost perfectly, and the inference could be drawn that it would similarly fit future situations. It must, however, be realized that the derivation of the regression equation is based on past data and, therefore, is subject to change if too drastic shifts are made in the transportation data of the future. This is a good point at which to reemphasize that simulation studies are a dynamic

---

[5] This study was made shortly thereafter.

business and that mathematical model-making requires continuous reevaluation on the part of the experimenter.

It is equally important to iterate that simulation studies are not a substitute for competent management. Mathematical models provide the executive with quantitative information; they do not substitute for his skill. This mathematical model, like any other, is a satisfactory tool, not an objective. A tool is designed to indicate trends in air-travel activity based on general economic forecasts and the offered air transport facilities. Care must be taken not to apply this model as a "cook book" formula, but to consider it as a working system which needs to be studied and evaluated in the light of every specific situation if it is going to be used in an able manner.

Case Study with a Loan Department

As another example, assume that the Personal Loan Department of the First Popular Bank desires to set up some rules for determining the kind of "calculated risks" the bank should take to improve its profit

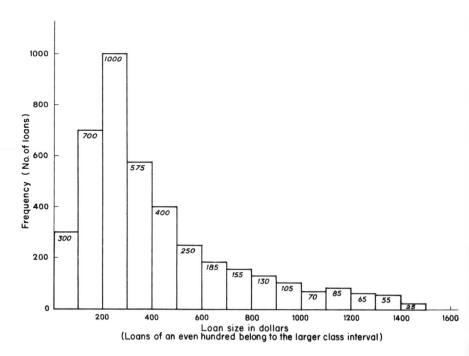

FIG. 4

figures.[6] Profit is a function of interest loan size, number of loans, and loans defaulted, among other things.

The mathematician who was in charge of this job first examined the records of the Loan Department for worthwhile historical data. The first piece of information compiled was the histogram of loan size versus the number of loans. This is shown in Fig. 4.

Applicants Name

Application No.

Position Held

Date of Applic.

Employer

Size of loan applied for

$$R = \frac{J-N-K-L-2B-3P-E-S-Q}{12}$$

Consideration		Excellent (4)	Good (3)	Fair (2)	Poor (1)
Job stability	(J)				
Income	(N)				
Income / Loan	(K)				
Lack of Indebtedness	(L)				
Ability to repay	(B)				
Paying habits	(P)				
Residents stability	(E)				
Personal habits	(S)				
Occupation (See table)	(O)				

Current Rejection Point

Applicants Rating (R)

Reviewers Recommendation

Remarks

FIG. 5. Loan review from.

A "loan review form" (Fig. 5) was developed with the purpose of aiding the Loan Department in establishing uniform practices, by making available to the individual interviewer a risk-describing function which

[6] For instance, too tight a policy in risk-taking, which would eliminate all risks in loan-making, may be as detrimental to the final profit figure of the bank as too loose a policy, which might include many bad risks.

could be related to the number of loans defaulted and the number of loans made.

A number of alternative formulas were tested as to their ability to calculate risk-taking versus profits,[7] on the rationale that "profit is a

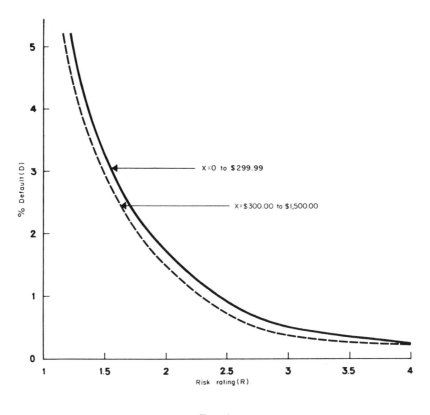

FIG. 6

[7] The following information was obtained from The Household Finance Corporation and was used in this work. A particular loan office makes 2000 loans per year in the $1 to $300 bracket. The distribution of these loans is sheer with the mean at $200. The interest rate is approximately 10%. They also make 20 000 loans in the $300 to $1500 bracket, where the average loan is $550 and the interest rate is 6%. Approximately 50% of the applications are accepted. Of these, 90% of the borrowers pay without any trouble; 5% pay after a few letters, notices, phone calls, and/or field calls; 3% pay after many calls, letters, notices, etc.; 1% pay noly after legal notice, or after the debt has been written off as a loss by the lender; and 1% never pay fully.

reward for risk-taking." Three alternative formulas were given a field test. Sufficient test data were collected to correlate "risk rating" R with % loans defaulted D and number of loans made. This information is presented in Figs. 6 and 7, respectively. The "risk rating" R was described by the equation

$$R = \frac{J + N + K + L + 2B + 3P + E + S + Q}{12}.$$

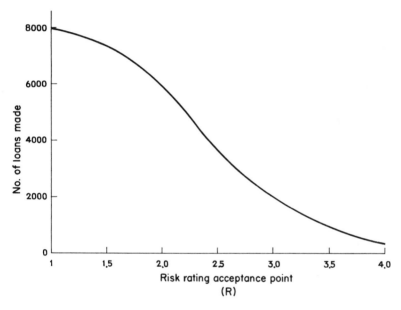

FIG. 7

The "ability to repay" B and "paying habits" P were considered to be two and three times more important, respectively, than the other factors (see Fig. 5). Profit was then described by a function

$$\text{Profit} = \Phi(A, I, D, Q),$$

where

$A =$ the amount of an individual loan,
$I =$ the interest rate applied to that loan,
$D =$ the % of loans defaulted,
$Q =$ the factor for dividend and operating expenses.

A curve of the percent profit may be plotted by selecting a "risk rating" figure R, then using figures the graphs presented [Figs. 4, 6, and 7] for the corresponding values for A and D. Obviously, to be of operational value, these graphs should always be kept current.

In the subject computations, the interest rate I is 10% for all loans up to $299 and 6% for loans from $300 to $1500. A profit is then established for several values of R to give a profit versus risk rating, as in Fig. 8. The risk rating R that gives maximum profit can then be used as a guide in accepting or rejecting applications.

In a similar project undertaken at another bank, a different profit equation was developed as a function of the loan level L of the frequency of customer demands at that level, f; of the probability (risk) of not

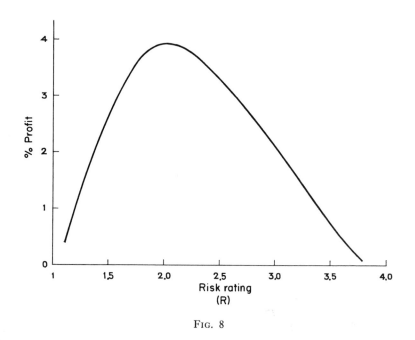

FIG. 8

being paid, r; and of the interest rate I. The researcher, for unknown reasons, later decided to eliminate f, thus reducing the profit equation to

$$\text{Profit} = IL - rL = L\,(I - r).$$

Table III presents profit figures for different loan levels at various rates of interest. By using this or similar equations we can develop families of profit curves. For instance, with the data of Fig. 9(a) we have the family of curves of Fig. 9(b).

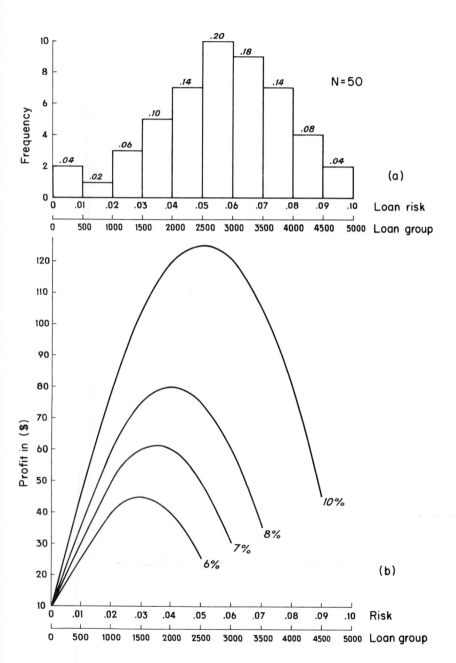

FIG. 9

TABLE III

	at 6% interest				at 7% interest		
L	0.06L	r	—rL	P	0.07L	—rL	P
500	30	0.01	5	25	35	5	30
1000	60	0.02	20	40	70	20	50
1500	90	0.03	45	45[a]	105	45	60[a]
2000	120	0.04	80	40	140	80	60[a]
2500	150	0.05	125	25	175	125	50
3000	180	0.06	180	0	210	180	30
3500	210	0.07	245	—35	245	245	0
4000	240	0.08	320	—80	280	320	
4500	270	0.09	405		315	405	
5000	300	0.10	500		350	500	

	at 8% interest				at 10% interest		
L	0.08L	—rL	P		0.10L	—rL	P
500	40	5	35		50	5	45
1000	80	20	60		100	20	80
1500	120	45	75		150	45	105
2000	160	80	80[a]		200	80	120
2500	200	125	85		250	125	125[a]
3000	240	180	60		300	180	120
3500	280	245	35		350	245	105
4000	320	320	0		400	320	80
4500					450	450	45
5000					500	500	0

[a] Points of maximum profit.

The foregoing clearly indicates that we can prove almost anything, given the freedom to develop our own equations. This is why we have so insisted that developing and testing equations is a very important subject in mathematical experimentation.

CHAPTER 11
Simulating Long-Term Effects

Ten years of experience with mathematical models, their construction, operation, and evaluation, offer ample evidence that the fundamentals of the approach which is behind a certain application may very well be transferable from one study to another, even if the environmental situation and the problem itself are completely different.

In 1961 the writer conducted a major study in simulation for a petroleum company in the Middle East. Much of the interest in this work had to do with the management of inventories. Some 100 000 items were involved. A regression analysis was made to help establish trends and variations. This was followed by a simulation of consumption levels, taking into due account confidence intervals and security stocks. The whole work helped develop new procurement policies which resulted in a very substantial reduction of the prevailing investments in inventories. These financial savings were of capital importance, since over a period of years procurement and management of inventories alone accounted for some 50% of the company's budget.

Treating its money supply as a materials inventory, a major bank in the European Common Market followed the same procedure and used the same mathematical tools with the Middle Eastern petroleum study. The two simulation projects were done absolutely independently from one another, and both the methods and the outcomes compared well after the work had been completed in both. This fact makes the homogeneity in tool usage among simulation projects even more striking.

Two Cases of The Model-Making Art

Examples of the broad applicability of certain methods, tools, and techniques can be found both in industrial and military practices.

One such case is the method divised to simulate the accoustics of concert halls and auditoriums using an electronic digital computer. The first step in the development of the model is to select a point on the stage. The major paths that the sound waves would take, between this source and a typical seat in the audience, are then drawn. One-bounce

and multi-bounce reflections from the walls and ceiling are then established. The machine calculates the time it takes a sound impulse to travel
over these various paths from source to listener and computes the
reverberation time of the hall.

For experimentation purposes, a sample of speach or music is recorded
in digital form on magnetic tape. The computer acts on these sounds
just as the floor or ceiling would. It produces an output tape, which is
also in digital form. This tape is then fed to another machine which
converts the digital information into an analog multitrack sound tape
suitable for playing on a multichannel tape recorder playback. This
recording is played over several loudspeakers in a free-space room which
does not add echoes and reverberations of its own. The sound has the
necessary echo delay, amplitude variations, and directionality to give
a good stereophonic resemblance to an actual hall. By changing the
machine program, the acoustic characteristics of the simulated hall
can be modified.

It can readily be seen that the over-all scheme used to study this
acoustics problem is no different than what has been done in a variety
of other cases involving mathematical experimentation. In their general
classification, these cases range from production planning to simulated
combat conditions and military logistics. But what about the finer
characteristics of the method? Is that where differences in the approach
and the tools to be used come into proper perspective?

At the present time, at least, model-making is an art. Performance
in systems design and in systems simulation depends on the artist.
Like a great doctor, lawyer, painter, or military commander, he is the
one who develops strategy and tactics in attacking a certain problem.
There is no point in stating in advance that this or that "could" or
"should" be done in simulation, just like it is impossible to establish
blueprints for winning any battle. All is determined by the thrust, the
ingenuity, and the skill of the commander.

In the present chapter we are primarily concerned with cases in
which long-range planning is at a premium. One of the most acute
problems in this class is the planning of birth rates.[1] We will therefore

---

[1] Commenting on this subject in the course of the Eleventh International Congress of
Genetics, which took place in September 1963, in the Hague, Dr. Dobzhansky said:
"Natural selection is at work when a defective child dies or when a dwarfed man fails
to find a mate. A high mortality rate is not necessary for natural selection to operate.
The great danger to man is not the suppression of natural selection but what is called
the "population explosion." Man must regulate his behavior for the benefit of future
generations. If he will not take measures to avoid the coming population crisis, he hardly
needs to bother about genetics."

consider a mathematical model of human birth rates and birth distributions.[2]

If all the women in a population had the same, constant expectation per unit time of bearing children for the same fixed period exposed to risk, the births would be spread randomly over the period, and the number per woman would follow a Poisson distribution. Clearly this is not even roughly the case in actual populations. The main discrepancies arise because, in most populations, some women are not exposed to risk, and the variances of the observed distributions are greater relative to the mean than the Poisson.

A more satisfactory model can be obtained if only births to mothers, hence, distributions truncated before one birth, are considered, and the expectation of bearing children is varied over the women. This variation in expectation must allow for differences, not only in fecundity but also in the intensity of exposure to risk and prenatal mortality. It is only for the lesser developed communities that the assumptions that the exposed-to-risk period is the same for all women and that the expectation of bearing children is constant over this period for each woman might not be unreasonable—although a simplification.

Let us suppose that the expectation of bearing children varies among the women in Pearson type III form. This function leads to a well-known distribution for the number of births per woman. When the two parameters that determine this function lie in appropriate intervals, the function is unimodal and has the value zero at the limits of its range, which can be taken as "nothing to infinity." Within these restrictions the shape is very flexible.

The following assumptions can then be formulated:

(i) All the mothers are exposed to risk for the same period T.

(ii) Each mother has an expected rate of child bearing E, which is constant over T.

(iii) The distribution of E among the women has an exponential form.

(iv) The births occur at random.

In order to test these hypotheses, the researcher needs to know the numbers of children born to a large number of women during the child-bearing period. These can be approximated by the distributions for women past the age of child bearing if there are no important effects of differential mortality of mothers according to the number of births, or of changing fertility. Such effects can be reduced by selecting, where

---

[2] Reference is made to the work of W. Brass.

possible, women in a narrow age range close to the end of child bearing.

To determine the mean ages of the women at births of different orders, the assumption can be made that the lower and upper age limits of T, as well as its length, are the same for all women. If the mean ages of the women at all and first births can be calculated from observations taken within a given population, then estimates of T, and of the lower and upper limits of the exposed-to-risk period, can be made. In observed populations these lower and upper limits are not the same for all women. However, Brass advanced the hypothesis that moderate variations in them, if independent of E, have little effect on the model with respect to the distribution of women by number of children born or their mean ages at different birth orders. The estimated lower and upper limits of T are, then, approximately mean values over all the mothers in the population.

In a population where fertility is constant and where there is no appreciable differential mortality of women by number of births, the integral over any interval including the reproductive period, of the mean number of children per woman at each age, is equal to $F(n - m)$. Here n is the upper age of integration, m the mean age of the women at all births, and F the mean number of children born per woman of completed fertility.

A number of sources of error might interfere with these calculations. The effects of differential mortality and approximations in the integrations could be slight, but changes in fertility may be important. Even where there is little or no consistent trend, fluctuations will influence the results. The estimates made, then, are of a rather rough nature.

Despite these weaknesses, Brass has shown that the fit of his models to the observations is sufficiently good for many useful applications. Much of his primary interest was to establish the broad features of birth distributions in a range of populations as a function of a limited number of parameters. With this he advanced the assumption that fertility characteristics of different communities can easily be compared, and the effects of changes in these characteristics examined. In itself this model could be particularly valuable in research on more primitive populations, where historical data are scanty and liable to error. In addition, when information is obtained from fairly small samples, theoretical distributions can be used to improve the statistical efficiency of estimates.

Location for Business

Along with the research on the evolution of the human population composing a certain market, establishing the optimal location of industrial or business concerns and estimating their respective productivity is one of the questions that attract managerial interest. One approach to this subject consists of the semi-nebulous quality called "experience." More often than not this kind of experience leads to wrong estimates.

Analytically, we could predict the production of a business center in any given location by an extensive statistical survey followed by a regression analysis. This approach is not unique, and we might conceive several alternative experimental models, more or less sophisticated. Apart from the data of the past, we also need to consider coming events. The establishment of a new center (business or industrial) in an existing location brings in itself a change in the parameters of the actual situation. This change will be greater or less depending on how the new center compares to the existing conditions.

Many formulated what might be called a "law of retail gravitation." This law was based on the assumptions that shopping centers attract trade from surrounding communities in direct proportion to the presentation of goods, and in inverse proportion to the square of the driving-time distances between the shopping centers and the surrounding communities. Hence, it was given the form

$$\frac{V_A}{V_B} = \left(\frac{P_A}{P_B}\right)^N \left(\frac{D_B}{D_A}\right)^n, \tag{1}$$

where $V_{A,B}$ are the "attraction" variables and $P_{A,B}$ and $D_{A,B}$ stand, respectively, for the population and distance variables. The exponents N and n are left to the ingenuity and skill of the researcher to define. In a certain study conducted a few years ago in Italy, the researchers chose to take $N = 1$ and $n = 2$. Needless to say, neither this choice nor Eq. (1) has ever been documented. This is at least one point in which the subject equation presents simularities with hundreds of others developed under the same conditions.

Another way of presenting this commentary on rationality is to say that several questions could be asked as to the development of Eq. (1) and its use. Nothing in it has been tested, nor has any valid hypothesis been formulated to start with. What is the difference if consumers travel by foot, car, or horseback? What about rivers, mountains, and other natural divisions of geographic areas? How should the relative gravitational merits of neighboring centers be estimated? What about political, psychological, or historic differences?

Important as they may be, none of the known models in the field tries to answer these questions. Instead they all stress how "the nature of these problems avails it to an easy formulation of a model." For an example to a second approach to the subject, say that we wish to consider building a shopping center in Stuttgart, Germany and decide to conduct a survey to estimate the productivity of the proposed center.

One may start by dividing Stuttgart into population areas. For each population area, the number of families (by income group) and the amount of money spent annually for general merchandise, apparel, and food[3] purchases (also by income group) can be determined from census statistics. Such annual purchases, for each population area, might be computed from the formula

$$P_j = (1 + f_j) \sum_i M_{ij} A_i \,,$$

where

M_{ij} = the number of families by income group (i) and by population area (j),

A_i = the annual amount of general merchandise, apparel, and food purchases per family by income group (i),

f_j = the percentage increase of such purchases for each population area (j),[4]

P_j = the total annual purchases in the forementioned commodities for each population area (j).

Each presently existing shopping center in Stuttgart should be surveyed and studied. From this survey and the census statistics, the annual presentation in millions of dollars for each shopping center can be estimated. Let K_k be the general merchandise, apparel, and food presentation (or "pull") for each presently existing shopping center k. Furthermore, a table can be prepared of the driving times from the center of gravity of each population area to each of the shopping centers. Let t_{jk} be the driving time from each population area j to each shopping center k.

For simplicity, we will assume that we intend to examine only one location for our proposed shopping center. We may prepare a table of the driving times from the center of gravity of each population area to this one location. We can build this shopping center any size, so let us consider a variety of presentations for said commodities. The proposed shopping center will compete with the existing shopping centers for the purchases from each population area. The amount of general merchandise, apparel, and food purchases which are attracted to the proposed

---

[3] Commodities which we will consider in the present model.
[4] This is an extrapolation factor to correct available historical data from a census.

shopping center (for each presentation) can be computed from the following formulas:

$$C_{jr} = \frac{Q_r/T_j^2}{\sum_k (K_k/t^2_{jk}) + Q_r/T_j^2} \, ,$$

$$\text{Sales}_r = \sum_j P_j C_{jr} \, ,^5$$

where

Q_r = the general merchandise, apparel, and food pull of the proposed center,

T_j = the driving time[6] from each population area j to the proposed center,

C_{jr} = the percentage of the subject purchases for each population area which are attracted to the center Q.

The researcher who developed this model stipulated that the answer to the problem would be a table showing the sales that would result from each presentation of the proposed center. The breaking point would be the point where such sales amount exceeds the general merchandise, apparel, and food presentation amount. This would represent the maximum economical size of the considered shopping center.

It is only reasonable to say that any such formula should be tested with various situations before it is trusted as an experimental tool.

Long Term Planning for Industrial Growth

In industry, experimentation on long-term trends has been treated in a variety of ways, ranging from the very simple to the most sophisticated. The "very simple" approach might, for instance, involve the use of game theory and other tools whose validity in management research waits still to be proved. But there also exist cases of very thorough investigations, and we will be concerned with one of them in the present section.

In the early fifties, the usage of game theory was thought to be of advantage in the investigation of cases where the wisdom of taking a certain action was rather doubtful. The models involved in some of these cases seemed at first glance to be quite fair. Deeper analysis showed

---

[5] For the subject commodities.

[6] Or, in the more general case, comuting time from residential areas to the shopping center.

that they were not. Contrary to this, we have available today examples of profitable usage of applied mathematics in the form of custom-made models, for complex industrial operations. This is the case of a study made by a major French manufacturer on long-term market evolution, concerning its major products, in France and in other European countries.[7]

As a point of reference, the subject study took the evolution of the market in the United States—a market in which the sales of autos, applicances, furniture, and other consumer durables set new records. In 1962, these sales rose 9% to a total for the year of almost $48 billion. Does this mark the beginning of a strong and sustained upward advance in these key markets? Or was the 1962 performance merely a result of the rise in income which went along with the business recovery? What could be the evolution of each European market as related to the American? Answers to these questions are important. Indeed, postwar experience lends support to the view that, as consumer durables go, so goes an industrial economy.

A rapid rise in sales of consumer durables provided much of the hiatus for the strong growth in the over-all economy during the first postwar decade. Between 1946 and 1955, durables sales in constant dollars more than doubled, yielding an average annual increase of 8%. However, since 1955, the advance in both consumer durable sales and GNP slowed markedly, with durables sales rising at a 2% rate. To be sure, a decided leveling in business investment in new plant and equipment contributed to the general lethargy of the economy. Still, it is significant that consumer investment in autos, appliances, and the like, which is about as large in dollar terms as business capital investment, also slowed after 1955. Was a similar trend going to develop in the European markets? If yes, at what time should it be expected and of what magnitude could it be?

In the American economy, part of the gain in 1962 sales of durables reflected the recovery in general business. As is typical, consumer purchases of durable goods sank during the 1960–61 business downfall. From the early 1961 "low" to the third quarter of 1962, the increase in spending for durables amounted to 15%. That was a somewhat smaller rise than in the previous three postwar business recoveries. Another difference was equally apparent. In two of the earlier periods[8]

---

[7] Reference is made to a very interesting study performed by A. Olmi, Director of Corporate Planning, Compagnie Française Thomson — Houston, which is covered in substantial detail in Chapter 8 of the French edition of the present book (Editions Dunod, Paris).

[8] That is, 1950 and 1955.

consumer durables reached their peaks fairly early in the recovery period, and then receded while general business activity continued to move ahead. In contrast, sales of these durable products advanced 5% during the fourth quarter of that year, almost entirely because of a surge in auto buying.

Concurrently, the home furnishings sales in the American market rose in a significant manner [Fig. 1(a) and (b)]. Twenty billion dollars

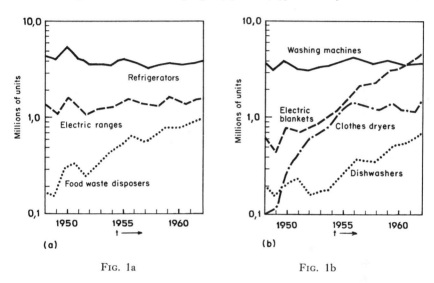

FIG. 1a   FIG. 1b

were spent in 1962 on appliances, home entertainment equipment, furniture, china, and other household durable goods. This figure was up almost $1 billion or 4% over 1961. Sales of many products included in this total, however, increased much faster:

(i)   Color television sales, which had covered around the 100 000-unit mark for several years, took off in mid-1961, and rose so rapidly that the total sales for that year reached 225 000. The swift climb continued throughout 1962 bringing sales to at least 400 000 sets.

(ii) Electric dishwasher sales rose 16% in 1962 to reach an all-time high of 720 000 units.

(iii) Food waste disposers also reached a new peak with sales up 11% to 890 000.

(iv) Many housewares—hair dryers, electric can openers, and electric blankets—also sold in record numbers. Major appliances which scored good gains but did not match previous peak levels include: gas ranges up 9%, washing machines and refrigerators up $8\frac{1}{2}\%$, electric water heaters up over 8%, and electric ranges up $7\frac{1}{2}\%$.

Factors underlying the market for durables give signs of becoming more favorable than they have been in the recent past. Demographic trends point to a rise in household formations in the years ahead. The change in the age structure of the population is already having an effect on household goods. An important factor in the near future is expected to be the rise in replacement potential. The average age of the stock of consumer durables owned by U.S. households has been increasing since 1951. This fact, combined with the high ownership rates for many products (more than 9 out of 10 families own a radio, refrigerator, washing machine, and TV set), means a large potential replacement market—but also a certain saturation.

What is the key to unlocking this potential in markets for consumer durables? The answer is that outlays for durables are particularly sensitive, not only to the level of income, but to its rate of growth and the outlook for continued growth. Higher expected future income is usually behind the willingness of young couples to spend a sizable proportion of their incomes on hard goods, and it is frequently behind their willingness to use credit. Furthermore, replacement potential alone cannot support vigorous growth in durables markets. Producers need to innovate by developing new features and new products. Studies of consumer markets show that such innovation speeds replacement sales and generates an increase in ownership of durables. The fact that many families are well stocked with hard goods is frequently cited as a damper on future sales. However, research projects contradict this supposition by indicating that many families want to improve or add to their stock of durable goods, and many have specific plans for purchases.

Seen in this light, the simulation work conducted by Olmi becomes of major significance. The researcher set as his first objective the development of general formulas containing the least number of parameters while being able to represent, in the markets under investigation, the past and future development of families of durable goods. For every family of articles, and for every country this study established two series of annual figures:

(i) the total number of articles which are in service,

(ii) the national production.

The total number of articles which are in service (which from here on we will call TAIS) includes all units which are installed in all public or private places and are ready for use with the exception of those which exist in different stores in order to be sold. While second-hand items are included, those items whose service has been discontinued, or which for any reason have been abandoned, are not included. The TAIS number has been evaluated by means of a sampling inspection.

The yearly production is known through the declarations of the different manufacturers, as analyzed, compiled, and presented by the manufacturers' associations. Hence, these production numbers are approximate. What interested the research workers most was the evolution of the sales and the behavior of the national market. The figures given by the manufacturers' associations are calculated on the basis of the national production data of the stocks that are available at the end and at the beginning of each period and on the import-export information.

In the calculation of the total sales figures, it is important to distinguish the sales of "first-to-be-installed" equipment from the replacement sales. Here, by first-to-be-installed equipment is meant the sale of units to household or other sites which were not provided thus far with this kind of article, and, therefore, acquired it now for the first time. This division is a very difficult one, because none of the currently available statistics allows an exact estimate.

The researchers advanced the following two equations as the core of their study:

$$V = V_e + V_r,$$
$$V_e = P_{n+1} - P_n,$$

where

P_n = the TAIS at the beginning of a certain year n,
P_{n+1} = the TAIS at the beginning of the following year, $n + 1$,
V = the total sales of the year,
V_r = the replacement sales of the year,
V_e = the first equipment sales of the year.

The Representative Curves of the TAIS and of the Sales

Over a long period of time, we consider the evolution of a certain market for durable goods whose function (as to the service offered to the user) shows no or very slow evolution. In this study of the French market, Olmi documented the established notion that such products have a characteristic curve of market penetration with inflation points when they move from the richer classes to the other strata of the population. This behavior can be graphically represented by means of an S curve.

In Fig. 2, the time is given by the abscissa and is indicated by x. Three curves have been established: P_1, P_2, P_3. These curves represent the evolution of TAIS on three different hypotheses concerning the growth of this population. If the population of a certain country remained constant, the asymptote αP_1 would obviously be an horizontal

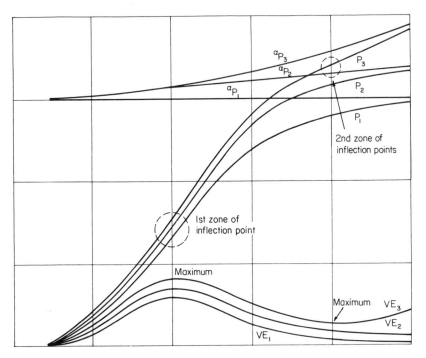

FIG. 2. $\alpha_{p_1}, \alpha_{p_2}, \alpha_{p_3}$: curves representing the variations of the saturation; $P_1, P_2 P_3$: curves representing the TAIS variations; VE_1, VE_2, VE_3: curves representing the sales variations of the first-to-be-installed equipment.

straight line. This is not true in the general case, and the growth of the population follows a certain function. As to the nature of this function, we can formulate the following two hypotheses:

(i) The absolute value of the increase is constant and forms an arithmetic progression.

(ii) The population of goods presents an accelerated increase. Thus, the subject curve will have an exponential asymptote.

Let's consider again the equation

$$P_{n+1} - P_n = V_e.$$

This was originally written for yearly intervals. But if the time interval becomes small enough, say Δx, and we call ΔP the increase of TAIS, we will obtain

$$\Delta P = V_e \Delta x$$

or

$$V_e = \frac{\Delta P}{\Delta x}$$

from which we obtain

$$V_e = \frac{dP}{dx} .$$

From this equation we can derive the theoretical form of the curves V_{e1}, V_{e2}, V_{e3}, which can be seen in Fig. 2. It is obvious that the beginning of the replacement curve presents a certain delay with respect to the origin of the first installation curve. While certain articles will unavoidably be repaired or replaced shortly after the installation has taken place, the total initial population will not die out until its useful life has expired. A sampling inspection has shown that, with durable goods, this total useful life varies between seven years for articles with short life curves to the level of fifteen to twenty years for articles with long life spans, such as refrigerators.

A basic interest of the researcher is to establish quantitative data able to represent the behavior of groups of articles as a function of their date of installation. In this way, the bulk of the replacement sales can be added to the current sales level as the life span for each item expires. The equation $V = V_e + V_r$ allows us to develop the theoretical curves V_a and V_b. These curves are obtained by summing the ordinates of the curve V_{e3} and the curves V_{ra}, V_{rb}. The indices a and b correspond to two different hypotheses as to the life span d of a certain article (Fig. 3).

Let us consider again the equations

$$\frac{dP}{dx} = V_e , \tag{2}$$

$$V = V_e + V_r . \tag{3}$$

The researchers searched a function of P for a TAIS corresponding to a human population of 1000. After a substantial number of trials they accepted the function

$$P = K + \frac{2K}{\pi} \left(\arctan \frac{x}{a} + \frac{ax}{x^2 + a^2} \right), \tag{4}$$

where K and a represent two parameters and x the time in years.

Equation (4) is homogeneous in x/a and P/k. Hence, a represents a number of years and K a number of articles (for 1000 inhabitants). A series of simple derivatives of this function can be taken:

$$\frac{dP}{dx} = V_e = \frac{4K}{\pi} \frac{a^3}{(x^2 + a^2)^2} , \tag{5}$$

$$\frac{d^2P}{dx^2} = \frac{dV_e}{dx} = -\frac{16Ka^3}{\pi} \frac{x}{(x^2 + a^2)^3} , \tag{6}$$

$$\frac{d^3P}{dx^3} = \frac{d^2V_e}{dx^2} = \frac{16Ka^3}{\pi} \frac{5x^2 - a^2}{(x^2 + a^2)^4} . \tag{7}$$

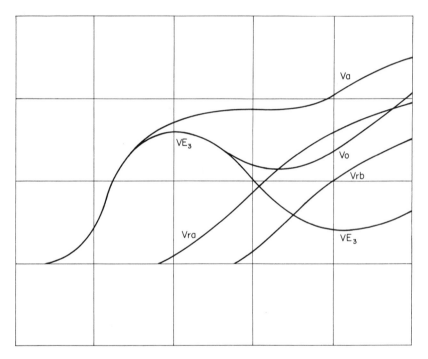

FIG. 3. Va and Vb are curves representing the total sales; VE_3, curve representing the first-to-be-installed sales; Vra and Vrb, curves representing the placement sales.

Since these equations depend on two parameters, a and K, we are faced with a double family of curves. This is graphically shown in Fig. 4.

The form of the V_e curve (fifth derivative of P with respect to time) is given in Fig. 5. It indicates that the forecast of sales of the first-to-be-installed equipment can be deduced from the corresponding TAIS

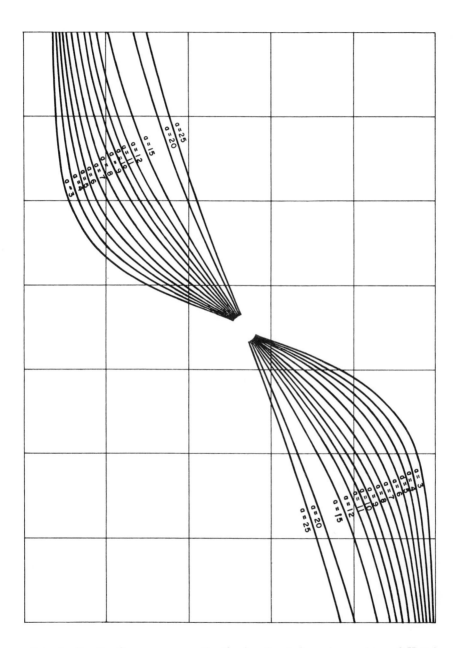

Fig. 4. Family of curves representing the function p for a given volume of K and many values of a.

forecast. To this should be added that the replacement sales are a function of the first-to-be-installed sales that preceded them. The two curves, V_e and V_r, can be superimposed, but the researchers found that in several cases the increase of V_r does not quite compensate for the decrease in V_e.

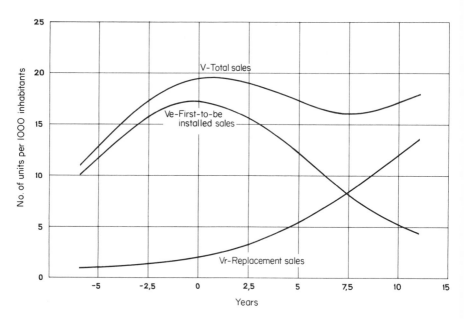

FIG. 5. Theoretical representation of the functions V, Ve, and Vr for the case where $a = 11$, $K = 150$, and $d = 15$.

In the sense of our discussion, the curve V has a certain maximum after which it decreases until a first minimum. These oscillations continue, TAIS being renewed each year by portions equal to $1/d$, so that it is completely renewed in d years. Figure 5 shows, for a certain case, the general characteristics of this phenomenon.

In order to study the structural recession of the market in a more detailed manner, the researchers advanced the hypothesis that the replacement sales at a certain year x would be equal to the sales of this type of equipment d years ago or, more precisely, at $x - d$. Hence, for year x the following equation holds:

$$V_r = \frac{4a^3 K}{\pi} \frac{1}{[a^2 + (x - d)^2]^2},$$

and approximating the total market potential $V = V_e + V_r$ the researchers established

$$V = \frac{4a^3K}{\pi} \left\{ \frac{1}{(a^2 + x^2)^2} + \frac{1}{[a^2 + (x - d)^2]^2} \right\}$$

Figures 6, 7, and 8 show the computed market potential data for TV
sets, refrigerators, and washing machines. It is seen that the U. S. curve

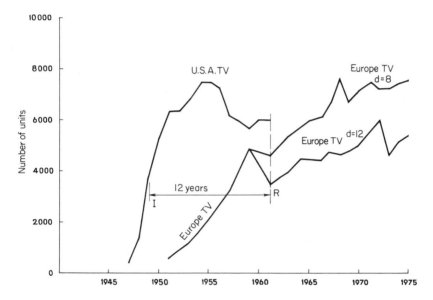

Fig. 6. U.S.A.—realized T V sales. Europe—actual and forecasted sales (to 1975).

for TV sets presents a structural recession whose origin was in 1955.
The European market shows no such effect. This is not surprising if one
considers the relative steepness of the two curves, the American one
having the highest inclination.

A similar analysis for refrigerators leads to inverse conclusions.
The relative slowness of the early years of market expansion in the United
States is followed by a mild recession. The curve of the European
market expansion shows considerable steepness, which in turn explains
the forecasted valleys in refrigerator sales. Finally, for washing machines,
the market behavior in Europe and the United States are quite comparable. Hence, the researchers took the average life span d equal to 13 or
14 years.

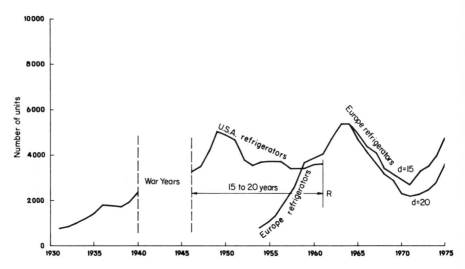

FIG. 7.   U.S.A.—sales of refrigerators (left curve).   Europe—actual and forecasted sales of refrigerators (to 1975). Two hypotheses have been used: mean time $d = 15$ and 20 years.

FIG. 8.   U.S.A.—sales of washing machines.   Europe—actual and forecasted sales of washing machines (to 1975). Three hypotheses have been used: mean time $d = 11$, 13, and 15 years.

CHAPTER 12

Experimentating in Industrial Operations

Demand for industrial products is generated by a complex interaction of product appeal, market saturation, spending mood in the market, efficient marketing policies, and other factors. If it were possible to describe accurately the effect of each of these factors and how they interact, we could forecast future demand in an effective manner.

For any particular industry, the ability to hold inventories to an effective minimum is very closely related to market forecasting and, in turn, this is a direct function of the actual state of the art of estimating the possible impact and interaction of a variety of factors which get into the marketing function.

Problems of this type have been tackled but are far from being solved in all their aspects. What we presently have available is a number of alternative approaches, each based on one or more hypotheses about how marketing factors interact with one another and how they affect market appeal for a certain industry or a certain product. Based primarily on assumptions and hypotheses, we have developed models which at times have shown a striking ability to predict. Often, predictions of this nature are close enough to reality to offer a basis for the derivation of certain rules.

Model-Making Procedures for Industry

Assumptions which need to be made with respect to a mathematical formulation of inventory problems concern

   (i) the nature of demand in the market, a crucial problem with which economists and econometrists have been playing for years;

  (ii) the cost of carrying inventories in raw material, semi-manufactured and finished form;

 (iii) the product flow within the manufacturing facilities of the company, and the associated delay times and production bottle-necks;

(iv) storage capacities and shipping delay times;

(v) price fluctuations (of the input commodities to the manufacturing process) and factors of obsolescence.

Management policies and the nature of the production system usually result in a different set of rules for keeping inventory at optimum levels. Nevertheless, a careful study of the various factors entering into several typical problems and problem types in inventory optimization indicates the existence of a number of principal economic factors. A substantial number of inventory optimization problems can be reduced to interactions between these crucial factors. This is the case with the purchase or selection of input material. Input evaluation has always been a major problem in industrial economics, in particular, if one considers all associated subproblems. For most industries a complex balance exists between optimum production capacity and low inventories and their ability to meet the demand in the market.

Most industries are faced with a variety of potential alternative solutions of varying properties, varying capabilities, and varying costs. For instance, increasing the capacity of the plant (manufacturing potential input) is one solution for meeting the actual or anticipated demand in the market, but this in turn implies commitments on the part of industrial management. At a given time and for a given process, the law of diminishing returns comes into play, and it may well be that the higher the established or wished level of production, the higher the cost of the incremental product unit will be.

Other factors have to do with the quantity in demand and the price offered in the market for a certain product. As the demand and price structure of the various products fluctuate, the optimum manufacturing pattern shifts. The determination of a certain pattern for any specific demand-price structure is of critical importance if inventories are to be controlled in an effective manner.

Similarly, the distribution facilities have to be examined so as to minimize waste, both in excess inventories and in transportation media, while satisfactorily meeting the demand in the market. This problem is further complicated by competition factors and the particular tie-ins in determining the proper relationship between volume and value for the marketable goods.

The foregoing are but a few of the factors involved in the evaluation of industrial operations and, as such, have bearing on inventory control methods and procedures. Although, in the past, production was considered to be the "most obvious" factor of all, we recently realized that plant operations are only one facet of a complex industrial ensemble and that optimizing only in respect to the operations performed within the plant may lead to a suboptimum in the profit picture of the whole enterprise.

A good example of the study of multifactor situations is the "limited-information estimation procedure," which has so far been applied in economic studies. Mathematically, this program is based on a generalization of the multiple linear regression technique to provide a model which contains many dependent variables. In this way, a simulator can reflect more fully the many interactions by which dependent variables affect one another, rather than assuming a more arbitrary and often over-simplified set of relationships between the variables.

Another approach, known as "nonlinear estimation," has so far been used mainly for the analysis of chemical and physical phenomena. For example, it has been used to investigate certain types of continuous processes in the petroleum industry, where it has helped to produce more precise descriptions of the complex interactions involved. These mathematical descriptions can then be used to predict the results when a change is made in one or more conditions relating to the process.

A Model for Inventory Control

Before 1955, inventory control theory was mostly concerned with the question of when to order. Many formulas had been suggested but they proved to be either ineffective or difficult. Practice had shown that forecasting the demand for the thousands of items necessary in a production system was a subjective rather than an objective matter. This fact alone was enough to upset the use of all subsequent formulas.

To make things worse, many companies used, and some still do, practices which did little to improve matters. Some industries reorder by checking on what has been reordered in the years before, irrespective of sales changes or stock levels. It is amazing how much of this sort of thing does go on in business almost everywhere, in spite of certain so-called scientific methods in use, and over-stocks and run-outs occurring in many items.

Because of this background of poor and inefficient practices, whenever faced with inventory control problems the researcher should establish the objective of the manufacturing system first. The necessary data can be obtained from sales forecasts, order analysis, customer records, production reports, and the like. With these quantitative estimates of the work done so far solidly worked out, he will be able to develop a list of "reasons" for past failures, for things to watch out, and sensible points to observe.

One of the points in which inventory management often fails is the accounting for "frequency of use" and "relative value" classifications of the items in stock. Methods of proportional separation of inventory items into distinct categories, such as the ABC classification, have been devised and could be used to advantage. In many cases 15 % to 20 % of these items account for 75 % of the investement. It is deadly irrational, even if frequently done, to treat all items with the same care, or lack of care, when such large discrepancies in value exist.

Figure 1 presents quantitative data from a manufacturing company. The actual data have been very closely approximated by a smooth curve. The percent of the items in stock represents close to half the value invested in inventories, or, more precisely:

% of Items	% of Value
10	47.5
20	67.5
30	77.0
50	91.0
70	98.0
90	99.8

In examing consumption reports, stock levels, and warehouse utilization, several considerations are important, considerations which have to do with the particular industry where the study is done and for which it will be useless if not dangerous to generalize. For a specific case, we will consider an application described by Brown.[1] It concerns a mathematical model built for a manufacturer of automatic controls.

This model can be simply phrased in three descrete steps:

(i) Subtract the actual demand in the current month from the expected value that was calculated last month. This expected value may be the result of smoothing the demand, a statistical forecast, or a modification thereof through managerial judgement.

(ii) Call this difference the current deviation.

---

[1] Robert G. Brown, Less Risk in Inventory Estimates, The Harvard Business Reviews. In his approach to the inventory problem, Brown makes a wide distinction between forecasting and prediction. This distinction is not rational, and we are not going to follow it or subscribe to it in any way. Nevertheless, we will be describing the mathematical model which has certain merits.

(iii) The new mean absolute deviation can then be expressed by the formula

$$\text{New estimate} = a \,(\text{new calculation}) + (1 - a)(\text{old estimate}). \qquad (1)$$

In Eq. (1), a is a parameter whose value can influence the relative importance of the new and the old means. According to Brown, this shows that, when the demand follows a very slowly changing pattern, a small

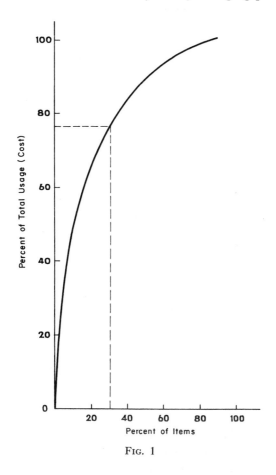

FIG. 1

multiplier or smoothing constant is appropriate. If recent developments in demand weight heavily, the new estimate can be oriented according to their trend by increasing the value of the multiplier a to, say, 0.3, 0.4, or 0.5. Here, of course, we encounter the first risk in the use of this formula: more often than not the estimating of this multiplier is subjective, and a small change in subjective judgement can make a great difference in results.

During the period this new multiplier is in effect, the routine calculations will respond quickly to whatever changes materialize. When the new pattern of demand is established, the parameter a can be returned to its original value, for instance, $a = 0.1$, to provide stability oriented to the long-term trend.

The method obviously requires a forecast of the impeding developments in demand, but Brown states it is not necessary to predict the magnitude or even the direction of the change. The model can orient its estimates to the actual change that materializes in the demand for each item, provided of course that the correct multiplier has been chosen. In essence, this is a simplified approach to the problem of including in one equation long-range and short-range average demand, or cycles with repeated peaks and valleys in demand at nearly the same time every year. As such it has its possibilities and its limitations.

In developing this scheme, the researcher used the Monte Carlo method to generate demand. He represented the size of each order by a random draw from a population with one exponential distribution, and the interval between successive orders for a particular stock number with another random draw from a second exponential distribution. The time constants of these distributions could be selected to approximate different situations met in practice.

A replenishment order generated in this system was posted immediately to the on-order file, together with a date due equal to one lead time later. The on-order file was posted to the on-hand file at the end of the date due, that is, after the demand for that date had been posted. The lead time was set at any integral multiple of the basic time unit. There was also an adjustable constant that made the total lead time equal to a fixed component plus a term proportional to the total size of the on-order file at the end of the previous review period:

$$L = L_0 + \delta U.$$

For a positive value of δ the situation was characteristic of a manufacturing system where the lead time increases with the backlog. A negative value of δ was more representative of a warehousing operation, where as business picks up the interval between full-truck-load shipments decreases.

The rules of this experimentation stated that the decision of whether or not to order should be based on an order point equal to the estimate of the maximum reasonable demand over one lead time. The order quantity was recomputed once per review period as proportional to the square root of the estimated current rate of demand. This represented the traditional order quantity formula where all factors other than demand were lumped into a single constant of proportionality

$$\beta = \sqrt{2Arv},$$

where A is the setup and ordering cost, in dollars per order placed; r is the carrying charge on inventories, expressed as percent per time unit; and v is the unit value of the item, for the computing of inventory investment. For $\beta = 0$, the system would generate a replacement order for each demand received.

A Linear Regression Scheme

Other research workers use different, alternative approaches. A simple or multiple linear regression has given satisfactory results in several cases. For a situation involving the interplay of more than one dependent variable, an accurate mathematical model may require a set of structural equations, so that each one reflects some structure of actual relationships between variables found in the system of real events around which the model has been fashioned. For instance,

$$X = aA + bB + cC + dD + e,$$

$$Y = fF + g(G + EK) + hH + j,$$

$$Z = kK + mM + nN + p.$$

Coefficients can be fitted to the data by the method of maximum likelihood. When, for reasons of accuracy, some of the equations of the model need to be nonlinear in one or more variables, the use of logarithms can help.

For an example of the use of regression analysis in production planning we will consider the case of a manufacturer faced with a job shop proposition, where many different varieties of a basic product are produced to customer specifications.[2] The problem was posed as follows: Given a manufacturing load in terms of units of unique apparatus in several broad product classifications or codes, what man-hour requirement is necessary in each shop section to meet the scheduled load ?

---

[2] The writer wants to express his thanks to Mr. J. B. Sheppard and Mr. F. L. Canning for the information they have provided on this subject and for their most cordial cooperation. Mr. Canning is credited with the development of the mathematical model.

When a certain plant is not manufacturing a line of standard products. the production planning department cannot always know the actual sectional man-hour requirements at the time the order is entered. Consequently, production planning must obtain a reliable estimate of the man-hour requirements of the individual orders and of the total load several months in advance of production, in order to realistically date new orders as a function of uncommitted capacity, to schedule and redate existing orders, to plan overtime and undertime, to adjust the size of the work force, and to subcontract segments of the load if necessary. Empirical averages of sectional man-hour requirements for each broad product classification do not provide the solution to this problem because of the wide variability of these times within each code.

Furthermore, the actual man-hour requirements, as determined from standard data by the sectional time study departments, are generally not available far enough in advance of production to enable production planning to take intelligent action appropriate to the load. The load requirements, therefore, must be obtained in some other fashion. The method which will be discussed in the following pages is that of "multiple linear estimation." Its industrial use came about along with the availability of an electronic computing facility, and it has been used with outstanding results.

In Chapter 9 we have stated that in a multiple linear estimation problem we attempt to estimate the dependent variable Z by a linear function of the independent variables Y_1, Y_2, Y_3, ..., Y_n. We said that the linear estimating function can be expressed as

$$Z = C_0 + C_1 Y_1 + C_2 Y_2 + ... + C_n Y_n.$$

The coefficients C_i can be easily calculated from historical data or, in the case of new products, from production specifications. In an actual application with the construction of power transformers a total of six variables has been used to predict the building time for each shop order. These variables and the method of determining each are as follows:

$Y_1 =$ Total number of stacks of punchings. There will be 8 on single phase and 12 to 16 on three phases.

$Y_2 =$ Rectangular area of the yoke in square inches. One decimal place is considered.

$Y_3 =$ Rectangular area of the short piece in square inches. For instance, this will be item 3 on three phases and none on a single phase. Again one decimal place is considered.

$Y_4 =$ Total weight (lb) of hypersil. Record taken directly from design specification.

$Y_5 =$ Volume (thousand cubic inches) of the blank dimensions considered a rectangular solid. This volume is taken equal to the blank width times the blank length times the blank height (rounded to the nearest hundred). Pressboard thickness is not included. After the product has been calculated, the decimal point is moved three places to the left, one decimal place is carried in the answer.

$Y_6 =$ Blank height (inches) rounded to the first decimal.

After the prediction information has been determined for the six variables Y_1 through Y_6 the values are substituted in the standard time equation. Included in this equation are seven constants (C_i, $i = 0 \ldots 6$) which have been determined through correlation techniques. These constants are subject to change as newer developments or changes come about. Should a change be necessary, a new set of constants is supplied by the mathematics group. The general form of the standard time equation used to predict the standard building time is as follows:

$$Z = C_0 + C_1 Y_1 + C_2 Y_2 + C_3 Y_3 + C_4 Y_4 + C_6 Y_6,$$

where Z is the predicted standard time in hours for one unit, Y_1 through Y_6 are the variables, and C_0 to C_6 are constants determined from sets of homogenous data by the method of least squares. The predicted standard time is per unit and that result is rounded to the first decimal place. The best estimating function is obtained by selecting as independent variables those having a strong correlation with the dependent variable and weak correlation with each other.

For an example of an application, say that eight physical variables, appearing on an engineering document available two months in advance of production and considered to be linearly related to core-building time (X), are selected as potential-independent variables. Their simple correlation coefficients with the dependent variable are then calculated from a random sample of 50 recent data sets. For the case in question the correlation coefficients are as follows:

$$r_1 = 0.72 \qquad r_5 = 0.95$$
$$r_2 = 0.89 \qquad r_6 = 0.78$$
$$r_3 = 0.95 \qquad r_7 = 0.79$$
$$r_4 = 0.91 \qquad r_8 = 0.83$$

After this calculation follows the step determining which (if any) of the eight variables were redundant. The intercorrelation coefficients between each potential-independent variable and all the other variables were calculated from the forementioned data sets. These are shown in Table I.

TABLE I

THE INTERCORRELATION COEFFICIENTS

$r_{1.2} = 0.56$
$r_{1.3} = 0.73$ $r_{2.3} = 0.93$
$r_{1.4} = 0.76$ $r_{2.4} = 0.89$ $r_{3.4} = 0.57$
$r_{1.5} = 0.71$ $r_{2.5} = 0.92$ $r_{3.5} = 0.58$ $r_{4.5} = 0.97$
$r_{1.6} = 0.70$ $r_{2.6} = 0.60$ $r_{3.6} = 0.61$ $r_{4.6} = 0.85$ $r_{5.6} = 0.82$
$r_{1.7} = 0.51$ $r_{2.7} = 0.64$ $r_{3.7} = 0.64$ $r_{4.7} = 0.82$ $r_{5.7} = 0.84$ $r_{6.7} = 0.89$
$r_{1.8} = 0.25$ $r_{2.8} = 0.81$ $r_{3.8} = 0.66$ $r_{4.8} = 0.79$ $r_{5.8} = 0.79$ $r_{6.8} = 0.63$ $r_{7.8} = 0.69$

To find the eight variables with the highest degree of multiple correlation with Z and the least among themselves would have required the calculation of 247 multiple correlation coefficients. Instead, Canning proceeded by using a simplified method, eliminating three of the eight potential predictors as redundant, and ending with a reduced model.

With the variables selected, it was then necessary to determine the intercorrelation coefficients from n different sets of homogeneous data, by least squares. Four hundred sets of unique relationships between core-building time and the five selected independent variables were obtained from the engineering documents of an equal number of shop orders over all product codes. The shop orders were transformers produced from the most recent engineering designs, and whose core-building times were determined from current standard data.

Testing the estimating equation thus obtained on a sample of 100 current shop orders, 30 % of the estimated times were within $\pm 1 \%$ of the actual core-building times, 75 % within $\pm 5 \%$, and maximum error (occurring twice in the 100 predictions) was $\pm 20 \%$. This distribution of percentage error has been closely followed each month since the estimating equation became operational. Under a full schedule, the total monthly corre-building load requirement has consistently been estimated within $\pm 1 \%$, but under a reduced schedule the percentage error rose slightly because the probability of estimating high or low on a majority of the units in the schedule increases as the number of units decreases.

Simulation in Steel Works

The present case concerns a steel transport problem. Internal transport in steel works is one of considerable magnitude. Before the finished product leaves the works, it has been moved quite often from one process to another. Apart from the involved cost, it is very important not to slow down production by failing to move produced goods or by not bringing in raw material fast enough. But in order to meet all the possible requirements of the different production units, the transport facilities needed for this peak would stand idle for a considerable time. It is, then, essential to balance the cost of idle time of production and of transport, so as to minimize the company's over-all cost figure.

The first step in determining the necessary transport facilities is to find out the tonnage to be moved in a given period. But this is not sufficient to fulfill this quantitative requirement. Say, for example, that the material to be moved consists of hot ingots. These have to be transported from the melting shop to the slabbing mill. During this time the ingots cool, and it is essential that this cooling should not exceed certain limits. So here not only the number of ingots to be moved per period but also the method in which they are to be moved are important.

In the specific case for which this simulator was developed, the concern had two steel production units, called melting shops. One of the melting shops disposes six open-hearth furnaces of 200 tons each, the other one converts 60 tons. When the steel is ready it is tapped in a big ladle. Then teeming starts; from the ladle the molten steel is poured into molds. These molds are rectangular and open at the bottom and at the top. They are standing on a train, two molds per bogey, and remain there during teeming and transport.

The molds in question are about 7 feet high, each containing 12 to 16 tons. Therefore, a train for the open-hearth shop consists of about 8 bogies ($8 \times 2 \times 12$) and for the convertor shop it consists of about 3 bogies ($3 \times 2 \times 12$). In the company where this study was made, transport handles these trains as a unit.

After teeming, the molten metal must cool down until the mould can be stripped off the ingot. This is done in a separate place, the stripping bay, common to both shops. The stripping must not be done too soon. The solidification of the molten metal starts at the outside, and the solid layer must be strong enough to keep the liquid center contained. But if one waits too long heat is lost which has to be added again later on.

A locomotive moves the ingot train from the melting shop to the stripping bay. Here, a crane lifts the mold of the ingot, at the same time pressing on the top of the ingot. An empty train is standing alongside and the molds are moved over, while the stripped ingots remain on the original bogies. In this operation, particular attention must be paid to the unequal temperature of the ingots.

The locomotive moves the train with the stripped ingots to the soaking-pit bay. There some twenty or thirty soaking pits are built parallel to the railway tracks. The train is brought alongside an empty pit and a crane lifts the blocks into the pit, which is then covered. The function of this pit is to equalize the temperature in the ingots. A comparison must be made between the ingot ready for the slabbing mill with the ingot when stripped. The time ingots have to stay in the soaking pit depends on the type of steel and on the track time, that is the time from teeming to charging the soaking pit.

The research workers were interested in the process between "end of teeming" and "ready for slabbing mill." In the course of the progress, the ingot is successively cooled, transported, stripped, transported, charged in a soaking pit, and reheated. The important fixed points of this process are a stripping crane, a number of soaking pits, and railway

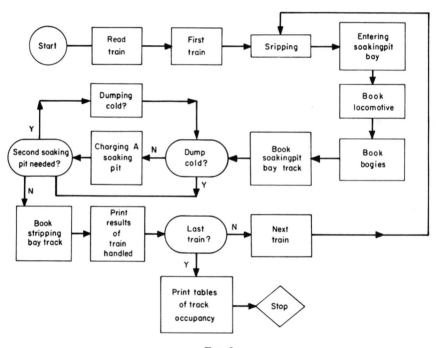

FIG. 2

tracks connecting the factories. Molds, bogies, and locomotives are used only during part of the process. At a certain point in the cycle they are not needed any more and become available for a new cycle.

We can follow better the sequence of operations with a cycle in the flow chart presented in Fig. 2. We see the cycle of the bogies from teeming through cooling, transport, stripping, transport, being unloaded, transport, being loaded with the molds of the following cycle, transport to the mold bay, where molds are changed and to the teeming by waiting for the next teeming. Depending on the length of the cycle and the interval between consecutive taps, five to ten ingot trains are rotating in this cycle for each melting shop.

Molds have a considerably longer cycle as they have to cool in the mold bay. Locomotives have a very much shorter cycle as they are required only after teeming and are available again as soon as the molds are back. Therefore, it is clear that cycles of bogies, molds, and locomotives are interconnected, and moreover any delay has an influence on future cycles.

The time a soaking pit is needed depends partly on the track time. Obviously, any delay after stripping has far more influence than a delay before stripping. A delay in a cycle not only influences the cycle of bogies, molds, and locomotives, but also lengthens reheating time. This might mean that, in a future cycle, ingots are delayed by having to wait until a pit is empty, causing still more delay for future operations. Thus delays are self-aggrevating and increase progressively. At such a moment it might be advisable to put the ingots aside, i.e., not charge them in the soaking pits, but put them outside and handle them later on, when the availability of the soaking pits is better. Of course, this causes extra heat loss and it may be that certain customers would have to wait.

To sum up, a delay in a cycle may tie up the next train waiting for empty bogies, train 4 or 5 waiting for the locomotives, train 8 or 10 waiting for bogies coming back, and still further on trains waiting for molds and for empty pits.

In the original statement of the problem, two melting shops were sending trains. To minimize interference, the tracks were laid out so that it is possible to strip an open-hearth train and have it brought to its soaking pit without a convertor train standing on the same track. There is still a snag in the track layout. When a stripped train is standing on one track it is considered dangerous to pass with a locomotive on the other track, because of the heat radiation. Finally, the locomotive might have to pass twice, once to fetch the empty bogies, the second time to bring the stripped ingots. There is a chance that the other track is unoccupied, the bogies are unloaded already, or its own bogies are nearer the stripping bay than those of the other train.

With this background, the questions asked by management could be phrased as follows: "Are the transport facilities adequate for a given production rate? If not, where do we expand? Will it pay to adapt a locomotive with heat protection? If the facilities are sufficient for the given conditions, at what rate of production will it be getting into trouble ?"

Problems like these could not be optimally solved from simple experience. Their complexity left aside, there is also the matter of human bias. The balance between risk and insurance is difficult to obtain. Big mishaps and trouble in the past leave a distinct impression, while normal operation does not. Also, a large number of small delays might not be sufficiently taken account of.

This problem can be approached by queuing theory, considering the process as two operations in series, stripping and charging in pits. The first operation has one channel, the second operation twenty to thirty channels in parallel. The service times are not independent. The clients for the operations are trains, but these fall into two distinct classes, each with its own rules (open-hearth and converter-steel). In each class there are subdivisions according to the type of steel.

The experimenters need, in this case, a simplified queuing model. They started off with a list of trains with their estimated time of arrival, type of steel, etc. They handled the trains in sequence of arrival, modifying the time of arrival with a chance number to simulate the usual uncertainty of teeming times.

A running account of the operation of cranes, tracks, pits, etc. was kept. If a train asked for a crane, the data processor who handled the model checked to see if the crane was available at that moment or not. If not, the processor kept note of the waiting time. If free, booked it for the known duration of the operation, adding a chance variable if the operating time was not constant. After booking, the processor advanced to the next operation.

The availability of a computer induced the researchers to continue the simulation over a reasonably long period[3] to obtain a complete distribution of data. Following this, they proceeded with the study of the effects of modifications in the installation. For instance, by adding a stripping crane, they searched for the resulting effect on the operations.

To prepare the program for a computer a description of the process had to be made. Because the simulator was too large for the available data processor, it had to be subdivided into two parts. The first part simulated the trains arriving during a period. The computer punched a card for each train, giving all particulars like time of arrival, type of steel, etc. Then, in the second half of the program, trains were handled in sequence of arrival according to the rules.

As an output, the computer printed a list of all trains, giving for each

---

[3] In the present case one hundred trains.

the times at which operations started and finished, the serial numbers of locomotives, bogies, and soaking pits being used, and any delays classed according to cause. At the end of the program a table of the occupancy of tracks was printed.

The printed results can be translated into graphs for ease of follow-up. Figures 3 and 4 show some results. In Fig. 3 the number of trains

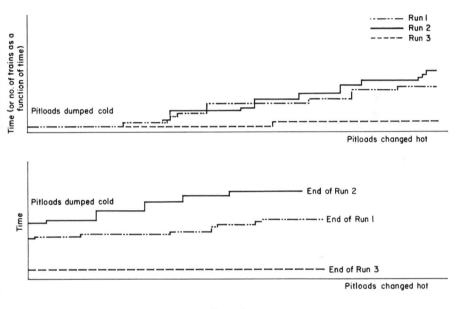

FIGS. 3

put cold is analyzed. As can be seen the present installation could not cope with the current load. Figure 4 shows the delays. While simulating one or two trains would not give a dependable answer, some hundred repetitions give already a useful indication.

Figure 5 gives an indication of the occupancy of soaking pits. Comparing pit 1 to pit 10 helps decide whether 10 pits would be sufficient or too much or whether some more pits would be useful. The researchers, in this case, concluded that a heat-protected locomotive made things not better, but worse. The explanation given to this result is that, once this locomotive is used, certain rules must be changed. With a normal locomotive it was always best to strip as soon as possible. With a heat-protected locomotive it seemed better to wait until being sure a soaking pit was available. The mixing of the two types was found to slow down the over-all process.

Models of the kind described in this chapter go well beyond the industrial practice followed until a few years ago when simple means, moving or weighted averages were used as the most sophisticated estimating processes. Yet we are still far from the ultimate and very much into an area which we are just starting to exploit. It is sound

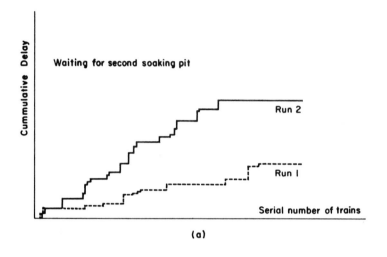

(a)

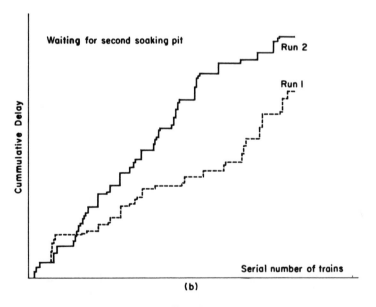

(b)

FIG. 4

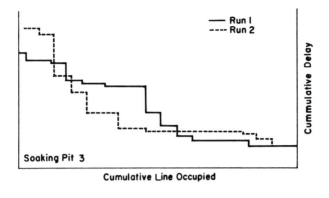

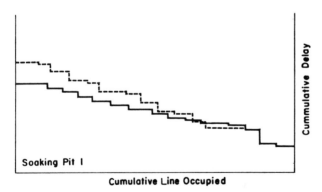

Fig. 5

practice that before formalizing any scheme the analyst carefully tests
both his model and his approach for sensitivity to the variation of the
crucial factors, unpredictable events and operational simplicity.

CHAPTER 13

Specifications for Inventory Control

In Chapter 12 we spoke of an inventory control example and made reference to the advantages to be gained through the rational management of a subject which, at times, accounts of some 50% of a company's operating budget. Exemplifying the fundamental concepts behind able inventory policies and procedures can help orient management thinking toward the nature of studies which it should undertake to obtain a more profitable basis for its operations. This is the objective of the present discussion. In this chapter we will present the guidelines of an analysis performed some three years ago at the request of a major petroleum concern.

Speaking from a top management point of view, in this particular case-study, reports over a number of years indicated that "something had to be done about inventories." But data were too general, and it was difficult if not impossible to establish responsibilities and to pinpoint soft spots, where effective control action was necessary. Most of the work was done through vague, indetermined averages[1] with the result that management was condemned to follow rather than to lead the facts.

To help establish both the calculating needs with respect to a rational treatment of inventory information and the potential savings from such application the following research took place. As the study progressed, a certain reorientation became necessary in order to determine the feasibility of applying sensitive analytic tools. We will consider only those general principles that were followed by the writer and his fellow-worker in the subject work.

In order to place the whole subject in perspective, the present chapter starts with a brief description of the basic principles established by management on inventory control techniques. This is followed by a summan discussion on inventory control simulation using electronic data-processing media.

---

[1] As everybody knows, but seldom cares to acknowledge, an "average" is a state of mind that makes one believe that if he puts his feet in an icebox and his head in an oven, on the average he will be most comfortable.

A Forward-Looking Inventory System

Inventory management was well aware of the serious effect inventory shortages may have on company operations. To avoid jeopardizing productive activities, it paid a certain price: that of accumulating and holding relatively high inventory levels. Slow handling of information, the time lags built into the system from the sensing of an inventory shortage to the actual rebuilding of such inventory, could also be blamed for excessive inventory accumulations. Excess inventory always costs more than it is worth, especially in cases where the demand for a product can fall within a short period of time.

The underlying purpose in an inventory control system is to reduce inventories while continuing to supply consumers adequately. All types of inventory control systems are based on a record maintained for each item. This record can be developed from physical inventories, purchase commitments, open production orders, and open requisitions. Whether a manual, mechanical, or electronic processing system is used, it is essential that accurate statistics on all aspects of materials administration be maintained and reported. It is also important, for control purposes, that these statistics be presented in a form that enables materials personnel to reach timely decisions, serving the company interests in the most profitable manner.

Among other things, inventory statistics should reveal the volume of procurement by country of source and how this compares with outstanding offers from the international market. The data should cover all types of procurement, such as procurement by the various organizational units, purchase indents "over-the-counter," or petty cash purchases and purchases made through the medium of long-range procurement contracts. The efficient handling of each item can be maximized by the use of a rapid, sensitive data-processing system which can help to establish an accurate control of materials supply and to pinpoint high and low stock levels at a time when corrective action can be effective.

In the study under consideration, computer use in inventory control could be seen under a variety of aspects. The more conventional approach would have been to maintain inventory file records. It was disregarded in favor of a more powerful use of electronic data-processing equipment: inventory control was projected in conjunction with discerning mathematical simulators. Properly constructed mathematical models programmed into properly selected computing equipment could provide the ability to predict demand and to take appropriate steps to meet it without building excessive stocks on hand.

With this background, the following objectives to be met by an improved inventory control system using computers were put forward:

(i) *The system should provide the basis for routine decisions required to maintain adequate, minimum stocks.* A rationally established materials administration system may be expected to perform three basic functions:

(1) Maintain a continuous record of the true current status of stocks.

(2) Analyze accurately a variety of transaction information in order to isolate exceptional matters.

(3) Report promptly to management and materials personnel each exceptional case requiring attention or decision to maintain stocks at the level demanded by current operations.

To perform these functions the development of a number of mathematical simulators, sensitive enough to ensure not only that excessive stocking is avoided, but also that chances of stock-outs are minimized within acceptable limits, will be required.

(ii) *The system should maintain an accurate, updated record of inventory flow.* The automatic inventory control system should provide an up-to-date record of the transactions of each item. This record should be developed from physical inventories, purchase commitments, open production orders, open requisitions, reservations, and other data. Program development should ensure that transactions are handled on the computer promptly as received, without batching or presorting on punched card equipment. This procedure contributes both to speed and to accuracy.

(iii) *The system should include master records, containing all fixed information and so designed as to minimize the actual flow of data.* One flexible solution might be that the input records include a master tape, in part-number sequence, for each of the items controlled. This may comprise such data as part number, description, average unit cost, requirements for each of the next six months, planned average daily usage, days of protective stock, days of lead time, economic order quantity, balance on order, and balance on hand.

Certain of these factors, such as the economic order quantity and average unit cost, should be periodically reevaluated by the computer. Differences and deviations should be brought to the attention of materials personnel and management in a timely manner.

(iv) *Data added to the system should be limited to information which varies with each transaction.* Because of its volume, fixed information relative to each item in stock should be permanently stored in the computer's memory, data added to the system being limited to changes only. Typical variable input data include on-order information for each of the orders placed each day; receipt information for each of the daily receipts indicating part number, quantity received, and unit cost; and issue information for each of the daily disbursements from stock, with part number, quantity issued, and the account charges.

(v) *To ensure dependability in data handling, parity checking should be incorporated in the system.* The company is currently implementing a new item-identification system. Completion of this work will coincide approximately with the conversion to electronic data-processing equipment. The inclusion of parity checks in the system can offer high dependability in data handling and should be carefully considered in overall design of the system. Two alternative approaches to parity checking are described in the latter part of this chapter.

(vi) *Routine decisions to replenish stocks should be developed automatically within the system.* The computer will be programmed to determine order point, quantity to be ordered, and expected delivery date. This would require the calculation of the planned average daily usage, and subsequently of the days of coverage. The latter is the number of days an operating department an word under present conditions based on the material on hand and on order.

The order point will be expressed in terms of days or of other time units depending on the specific item on hand, based on the daily usage of items and on lead time, or the number of days elapsing between the time an order is placed and the time the material is received and p!aced in stock.

(vii) *Simulation studies should be carried out by the computer to evaluate costs of articles versus delivery delays.* Mathematical simulators would be developed for computer processing to help evaluate alternative bids and item costs versus the delivery delays proposed. Such simulators should be run in connection with most reorder decisions.

(viii) *The system should evaluate alternative suppliers.* In connection with the evaluation of delivery delays versus cost savings, a total market and supplier evaluation should be run by the computer, taking into account individual prices, supplier's dependability, transportation costs, resulting insurance, and the like.

(ix) *Routine decisions to expedite receipts should be made by the system.* The determination of whether expediting is necessary can be effectively handled by the data-processing system. For this, the machine will need to calculate the days in stock as the ratio of the quantity on hand to the planned average daily usage. When the days-in-stock is lower than the days-of-protective-stock, this will be taken as an indication that material in the protective (minimum) inventory is being used and that a rush order is necessary.

(x) *The system should automatically analyze individual stock movements and report exceptional patterns.* A count should probably be kept by the computer of the number of requests received for each item at each warehouse during a predetermined period of time. If an individual warehouse is not carrying an item for which the demand during the past months reached a certain level, the data-processing system should indicate the need to change the distribution so that the item will be stocked in the future.

On the other hand, if a warehouse is carrying an item in stock and the orders for this item have fallen below a minimum level, the computer will indicate the need to change the distribution pattern so that the item is no longer stocked at the warehouse. When the level of stock of any item in a warehouse rises above a maximum level calculated on past demand, the data-processing system will indicate a surplus condition.

(xi) *Certain sensitivity tests should be performed by the machine to detect over-all shifts in consumption.* While long-term historical consumption data will probably be used as the basis for routine inventory control including purchasing, short-term data should be used to help decide on possible shifts in consumption.

(xii) *Required historical records and reports should probably be automatically prepared within the system.* At intervals the computer should probably be used to prepare a consolidated stock status report covering the inventory for all warehouses. Certain file maintenance functions should also be performed at this time, for example, new items added to the inventory, obsolete items removed, requirements computed for each of the next six months per item, and the like. Depending on management policies and control requirements, a portion of the file or all of the item records in the file might be listed on stock status reports at regular intervals. Such reports should show both the current position and historical statistics.

Two Analytic Studies

Analytical studies were performed in order to illustrate, within the prevailing conditions, the benefits of statistically forecasting inventory movement patterns. These studies also considered the statistical confidence which can be placed on the ability of the forecasts to meet actual consumption needs.

To start with, a statistically significant sample was chosen out of the total inventory. It was selected on a random basis. Four-year patterns of quantitative materials served as the basis for the studies.

A preliminary examination of the available four-year data for the fifty sample items indicated that it would have been possible to forecast with reasonable accuracy the demand for about half of them. Data for the remaining items were either incomplete or so widely scattered that further statistical analysis was not justified. Ten of the items whose data are prone to statistical analysis are taken as examples.

As the study progressed, demand trend analysis of the sample items illustrated an effective basis for forecasting. Regression analysis techniques were used to calculate trend lines for the consumption of each item. Diagrams for each of these items are presented in Figs. 1 through 10. It will be noted that each of the ten items has a characteristic demand pattern of its own. For example, it can be seen that the demand trend in Figs. 3 and 6 shows no significant variation as a function of time. The demand for Item 3 fluctuated around the line that is essentially parallel to the horizontal axis at the 842-unit level.

As another example, the demand for Item 2 substantially shifted upwards about the end of 1958. Therefore, a forecast of demand for this item, calculated over the total time period (four years), would be misleading in meeting current requirements. In order to detect shifts in demand for items such as No. 2, the data-processing system should be programmed not only to compare short-range against long-range trends, but also to determine the optimum length of the short-range timing period.

For the purposes of this preliminary analysis, the most recent six-month period was arbitrarily selected as the basis for calculating short-range demand trend lines, again using regression techniques. In certain cases (Items 3 and 6), the regression line for the short-range trend appeared to reflect reasonably accurately the long-range trend. In other cases, such as for Items 1, 8, 10, and others, the short-range trend line gave misleading or inconclusive information relative to the longer-term picture. In summary, then, this analysis did not substantiate the hypothesis that the last six-month period would be sensitive enough to detect shifts in demand and accurate enough to reflect over-all consumption patterns.

The statistical study of selected materials items can, of course, be carried out in greater detail. Much of the value of a petroleum company's inventory is tied up in a relatively small number of stock items, and the

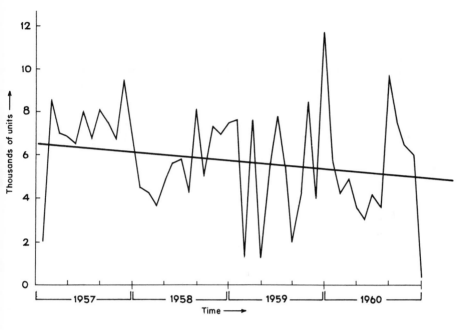

FIG. 1

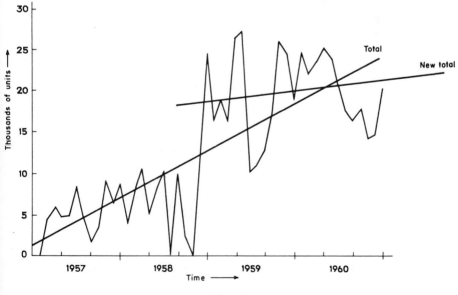

FIG. 2

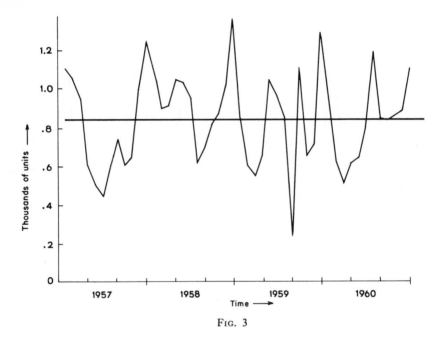

FIG. 3

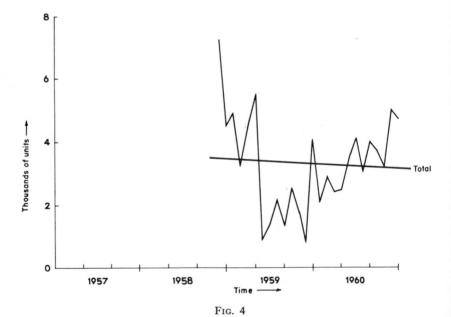

FIG. 4

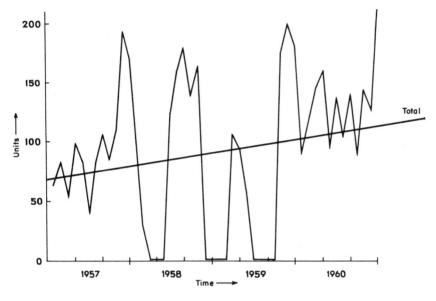

FIG. 5

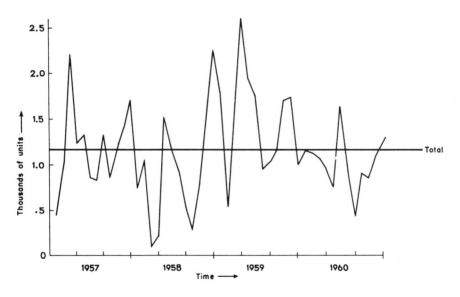

FIG. 6

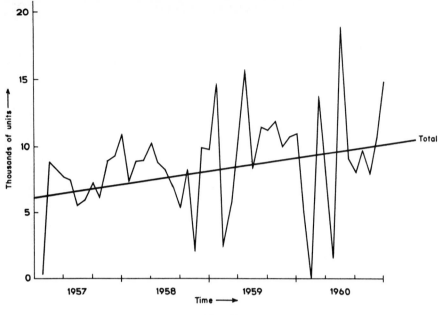

FIG. 7

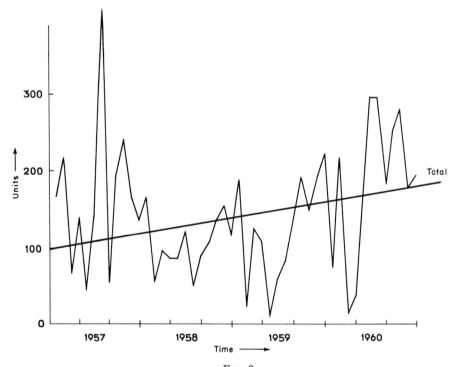

FIG. 8

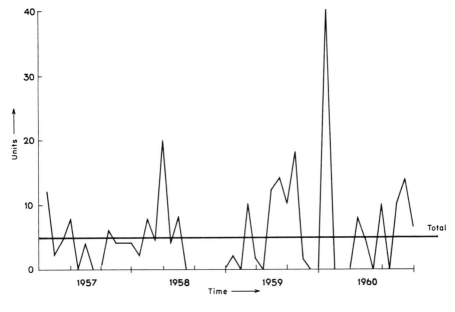

FIG. 9

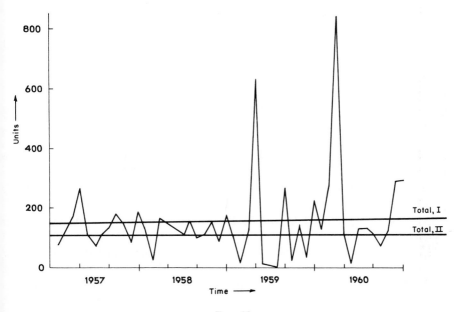

FIG. 10

behavior of these items particularly warrants careful study in a time-sensitive manner. In order to evaluate inventory levels, a mathematical simulation model was developed on the basis of four independent variables:

(i) time (expressed in months),

(ii) inventory at the $(n-1)$ time,

(iii) item demand for the current months,

(iv) item receipts for the current months.

The calculated value was that of the new inventory level per item.

The available data on inventory replenishment orders indicated when an order was placed. Actual delays from order to receipt varied between three and six months, and a few items had even longer delivery delays. For this reason, three alternative delay periods of three, six, and nine months were used in the calculations of the simulation model, as shown in Figs. 11 to 20, which also show the respective consumption curves.

This study effectively illustrates the large-scale economies available through better management of inventories. For almost all items, it would appear obvious that inventory levels were unreasonably high. In certain cases, as for Items 5, 7, and 8, reordering was utterly ineffective. In other cases, for example, Items 6 and 9, fear of inventory depletion had created unreasonable buildups. Finally, the one-year periodicity of ordering for Items 1, 2, 3, and 6 did not seem rational, relative to the consumption pattern.

Effects of a nontimely inventory follow-up can be seen in several items, as for instance with Item 2 where the minimum inventory was practically zero against a mean consumption value of 13,112. Conversely, the maximum inventory was about eleven times higher than this value. For this same Item 2, it is more rational to consider the mean of only the last two years, since consumption data indicate that two distinct distributions existed. The two-year mean value is 19 540 items and, with probabilities of meeting demand of 84 %, 97.7 %, and 99.8 %, the respective necessary inventory levels are 23 960, 28 380, and 32 800 units. The maximum inventory level held in stock was $4\frac{1}{2}$ times higher than the one required at the 99.8 % level of confidence in meeting demand.

Tables I and II indicate rational inventory levels and their carrying costs at the 50 %, 84 %, 97.7 %, and 99.8 % levels of confidence for meeting actual demands. For comparison purposes, the actual minimum and maximum inventory levels for Items 3 and 10 are also shown.

It can be seen that for Item 3 the minimum quantity held was well

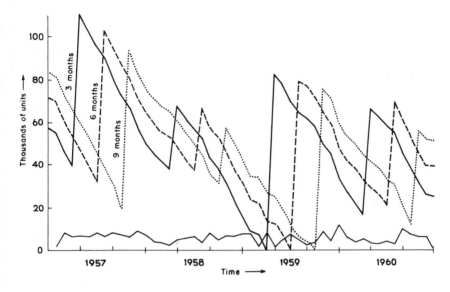

FIG. 11

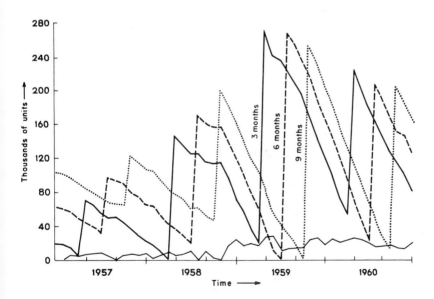

FIG. 12

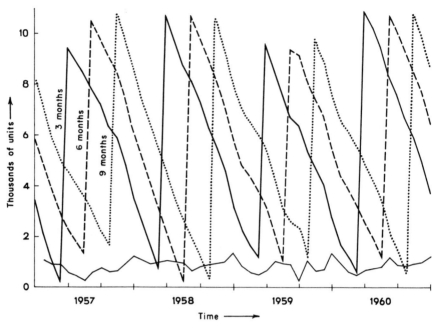

FIG. 13

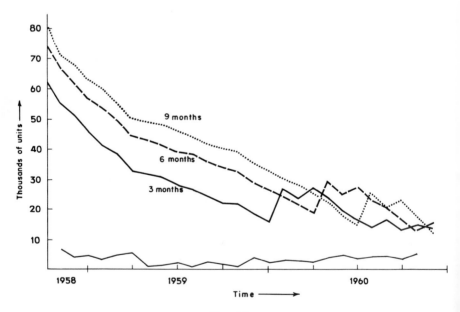

FIG. 14

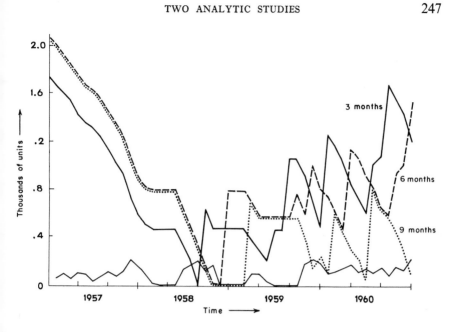

FIG. 15

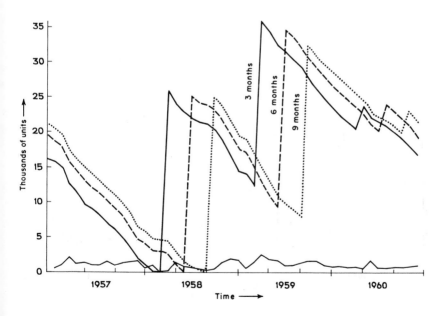

FIG. 16

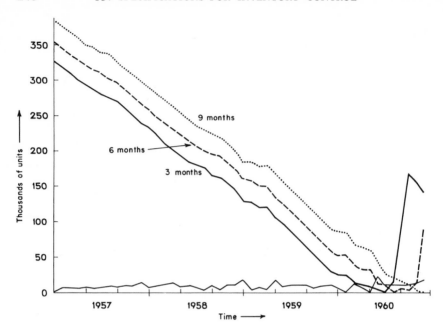

FIG. 17

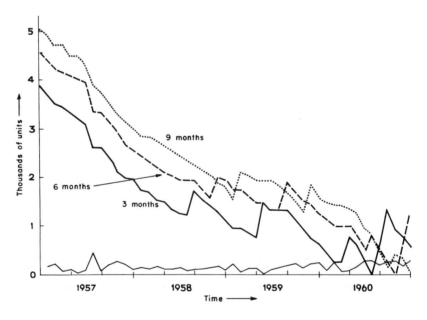

FIG. 18

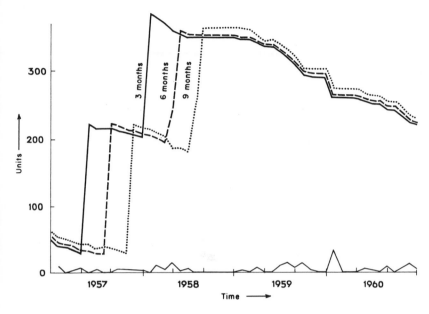

FIG. 19

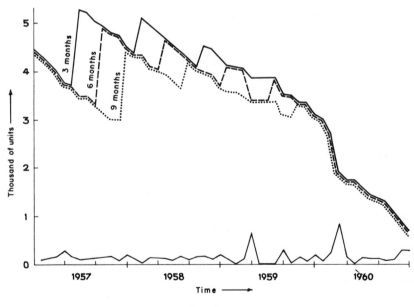

FIG. 20

TABLE I

EXCESS INVENTORY LEVELS AND THEIR CARRYING COSTS FOR ITEM 3.
THE UNIT COST WAS $16.80; MINIMUM QUANTITY HELD, 315 UNITS; AND MAXIMUM
QUANTITY HELD, 5215 UNITS

Calculated inventory level	Probability of meeting demand	Value in dollars
842	50.0%	14200
1092	84.0%	18400
1342	97.7%	21300
1592	99.8%	25100

TABLE II

EXCESS INVENTORY LEVELS AND THEIR CARRYING COSTS FOR ITEM 10.
THE UNIT COST WAS $ 2.97; MINIMUM QUANTITY HELD, 581 UNITS; MAXIMUM
QUANTITY HELD, 2481 UNITS

Calculated inventory level	Probability of meeting demand	Value in dollars
Alternative I. All data included		
154	50.0%	460
345	84.0%	1040
536	97.7%	1620
727	99.8%	2170
Alternative II. Points "out of control" omitted		
127	50.0%	380
190	84.0%	570
254	97.7%	760
317	99.8%	950

below the expected level of demand, while the maximum quantity was
$6\frac{1}{2}$ times the inventory necessary at the 99.8% confidence level. Since many
expensive items, like this existed, savings from their carrying cost
might have been, in themselves, enough to offset a major part of the cost
of an electronic data-processing installation, provided the proper prepar-
atory work was done.

An interesting case is presented by the demand curve for Item 10,
which has two "out-of-control" points. The inventory carrying level

is significantly different depending on whether or not these points are incorporated in the regression calculation. The expected levels with and without consideration of the two peak demands are, respectively, 167 and 129. The regression lines are correspondingly identified as total I and total II. At the 99.8 % level of confidence for meeting demand, the inventory carrying levels are, respectively, 727 and 317 lb.

This example shows that the exclusion of the "out-of-control" points can bring a 50 % reduction in inventory carrying cost. Such possibilities become evident only by means of statistical analysis; otherwise they remain hidden under a great bulk of nonsignificant data. Further, the timely identification of "out-of-control" points can permit early corrective action on the part of management, or, if this reflects structural need in consumption, can help establish efficient forecasts. This is exactly what happened with Item 10, after establishing the reason behind the yearly periodicity of the high consumption points.

In conclusion, while it is not statistically valid to generalize from the sample of 10 items, it would appear evident that the inventories for these items are unreasonably high. With similar patterns existing for other items, the resulting costs were enormous. Statistical inventory control procedures placed, by their own usage, a distinct data load on the electronic data-processing facility.

Parity Checks

Within the framework of the inventories study, and in order to achieve a high degree of accuracy in classifying, describing, and specifying all materials purchased, stored, and used, some thought was given to how electronic data-processing media can make more dependable the numbering system which was selected for classification and identification purposes.

The numbering system provided that only one code number be assigned to the same material wherever it may be stocked. The obvious advantages of this approach was mellowed by a relatively high proportion of errors in transcription. The fact that the subject system used an all-numeric 10-digit code served to ease the error-detection problem. Two different approaches to single detection parity checking are presented below as examples of what can be done in the direction of improving the dependability of item codings.

A code number, in the numbering system in question, consists of ten digits:

XX.XX.XX.XXX.X

The following digits	Indicate	and can range
XX.	Group	00.99
XX.	Subgroup	00.99
XX.	Sub-subgroup	00.99
XXX.	Item number	000.999
X.	Indicator	0.9

The arrangement of materials into specific groups is not done according to a strict relationship in function or end use, but on the basis of a similarity in purchasing, storage, and administration of materials. Equally, the division of a group into subgroups and sub-subgroups depends on the kind of material; it is not done according to a fixed pattern.

With the first of the parity systems, a check digit should be added to the item number to ensure the validity of the transcription. This check digit will be computed from the base digits of the number as follows:

Item number: 1163245798

(1) Take the alternate digits starting with the digit on the extreme right (i.e., digits 8, 7, 4, 3, 1).

(2) Double the value of each digit (i.e., 16, 14, 8, 6, 2) and sum each individual resulting digit:

$$1 + 6 + 1 + 4 + 8 + 6 + 2 = 28.$$

(3) Take the sum of the alternate digits starting with the second from the right $(9 + 5 + 2 + 6 + 1 = 23)$ and add it to the result of step (2): $28 + 23 = 51$.

(4) The check digit is the difference between nine and the least significant digit (digit to the extreme right) of the result of step (3), $9 - 1 = 8$.

(5) The item number including the check digit becomes

Numeric sequence	Check digit
1163245798	8

This method of obtaining a self-checking number is effective against most of the common transcribing errors, like alternate column transportation.

PART IV

Applications with Stochastic Processes

CHAPTER 14

Using PERT in Schedule Control

PERT is, basically, a statistical technique, prognostic and diagnostic. It is used for the purpose of quantifying knowledge about the uncertainties faced in completing research, production, or other activities. Its use may aid the timely achievement of program deadlines by drawing attention to danger signals that require remedial decisions.

The system works by using a constellation of probabilities to evaluate past performance. On this basis it can be used to predict future evolution of events and to locate soft spots through "exceptions." Trouble areas can thus be spotted, and management be given the option of transferring funds or manpower from parts of a certain program that are ahead of their schedule to parts that are behind.

Once established, this information scheme allows the running of test cases on alternatives to an existing program, with the aim of cutting the time needed to complete a project or a major subpart of it. By using PERT, one missile contractor, who had found himself lagging considerably behind schedule, was able to locate the trouble spots and eliminate two-thirds of the time beyond the deadline he would otherwise have required. Yet, interesting as its accomplishements might be, it is important to realize that PERT is not an "all-weather" solution to industrial problems; if its use offers advantages it also involves pitfalls and presents certain problems.

Rather than thinking of PERT as the medicine which will cure production delays and other ills, management is advised to follow a cautious approach considering it as a tool which may (just as it may not) pinpoint potential deadlocks and bottlenecks. Depending on the case and on the skill invested in its use, PERT might provide a periodic evaluation of a certain program, backed by supporting summaries of the more detailed project areas. Where trouble spots are indicated, alternatives can be evaluated and the preferred course of action determined in an effective manner.[1]

---

[1] For problems concerning the management of research and development projects, their time-estimation and scheduling, see D. N. Chorafas, "Les Fonctions de Recherche

Fundamentals on PERT Development

As a technique developed for measuring and controlling the progress of a weapons system program, PERT may help bring to the attention of management the significant factors affecting or being affected by a certain project. Military officers and industry executives concerned with the scheduling of weapon systems know that the development of these systems cannot be accomplished with split-second precision. The more complex the programs become, the greater the need for procedural tools to aid management in comprehending and controlling the operations which are involved. This is the reason why we are looking for powerful tools to use.

The fundamental approach of the "program evaluation and review technique" encompasses the selection of identifiable events along with the sequencing and establishing of interdependencies. Based on these interdependencies of events, a program network is developed. This is drawn up in reverse order, moving from end product to the present status of the given project.

Once the framework has been established in a chart form, it is given out to the contractors or agencies working on the various parts of the ensemble, with the request that the scientists and engineers in charge return this chart with its time estimates on completion dates. They are asked to give three estimates:

(i) most likely completion date;

(ii) most optimistic date, given an unexpected breakthrough;

(iii) most pessimistic date, assuming practically nothing works out as expected.

These figures must be edited for "reasonableness." Understandably, differences of opinion may and do develop as to the value of the three estimates. Such differences have to be ironed out or the benefits to be derived from the use of PERT will be minimal. The simulated time estimates are based on the initial data. If these are not agreed upon the use of both the prognostic and diagnostic data will not function as a time plan for the studied operations.

Equally important to the reasonable precision of the initial estimates is the timeliness with which these are processed. This is the background reason why we most often make reference to the use of a computer.

---

dans l'Entreprise." Editions de l'Entreprise Moderne, Paris, 1960; and D. N. Chorafas, "Die Aufgaben der Forschung in der Modernen Unternehmung." R. Oldenbourg Verlag, Munich and Vienna, 1963.

The machine calculates the relation between the various parts of the whole in a certain point of time, simulates their interactions, and evaluates how long it will probably take from each "event" to the next. These computations establish which of the flow lines is most "critical," that is, which is most likely to take the longest time to be completed.

The installation of an evaluation procedure to process and manipulate critical data and the establishment of channels to bring actual achievement and change data to the evaluation point are the indispensable links in a PERT program. This program starts with the "flow plan." The flow plans are established by assuming initially that an ordered sequence of events (with associated resources and performance) can constitute a valid model of the research and development schedule. The flow plan is in itself a sequence of events that are necessary to the accomplishment of the end objective. These events must be distinguishable points in time that coincide with the beginning or end of a specific task.

Establishing a "flow plan" consists essentially of placing the events in a pattern which shows their interrelationships and fundamental time precedences. Figure 1 presents a plan which will form the basis of sub-

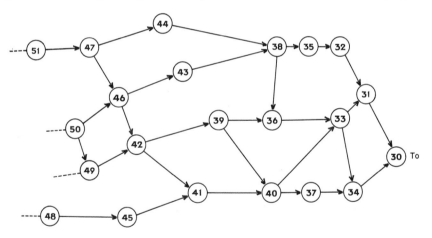

FIG. 1.   System flow. The arrows indicate the elapsed time of each interval between the project's "events."

sequent analytical treatment. The numbered circles represent events. The arrows between events represent the times necessary for accomplishing the activities. An activity cannot be initiated until the immediately preceding event has been accomplished.

In Fig. 1, we consider event "30" as being the "objective" of the system at time T_0. The interval between events 31 and 30 has been associated with an estimate elapsed time $t_{31,30}$. This is one of the elapsed-time estimates to be obtained from competent research or applications engineers, responsible for performing the job. But before mentioning these estimates we still have to see how this flow plan itself is established.

We start with a reference to past, familiar program-planning techniques. Bar charts have long been the standard method for indicating schedule plans and progress. A sample master phasing chart is presented in Fig. 2(a). As can readily be seen, with the complexity of present day

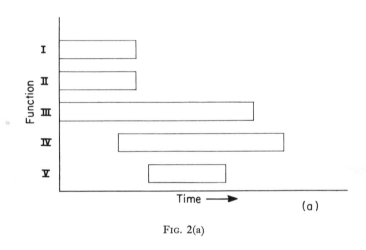

FIG. 2(a)

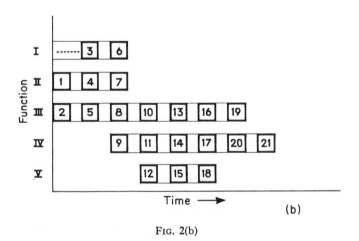

FIG. 2(b)

technological systems, it is difficult to define and confirm progress against a bar chart. This is particularly true if the chart is supposed to represent a broad effort over a relatively long period of time. Consequently, events or milestones are inserted in the bars to better identify crucial points. With this change, Fig. 2(a) would be changed to something similar to Fig. 2(b).

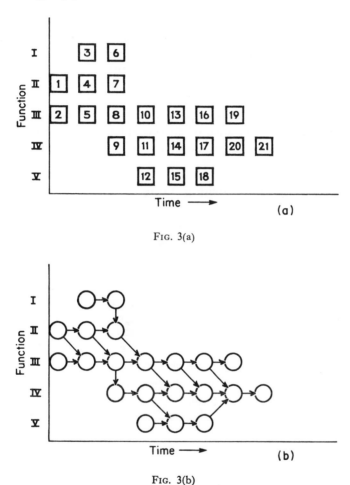

FIG. 3(a)

FIG. 3(b)

The division of a bar chart into discrete events proved to be an aid in progress reporting. However, this approach too neglects to indicate the interrelationships within or between bars. The subtasks within a major program are not "independent" as in Fig. 3(a) but interdependent

[Fig. 3(b)]. Hence, it is necessary to clearly indicate the interrelationships depicting the necessary paths of action. With these additions the original master phasing chart would appear as a network reflecting the true sequence of events, tasks, and subtasks facing the management of the project. The flow plan in Fig. 3(b) is no different in its structure than that in Fig. 1.

We have already stated that, in PERT terminology, the components of the network are "events" and "activities." *Events*, or milestones, are the clearly identifiable points in time which mark the beginning or completion of a specific operation in the program and are represented in the flow path by numbered circles or squares. An *activity* is the time-consuming link between two related events, and it is shown as an arrow-line. Activities will not normally commence until the preceding event has been completed. While these are matters of definition, the fact to remember is the importance of an unambiguous, accurate description of events so there can be no question as to their completion.

Establishing Time Estimates

We have briefly mentioned that estimates of time necessary for performing the activities are made under the assumptions of optimistic, pessimistic, and most-likely conditions. Statistical techniques are then applied to the raw data in order to put them in a form amenable to analysis. The three estimates are shown on the top line of Fig. 4 and are represented by points *o*, *m*, and *p*, respectively.

The lower portion of Fig. 4 gives a characteristic of the probability

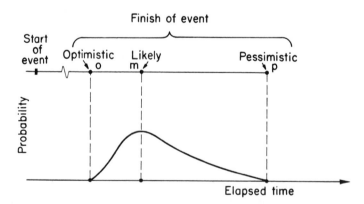

FIG. 4.   Estimating the time distribution.

distribution of the time involved in performing the subject activity. The scheme postulates that the three estimates can be used to construct a probability distribution. This distribution has one mode, with the most probable time estimate m being representative of that value. Similarly, it was assumed that there is relatively little chance that either the optimistic or pessimistic estimates o or p would be realized. Hence, small probabilities are associated with these points. No assumption is made about the position of the point m relative to o or p. It is free to take any position between the two extremes, depending entirely on the estimator's judgement.

Event times are derived through a computation based on the activity times. This computation takes the sums of the established time estimates. Hence, by virtue of the central limit theorem, event times will be roughly normal or distributed even if the distribution of the activity times is not normal.

For an example, we shall use the expected values and variances of the activity times. From these we shall calculate expected values and variances of event times. The problem, then, is to estimate the expected value and variances of an activity time from the likely, optimistic, and pessimistic times discussed above.

For uni-model frequency distributions, the unit standard deviation can be estimated roughly as one-sixth of the range.[2] It is thus accepted to estimate the standard deviation s of an activity time as one-sixth of the distance between the optimistic and pessimistic time estimates $(p - o)/6$. The estimation of the expected value of an activity time is more difficult. We do not accept the likely time as the expected value. An activity mean time will (probably) more often be greater than the likely time than less. Hence, if likely times were accepted as expected values, a bias would be introduced.

For calculation purposes, we will use an estimate of the expected time which would seem to adjust for the bias present if likely times were accepted as expected times. As the model of the distribution of an activity time, we chose the beta distribution with mode the likely time, range the interval between optimistic and pessimistic times, and standard deviation the one-sixth of the range. The probability density of this distribution is $f(t) = k(t - o)^\alpha (p - t)^\rho$ where o and p are the optimistic and pessimistic time estimates, respectively, k is a constant, α and ρ are functions of o and p, and the likely time t is equal to the modal

---

[2] This is, of course, an oversimplified assumption. Though it constitutes an established practice in PERT usage, the writer would like to note here his preference for data reduction, using a mathematically sound approach.

time, From this, we obtain the estimate of the mean and variance for ranges of distribution to be encountered:

$$\sigma_t^2 = \left(\frac{p - o}{6}\right)^2,$$

$$t = \frac{o + 4m + p}{6} = E\,(t)$$

Hence, the expected time $E(t)$ is the weighted mean of m and the mid-range $(o + p)/2$ with weights 2 and 1, respectively. Other users of PERT do not agree to this computation, choosing what they define as "realistic time estimates" for each activity. For them, the single-point time estimating technique is preferred for it simplifies and ex-pedites implementation without much loss of system objectives.

With this approach, the realistic time estimates represent the most likely time for accomplishing each activity, with consideration being given to

(i) maintain the planned application of resources, without biasing,
(ii) the expected mix of favorable and unfavorable conditions, and
(iii) not allowing predetermined schedules to bias the estimates.

After the estimates have been established, the network is reviewed to assure adequate frequency of events to provide proper reporting and visibility for management. As a rule, with this approach activities should not exceed eight to ten weeks in length. By addition of the activity-time estimates and event descriptions, the completed network can then be programmed for electronic data processing.

Other users follow different practices. For instance, if the optimistic, most likely, and pessimistic estimates show that little time will be gained if things go better than expected but that considerable additional time will be required if things go badly, certain companies prefer to use an expected time t that is somewhat longer than the most likely, but less than the pessimistic estimate. If the three estimates indicate that there will be little time lost if things go badly, but considerable time may be gained if things go well, then the expected time is taken as somewhat shorter than the most-likely estimate.

Sequencing Events and Preparing Listings

In planning and controlling time schedules, sufficient emphasis should be placed on the fact that a seemingly unimportant event at a system level, which could easily escape the attention of an over-all weapons system manager, could mean a major system delay some months later. This has often proved to be the case when planning might have been based on independent, singular, rather than interrelated events.

It is amazing indeed that it took a major research project to discover that while one-week delay in the shipment of a tiny bearing for a gyroscope might seem unimportant to the system manager of a missile or space program, it could result in a three-week delay in shipment of the initial guidance system and a possible two-month delay in delivery of the missile for flight test. It is the scheduling and monitoring of thousands of items which make up a complex weapons system, many of which involve research and development difficult to schedule and predict, that brings about the need for

(i) measuring criticality in terms of the probability of elements being available when required to match with related elements of other subsystems;

(ii) evaluating the effect of slippage or gain in schedule, with the realization that a small change in the achievement of an objective in one subsystem can have a major impact on the over-all system schedule;

(iii) establishing the incompatibilities in schedules of interrelated subsystems to identify potential trouble spots before they become apparent through their own thrust;

(iv) predicting the effect of trade-offs in funds, manpower, or time on over-all program schedule.

But to accomplish these objectives the work does not consist simply of establishing a flow plan and making the three time estimates. After the raw data have been translated into usable form, it is necessary to structure the information into a pattern which will lend itself to analytical treatment.

The first step in organizing the data is to order the events in a particular sequence. Starting with the objective, these events are placed sequentially on a list until they are all noted and the present is reached. The rule of ordering is that no event is placed on the list until all of its successors have been listed. For example, the events of Fig. 1 have been ordered in this sequence in the first column of Table I.

Columns (2), (3), and (4) of Table I concern events that immediately precede those in column (1). For the activities indicated (arrows on the flow plan), the mean and variance of the distribution of times are listed. Columns (5), (6), and (7) show similar information for those events

TABLE I

LIST OF SEQUENCED EVENTS WITH ELAPSED TIME ESTIMATES

(1)	(2)	(3)	(4)	(5)	(6)	(7)
	Immediate preceding events			Immediate following events		
Event No.	Event No.	Elapsed time estimate		Event No.	Elapsed time estimate	
		Mean (t)	Var. (σ_t^2)		Mean (t)	Var. (σ_t^2)
To 30	31	6	2			
	34	9	3			
31	32	12	3	30	6	2
	33	14	4			
34	37, 33	17	5	30	9	3
32	35	13	6	31	12	3
33	36, 40	11	4	31, 34	14	4
35	38	8	3	32	13	6
36	39	10	4	33	11	4
	38	21	6			
37	40	19	2	34	17	5
40	41	9	2	33	21	6
	39			37	19	2
41	42, 45	12	3	40	9	2
·	·	·	·	·	·	·
·	·	·	·	·	·	·
·	·	·	·	·	·	·
Actual						

immediately following column (1). The computation of "earliest times" for events starts with the consideration of the events in inverse order from their appearance on the list of sequenced events. In that sequence, the activities currently under way are examined. From all the activities that lead to the first event on the list, we choose the one with the longest expected time. This expected time and its associated variance are listed in columns (2) and (3) of the output sheet, as in Table II. Sequentially, each of the events (in their inverse order) is handled in this fashion.

The latest time at which an event can be accomplished is found by fixing the objective event at some future date and working backwards through the earlier events. The procedure for arriving at the latest dates for events is performed in the same general fashion as that for the earliest times. They are taken sequentially in the same order as the events appear in Table II. The objective event is assigned a mean that corresponds

TABLE II

OUTPUT SHEET[a]

(1)	(2)	(3)	(4)	(5)	(6)	(7)	(8)	(9)	(10)	(11)	(12)
	Earliest Time		Latest Times		Slack	Prob.	Prob.				
Event No.	T_E Expec.	Var.	T_L Expec.	Var.	$T' = T_L - T_E$	of no slack	of meet. sched.	Orig. sched.	Calcul. variat.	New sched.	New slack
30	.	.	.	.							
31	.	.	.	.							
34	.	.	.	.							
32	.	.	.								
33	.	.									
35	.										
37											
A											

[a] Time may be shown in weeks from time A (actual), or in any other convenient measure.

to its desirable date with zero variance. Then, utilizing the information in the last two columns of Table II, earlier events are specified by subtracting their activity times from the expected times of the succeeding events.

Hence, after the events of a project have been defined and their interrelationships properly established, the next step is to establish all the individual expected activity times along every possible path in the network running from the final to the starting event. Having done this, we must examine the total activity times of the many possible paths to find the longest, which is called the *critical path*. It represents that sequence of activities and events which will require the greatest expected time to accomplish.

Figure 5(a) shows the earliest time T_E for a small complex of events, with the time intervals between them t_e. If the 22nd week is satisfactory

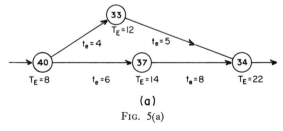

(a)

FIG. 5(a)

for accomplishing the event 34, the system can be "anchored" at this point, and the latest times computed in backwards computation, as discussed above.

Figure 5(b) presents the time relationship of the earliest and latest times for event 33. The dashed circle of this event represents the latest

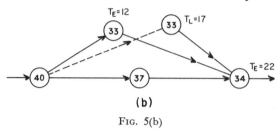

(b)

Fig. 5(b)

time T_L. It indicates that the event has slack, and could be scheduled anywhere within its slack range of S weeks without disturbing the expectation of timely accomplishment of the final event at week 22.

Slack time represents the difference between the total expected activity time required for any specific path and the total for the critical path. It is a measure of the spare time that exists at the moment in each of the other sequences of events. For rescheduling purposes, it may prove helpful to calculate the expected slack time for each event along many paths in the network.

The slack for each event appears in the sixth column of Table II. A zero slack indicates the earliest and latest times are identical. "Positive" slack indicates an ahead-of-schedule prediction, while "negative" slack forecasts a behind-schedule condition. If zero slack events are joined together, they will form a path that will extend from the present to the final event. This is exactly the basis for the critical evaluation. Should any event slip beyond its expected date of accomplishment, the final event can be expected to slip a comparable amount.

Thus far, the analysis of slack has not taken into account any scheduled dates except objectives. The actual situation may show scheduled dates for many of the interim events. Figure 6 graphically illustrates the uncertainties involved in predicting the precise time at which an event will occur. Event 30 might have been scheduled at time T_{os}; however, a time analysis could indicate that the event is expected to occur at time T_{oE} with a standard deviation as indicated

The probability distribution of times for accomplishing an event can be closely approximated with the normal probability density. Hence, we can calculate the probability that the event 30 will have occurred by time T_{os}. This is represented by the shaded area in Fig. 6.

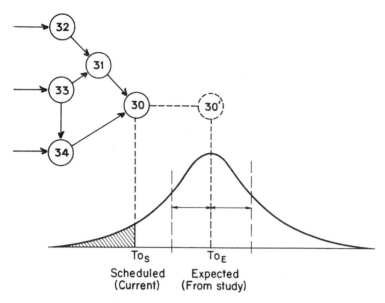

FIG. 6. Estimate of probability of meeting scheduled date T_{0_s}. Shaded area is an estimate of the chances that event 30 will occur by T_{0_s}.

Table II outlines the probabilities of meeting the scheduled date if all activities are carried out as soon as they can be. If the probability is low; the schedule is unfeasible. High probabilities would indicate the schedule will be met. If it is decided that a scheduled date is unfeasible, then resources and performance must be altered or a rescheduling must take place. Competent technical advice could provide a new plan, and appropriate directives could be acquired from these estimating sources.

Procedural Evaluation

For reasons of accuracy, complexity, and timely preparation most PERT users rely on electronic data processing. The network, events, activities, and time estimates can easily be arranged into computer input form. After processing the machine can prepare print-outs of the data in almost any sequence desired (Fig. 7). This matter depends mainly on company policy and control aims. The same is true for the timing of these reports. For instance, a certain manufacturer prefers biweekly print-outs of each network's critical paths. Another major manufacturer times these reports according to the degree of criticality.

THE ABC COMPANY
Electromechanical products division

SAMPLE NETWORK

MOST CRITICAL TO LEAST CRITICAL ACTIVITY

PRECEDING EVENT CODE	SUCCEEDING EVENT CODE	ACTIVITY TITLE	EARLY TIME	LATE TIME	SLACK	SCHED. DATE	EARLY DATE	LATE DATE

FIG. 7

Similarly, while certain companies use PERT as a "time pressure" device, others place more emphasis on its use in experimentation. This is quite sound since a remedial action is employed to reduce completion times along the critical path, another network segment may become the new constraint. Hence, a timely updating may include completions, additions, corrections, and deletions of event and activity information which will be fed back into the computer for inclusion in subsequent print-outs.

In this sense, the service performed by the computer is to locate and measure variations in performance along the different paths through a network. This still leaves quite valid the need for competent people, closely associated with the work along the critical path, who would analyze the progress or lack of progress that is taking place. Corrective action should normally be initiated at the time the analysis is concluded. Both the analysis and the corrective action need to be summarized for reporting to higher levels of management. In addition to written reports, graphic presentations can be used to summarize program status, provided that this graphic reporting is tailored to accommodate individual requirements.

The discussion of the use of the output aids in understanding. Far from performing any miracles, the PERT approach could pinpoint for program managers those activities which are part of the critical path and those which have considerable slack time, permitting the shift of manpower or funds, where feasible. The analyst, then, should take due care to consult with the responsible company people before finalizing the framework of a PERT system. The same is true about consulting with subcontractors and suppliers.

In the case of a major project, if a supplier or a contractor proposes a change in the program, its effect on the expected completion data can be quickly determined. In present-day practice contractors are often asked to report whether or not they have completed events before the scheduled date of completion, and also any changes in estimates for future events.

To help provide homogenity in procedures and practices, a major industry with considerable experience in the use of PERT issued the following directions regarding systems analysis, data collection, and data handling.

(1) *Each network shall begin* with an appropriate data date, expressed as event 0000, and shall contain events with appropriate description and assigned numbers, a title, network code, and time estimates and dates.

(2) *Networks shall contain* sufficient events to adequately monitor progress along each main stream of effort leading toward the terminal objective. A six- to ten-week time span between events is considered to be a practical level. Activities involving time intervals of less than one week shall be avoided unless required to add clarity to the network or designate a change in responsibility.

(3) *Time estimates shall be* in weeks including the nearest tenth of a week. The estimates are to reflect elapsed time under normal operating conditions, including the normal number of shifts. Estimates shall be made based on a level of resources currently available or attainable at the time required. These resources shall be compatible with current planning. The level of resources, such as manpower, will be a prime factor in establishing the three estimates, but these resources shall not be the basis for optimism or pessimism.

(4) *A single point of over-all responsibility* for any activity on a network shall exist so that reporting and updating is consistent and its source definite. If dual responsibility should exist due to the nature of an activity, one organizational element will be given prime cognizance. This responsibility is expressed through the use of a "responsibility code."

(5) *An activity listing by responsibility* should be prepared consisting of activity data arranged on separate sheets by responsibility code. The activities within each responsibility must be grouped in three categories on a sheet and classified as follow:

(i) completed activities, including all those from start of network to data date and especially identifying those within one, two, and three months prior to data date;

(ii) activities in progress, or those having their beginning events completed, should appear in a second category; they must be reported on each updating period;

(iii) future activities comprise the remaining; placement in this area indicates that the start of this activity is still constrained by other activities.

(6) *A semi-montly PERT report* shall contain the following data:

(i) Revisions to existing events and activities including reestimates, revisions to codes or descriptions, insertion of actual completions or schedule dates;

(ii) additions or deletions of activities and events;

(iii) any required supplementary remarks.

After processing, the data contributor is expected to analyze the output and prepare a PERT Analysis and Corrective Action Report, in accordance with the specific requirements put forward by project management. Special attention is to be given to the most critical path, significant negative slack paths, and any major network revisions.

Other Practices

Almost every PERT user develops rules and procedures that suit him best. A manufacturer who acts as systems manager for a large scale project has outlined the following step-by-step approach:

(A) *Identification of major tasks and subtasks.* During this step, the task breakdown must be accomplished and subtasks identified.

(B) *Preparation of networks.* This involves all parts of the project including those of the prime contractor and the subcontractors.

(C) *Establish system techniques and management report requirements.*

(D) *Install the data processing system.*

(E) *Provide for continued reporting and maintenance.*

To facilitate rapid implementation and to afford ease of understanding, only the basic system requirements have been standardized. As additional data uses and handling techniques are developed or improved, the PERT installation is expected to undergo refinement. For every project, and in order to facilitate early implementation, technical briefings are conducted outlining PERT methodology and techniques. Subcontractors are made particularly aware of the fact that the compatibility of systems for gathering and transmitting essential data is a prerequisite and that time is of paramount importance.

In order to adequately identify events in a form amenable to computer analysis and to transmit information about events in an unclassified manner, this manufacturer has assigned code numbers to the various events. These code numbers consist of two parts: a six-digit prefix and a three-digit suffix, separated by a hyphen. The prefix identifies the highest level plan number upon which the event appears. For instance, all events on a component plan numbered 003244 would carry this particular six-digit prefix. These identifications involve Code number, other identification number, description, responsibility, and schedule date.

One of the delicate problems in the use of PERT is the coordination of practices between the prime contractor and its subcontractors. The systems manager must make sure that the integration of various data will be possible. One major aircraft manufacturer outlines its approach in five steps:

(i) indoctrination of selected subcontractors' personnel;

(ii) assistance in briefing and guiding secondary subcontractors;

(iii) provision of manuals, sample networks, and forms;

(iv) assistance in planning the installation of the PERT system;

(v) guidance during its operations.

Another concern assigns this work to an evaluation team. After this evaluation team has been properly trained, a meeting with the contractor-assigned members of the team is held to select the events to be included on the flow plan. The team's assignment includes the analysis of each event description considered for use on the flow plan. For evaluation purposes a number of appropriate questions are asked, among them:

(i) Does the event represent a definite, identifiable beginning or ending point of some activity or group of activities?

(ii) Is the description detailed and complete? Does it tell who does it? How, where, and what is done?

(iii) Does the technical man, who is to do the estimating, understand the events as beginning and ending points of some clearly defined activity?

(iv) Is the man in charge able to fix in his own mind what has to take place at the completion of the preceding event, before the immediately succeeding event is reached?

CHAPTER 15

Markoff Chains in Simulation Studies

We have already made reference to the use of mathematical statistics in simulation studies. We spoke about regression analysis, the meaning of randomness, and the use of the Monte Carlo method. We said that most often our work in these fields concerns fundamental micro-events and micro-reactions. These reactions may be natural or artificial, fission of atomic nuclei, scattering phenomena, and the like. By superimposing the reactions taking place within a sample, the over-all or macro-behavior of the process is formed. This macro-behavior is most important to the evaluation of possible applications in technology.

Several ways exist for the development of macro-laws from the regularities of the micro-event. The usual approach, in most cases, begins with writing a formula that represents the single micro-event in its most general form. This is followed by a summing up process, provided this approach can be based on physical laws or on tentative statements. Similarly, when studying the behavior of any other natural or man-made system we may start with micro-events, which we eventually synthesize into a working ensemble. But what about the minute changes which interfere?

Consider, for instance, the process of natural selection. If two variants are present in equal numbers in a population, and one has a selective advantage of, say, 3 % over the other, the proportion of the two in the next generation will be shifted from the 50-50 basis and it will be even more so in the following generation. One can say that 3 % is a high degree of selective advantage. Nevertheless, the result would be just the same with a selective advantage of 0.001 % (which is undetected for any practical purpose) although it would necessitate a substantially larger time range.

In the present chapter we examine the use of transition probabilities, or Markoff chains, in the analysis of the behavior of a system. After a brief introduction to the theory of Markoff chains, we will consider several examples.

Introduction to Markovian Process[1]

The theory of Markoff chains is concerned with probabilistic processes in which the outcome of a certain stage depends on the outcome of the immediately preceding trial, and only on it. The outcome of A_j has no longer a fixed probability p_j, but to every pair (A_i, A_j) corresponds a conditional probability p_{ij}, given that event A_i has occurred at some trial.

Since the outcome of the nth trial depends on the outcome of the $(n-1)$th trial, it follows that to complete the series in addition to p_{ij} we should be given the probability p_i' of the outcome A_i at the initial trial. The probabilities of sample sequences are then defined by the following equations:

$$P(A_i, A_j) = p_i' p_{ij}; \qquad P(A_i, A_j, A_k) = p_i' p_{ij} p_{jk};$$

$$P(A_i, A_j, A_k, A_l) = p_i' p_{ij} p_{jk} p_{kl}; \qquad P(A_i, A_j, A_k, A_l, A_m) = p_i' p_{ij} p_{jk} p_{kl} p_{lm};$$

$$P(A_{i0}, A_{i1}, A_{i2} \cdots A_{in}) = p_{i_0} p_{i_0 i_1} p_{i_1 i_2} p_{i_2 i_3} \cdots p_{i_{n-2} i_{n-1}} p_{i_{n-1} i_n}.$$

It follows that independent trials can be considered as a special case of Markoff chains with $p_{ij} = p_i'$ for each i. If p_i' is the probability of A_i at the initial trial, then $p_i \geqslant 0$ and $\Sigma^i p_i' = 1$. Furthermore, each A_m must be followed by an A_n and for all m and n,

$$p_{m1} + p_{m2} + p_{m3} + \cdots = 1, \qquad \text{where} \quad p_m \geqslant 0.$$

Based on the foregoing, a sequence of trials with possible outcomes $A_1, A_2, A_3, \cdots, A_n$ will constitute a Markoff chain if the probabilities of chain sequences are defined by the general equation

$$P(A_{i0}, A_{i1}, A_{i2}, \cdots A_{in}) = p_{i_0}' p_{i_0 i_1} p_{i_1 i_2} \cdots p_{i_{n-1} i_n}$$

where p_{i_0}' is an initial probability for A_i and p_{ij} are the conditional probabilities for the events A_j given that for each such event a corresponding event A_i has occured during the immediately preceding trial. We can now construct a *matrix of transition probabilities* p_{ij} or, in different terms, of probabilities defining the transition of the system from state A_i to state A_j. Indeed, such probabilities p_{ij} can be arranged in the form of a square matrix (stochastic matrix) where all elements

---

[1] See D. N. Chorafas, "Statistical Processes and Reliability Engineering."

will be nonnegative and in which the sum of each "transition of state" (whether written by row or by column) will be equal to one:

$$p = \begin{bmatrix} p_{11} & p_{12} & p_{13} & \cdots & p_{1n} \\ p_{21} & p_{22} & p_{23} & \cdots & p_{2n} \\ \vdots & \vdots & \vdots & & \vdots \\ p_{n1} & p_{n2} & p_{n3} & \cdots & p_{nn} \end{bmatrix}$$

A stochastic matrix together with the initial probability p' completely define a Markoff chain. The probabilities used in the matrix are determined by the observation of behavior over long periods of time, which leads to the calculation of the relative frequencies. Hence the matrix is actually a summary of past behavior.

For an example, say certain nomad tribes migrate between the mountains (M), the plains (P), and the seaside (S). Then suppose that over each unit of time there is a probability that a nomad population will move to another area. If the behavior of the nomads is given by the sequence of letters:

$$M\,P\,S\,S\,P\,M\,M\,M\,S\,P\,P\,S\,P\,S\,M\,M\,P\,S\,S\ldots,$$

we can develop a matrix of transition probabilities:

↓	M	P	S
M	0.18	0.60	0.28
P	0.44	0	0.72
S	0.38	0.40	0

Assume that we are studying a population of 800 families and that all are in the plains. Then the initial distribution would be $(0, 800, 0)$ for (M, P, S), respectively. After the first interval of time, the distribution would be different according to the transition matrix, namely, $(480, 0, 320)$. When several intervals of time have elapsed the system begins approaching a steady state of equilibrium, which can be readily computed from the given data.

A requirement for a sequence of states to be a Markoff chain is that the probabilities of transition must not depend on states earlier than the operand. An example where independence does not hold is given by

$$A\,B\,B\,A\,B\,B\,A\,B\,B\,A\,B\,B\,A\,B\,B\,A\,B\,B\,A\,B\,B\,A\,B\,B\,A$$

In a chain like this, B is followed by A and B about equally. If this sequence is studied we notice AB was always followed by B. BB was followed 8 times by A and 0 times by B. It follows that the process is dependent on what state preceded the B. Thus, this is not a Markoff chain.

When a system is found to produce trajectories where the transition probabilities depend in a constant way on what state preceded each operand, the system though not Markovian could be made so by recoding.

Suppose that a market analyst did a thorough investigation of the behavior of a tourist population with regard to its preference for the three popular resort areas K, L, and M. Say that over each one-unit interval of time (for instance one year) there is a constant probability that a person having been to resort K will shift to resort L, and similarly for the other possible transitions. Say that these transition probabilities have been calculated and that their numerical value is as follows:

	K	L	M
K	0.3	0.1	0.6
L	0.5	0.3	0.2
M	0.2	0.6	0.2

We could derive these probabilities by observing the behavior of the population (in respect to its vacation-going habits) over a relatively long sequence of time, computing the frequence of the different transitions (e.g., $K \to K$, $K \to L$, $K \to M$, etc.), and then finding the relative frequencies which are the p_{ij} elements of the matrix of transition probabilities.

In a transition matrix, written as in the foregoing K, L, M example, when both the column sums and the row sums are equal to unity, then the matrix is called "doubly stochastic."

Sometimes, the term Markoff chain is applied to a particular trajectory produced by a system, and on other occasions it is applied to the system, and on other occasions it is applied to the system itself which is capable of producing many trajectories. In that case, the matrix will yield information about the tendencies of the system, although not necessarily about specific details.

Once the transition probabilities of the system have been established, in the long run it would be irrelevant which initial value the variables K, L, and M had. If we were observing the behavior of a random sample of 6000 from the vacationing population, the initial vector (V_K, V_L, V_M) of the three subpopulations might have been $(0, 6000, 0)$ or $(3000, 0, 3000)$, or $(2000, 2000, 2000)$. This initial distribution would not influence the equilibrial values of the system.

The equilibrial values of a Markoff chain can be readily computed. If V_K is the value of K at time t and $V_K{'}$ the corresponding value of K at time $t + 1$, and if the same holds for the other variables, then from the matrix of transition probabilities we compute

$$V_K{'} = 0.3V_K + 0.1V_L + 0.6V_M,$$
$$V_K{'} = 0.5V_K + 0.3V_L + 0.2V_M,$$
$$V_M{'} = 0.2V_K + 0.6V_L + 0.2V_M.$$

But, at equilibrium the values are unchanging, hence, $V_K{'} = V_K$, etc. Therefore,

$$V_K = 0.3V_K + 0.1V_L + 0.6V_M,$$
$$V_L = 0.5V_K + 0.3V_L + 0.2V$$
$$V_M = 0.2V_K + 0.6V_L + 0.2V_M$$

or

$$-0.7V_K + 0.1V_L + 0.6V_M = 0,$$
$$0.5V_K - 0.7V_L + 0.2V_M = 0,$$
$$0.2V_K + 0.6V_L - 0.8V_M = 0.$$

These three equations are not all independent, for, in this example, the sum of the three populations must be equal to 6000. Hence we can drop one of the equations and replace it with

$$V_K + V_L + V_M = 6000.$$

The system now becomes

$$-0.7V_K + 0.1V_L + 0.6V_M = 0,$$
$$0.2V_K - 0.7V_L + 0.2V_M = 0,$$
$$V_K + V_L + V_M = 6000,$$

and the definition of the state of equilibrium has been reduced to the solution of a simple linear system composed of three equations with three unknowns.

Based on the property of Markoff chains, to lead to an eventual state of equilibrium which is a function of the matrix of transition probabilities, Professor H. Greniewski, of the University of Warsaw, developed the theory "of economic systems with feedback." This theory states that in economic planning it is virtually irrelevant if one starts with a poor plan of initial conditions, provided the proper feedback has been established to allow a self-regulatory function to go on.[2]

Seen from this perspective, the whole process of economic planning and government control becomes dependent on the functional aspects of information feedback. From this, Greniewski advanced the proposition that the construction of a model of the national economy can be made in its initial state *as if* it were a completely isolated system, with abstraction from natural boundaries, social factors of noneconomic qualification, and world-wide interactions. The influence on this theory of the fundamental concept of a totally planned economy is self-apparent. It should be stated, however, that Professor Greniewski carefully introduces variants to account for the behavior of "the event" and its influence on "the plan"—and by varying the weight of the independent event he avails for experimentation under different economic systems.

Furthermore, with the forementioned approach to planning through feedback and transitional probabilities, a definite distinction should be made between "planning at the national income level" and "corporate planning." The difference is essentially one of shock-absorbtion capabilities, until the system finds, by trial and error, the stability condition it is seeking (if ever). In a planned economy the state can absorb the penalties imposed by system deviation (until the collapse of the economy itself, should inefficiency play a major role). Contrary to this, a company operating within a free enterprise system may be unable to survive until reaching such stability, because of the continuous flux in the financial environment, which would upset the "transition" by competitive action. This exemplifies the need for management to use foresight in replacing the physical time-consuming regulation, even if such tendency toward a far-away state of equilibrium can be proved to exist.

Evaluating the Use of Markoff Chains with a Popular Game

A mathematical statistician has been asked to investigate certain characteristics of the popular American game of baseball. He has avail-

---

[2] This reflects personal discussions the writer had with Professor Greniewski, during November 1962, while lecturing in Warsaw on the invitation of the Polish Academy of Sciences. See also for reference: H. Greniewski, Cybernetics and Economics Models, The Review of the Polish Academy of Sciences, 1959.

able a wealth of historical data, and he is faced with the problem of determining a method of applying Markoff chains. Several approaches were considered, and after extensive discussions with the specialists on the game itself and certain unsuccessful results, all but one approach were abandoned.

Before considering this application of Markoff chains, some introduction into the particulars of the baseball industry may be of advantage. The two leagues comprising what are referred to in the United States as the Major leagues are the American league and the National league— each league consisting of eight teams. During the baseball season, each team vies for the first place standing in its own respective league. Of course, only one team can finish first in each league; the remaining teams are forced to fall into the subsequent positions according to their relative successes during the season.

This situation lends itself to the operand-transform matrix. This matrix is formulated by taking as the operand the team's standings of any given year and as the transforms the team's standing of the following year. As an illustration, let us arbitrarily choose the American league matrix resulting from the transformations in league standings from the 1956–1957 season (see Table I). Teams are indicated by numbers since there is no point of confusing the issue of various names.

TABLE I

AMERICAN LEAGUE STANDINGS AT THE CLOSE OF THE 1956 SEASON

↓	1	2	3	4	5	6	7	8
1	×							
2			×					
3				×				
4					×			
5						×		
6		×						
7								×
8							×	

The tranformation is from column to row, an x in the matrix indicates that the mean has moved from position m in 1956 to position n in 1957. For instance, the first-place team of 1956 remained in first place in 1957, the second-place team dropped to the sixth position, and so on through the remainder of the matrix.

However, by definition the Markoff chain is a sequence of states in which, over long various stretches, *the probability of each transition is the same.* The last eight words of this sentence are the part with which we need be initially concerned. Will our data display enough of a trend toward constant probabilities to permit us to reasonably assume a Markoff chain situation? This is the first question to which we must search for an answer through an analysis of the respective historical data.

The earliest records of team standings which could be found useful were those of the year 1917. The first step, after the time range was selected, was to develop the transformations from the years 1917 to 1957.[3] The two leagues (American and National) were considered separately for the expressed purpose of comparing the results of each for differences and simularities at a later time. After the forty matrices of each league were completed, they were collected into four groups of ten years each (see Appendix II). These four groups were then compared to see whether or not any trend existed toward constant probabilities. The results are as follows:

In the American league the probabilities of a first place team remaining in first place were $\frac{4}{10}$, $\frac{5}{10}$, $\frac{4}{10}$, and $\frac{6}{10}$, respectively, for each of the ten-year groups. The probabilities of the second-place team going to first place were $\frac{2}{10}$, $\frac{3}{10}$, $\frac{1}{10}$, and $\frac{2}{10}$, respectively. In the National League the corresponding probabilities of a last-place team remaining in last place were $\frac{5}{10}$, $\frac{5}{10}$, $\frac{4}{10}$, and $\frac{3}{10}$. Similar trends appear throughout the matrices. Certain inconsistencies can, of course, be found, but these inconsistencies are considerably fewer in number than the constant trends and are relatively small in magnitude.

In addition, it is likely that the small sample size had much to do with the inconsistencies in question. It is possible that a large sample size would tend to reduce discrepancies. The experimenter has tested this supposition and found it to be the case. Numerical data are shown in the matrices of Appendix III. They represent groupings of twenty years—combining the first and last ten-year groups and the second and third ten-year groups, respectively. The data were taken from the matrices of Appendix II.

---

[3] To avoid using long extensive tables in the text, the data are shown in Appendix I.

Some of the probabilities appearing in the twenty-year matrices are as follows:

In the American League:

1st place to 1st place	$\dfrac{10}{20}$	and	$\dfrac{9}{20}$,
8th place to 8th place	$\dfrac{7}{20}$	and	$\dfrac{8}{20}$.

In the National League:

1st place to 1st place	$\dfrac{5}{20}$	and	$\dfrac{5}{20}$,
8th place to 8th place	$\dfrac{8}{20}$	and	$\dfrac{9}{20}$.

These ratios show signs of tending toward constant values. It appears likely that if, say, forty more years of data were available, the results would be even more conclusive. Appendix IV contains the matrices showing a summation of the transformations of each of the two major leagues through the forty-year period from 1917 to 1957. It can be seen from these matrices that in no instance has any team ever gone from first to last or from last to first place in either league. There also appears to be a tendency for teams to remain essentially at or near their previous year's standing since the higher probabilities tend to hover around the main diagonals in each matrix.

It is further interesting to note that the varieties are smallest in the first and last columns of each of the matrices, both the largest and the smallest probabilities occuring in these columns.

Runoff Volume as a Markoff Chain[4]

The problem approached here is the prediction of the runoff (water yield) of a river basin from year to year. While daily variations in stream flow are mostly random, the annual flow usually follows specific probabilities. If this is so, then the order of events follows a Markoff chain. In problems of this sort the relatively small number of observations and their great variety make analysis difficult. This is why the experimenter

---

[3] This case was prepared as a term project by A. Schwartz in a graduate course in Systems Engineering taught by the author at the Catholic University of America.

decided to use five "runoff classes." These were established on the basis of "percent of average annual runoff" as follows:

Class 1 (much below average)	less than 60%
Class 2 (below average)	60–89%
Class 3 (average)	90–109%
Class 4 (above average)	110–139%
Class 5 (much above average)	140% and up

In total, twenty-nine streams in the Potomac basin having an aggregate of 553 years of record were used. The computation of the probability matrix was programmed on a small digital computer. The input was the class limits, the station average, and observed flows; the output were tables of flow in percentages, class limits for each station, and the cumulative transformation matrix. The raw data arranged in a matrix form are as follows:

↓	1	2	3	4	5
1	8	18	13	13	7
2	16	51	52	27	24
3	15	42	45	32	10
4	16	34	23	27	16
5	10	25	13	11	5

From this we can easily derive a matrix of transition probabilities:

↓	1	2	3	4	5
1	0.124	0.106	0.088	0.115	0.112
2	0.246	0.300	0.356	0.243	0.387
3	0.230	0.247	0.310	0.290	0.162
4	0.246	0.200	0.088	0.252	0.258
5	0.154	0.147	0.158	0.100	0.081

This matrix is very significant indeed. It shows that the system has a high probability toward the average and below-average state. As can be seen, for instance, a year of average flow is followed by a lowering of runoff in 65 out of 146 cases and a rising in only 36 out of 146 cases. When in a state on either extreme, a change towards the other end occurs in 57 out of 65 and 57 out of 62 cases, respectively.

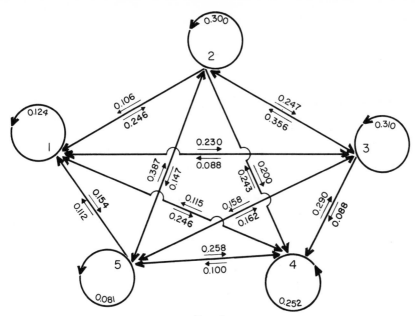

Fig. 1

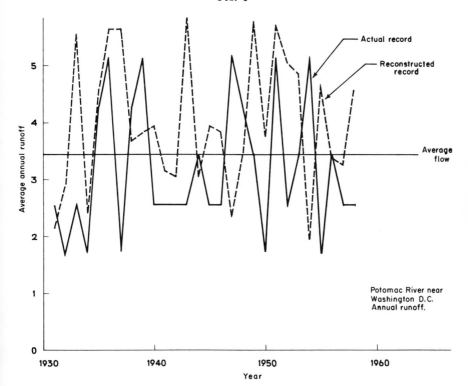

Fig. 2

A kinematic graph[5] was drawn for the transformation, based on established transition probabilities. The data for the graph in Fig. 1 have been derived from the transition matrix.

A stochastic model was devised using random numbers in accordance with the probabilities indicated by the matrix for the transformation from each state. Figure 2 shows the results together with the actual experience at the Potomac River gate in Washington, D. C. It can be seen that, while the over-all distribution is faithfully reproduced, the forecasting of individual years (simulated data) presents deviations from the actual distribution. These deviations, however, might be due to the relatively small sample sizes or a compensating factor should be applied, to shift the simulated data in phase with the real. The whole subject needs further investigation.

APPENDIX I

TABLE II

STANDINGS OF THE AMERICAN LEAGUE TEAMS AT THE CLOSE OF THE 1917 AND 1918 SEASONS

1917 / 1918	Chi 1	Bos 2	Cleve 3	Del 4	Wash 5	N.Y. 6	St. L 7	Phil 8
Bos 1		×						
Cleve 2			×					
Wash 43				×				
N.Y. 4						×		
St. L 5							×	
Chi 6	×							
Det 7				×				
Phil 8								×

[5] See the discussion on "incessant transition" in D. N. Chorafas, "Statistical Processes and Reliability Engineering," Chapter 27.

TABLE III

STANDINGS OF THE NATIONAL LEAGUE TEAMS AT THE CLOSE OF THE 1917 AND 1918 SEASONS

1917 / 1918	N.Y. 1	Phil 2	St. L 3	Cin 4	Chi 5	Bos 6	Bkn 7	Pitt 8
Chi 1					×			
N.Y. 2	×							
Cin 3				×				
Pitt 4								×
Bkn 5							×	
Phil 6		×						
Bos 7						×		
St. L 8			×					

TABLE IV

STANDINGS OF THE AMERICAN LEAGUE TEAMS AT THE CLOSE OF THE 1918 AND 1919 SEASONS

1918 / 1919	Bos 1	Cleve 2	Wash 3	N.Y. 4	St. L 5	Chi 6	Det 7	Phil 8
Chi 1						×		
Cleve 2		×						
N.Y. 3				×				
Det 4							×	
St. L 5					×			
Bos 6	×							
Wash 7			×					
Phil 8								×

TABLE V

STANDINGS OF THE NATIONAL LEAGUE TEAMS AT THE CLOSE OF THE 1918 AND 1919 SEASONS

1918 / 1919	Chi 1	N.Y. 2	Cin 3	Pitt 4	Bkn 5	Phil 6	Bos 7	St. L 8
Cin 1			×					
N.Y. 2		×						
Chi 3	×							
Pitt 4				×				
Bkn 5					×			
Bos 6							×	
St. L 7								×
Phil 8						×		

TABLE VI

STANDINGS OF THE AMERICAN LEAGUE TEAMS AT THE CLOSE OF THE 1955 AND 1956 SEASONS

1955 / 1956	N.Y. 1	Cleve 2	Chi 3	Bos 4	Det 5	K.C. 6	Bal 7	Wash 8
N.Y. 1	×							
Cleve 2		×						
Chi 3			×					
Bos 4				×				
Det 5					×			
Bal 6							×	
Wash 7								×
K.C. 8						×		

TABLE VII

STANDINGS OF THE NATIONAL LEAGUE TEAMS AT THE CLOSE OF THE 1955 AND 1956 SEASONS

1956 \ 1955		Bkn 1	Mil 2	N.Y. 3	Phil 4	Cin 5	Chi 6	St. L 7	Pitt 8
Bkn	1	×							
Mil	2		×						
Cin	3			×					
St. L	4							×	
Phil	5				×				
N.Y.	6			×					
Pitt	7								×
Chi	8						×		

TABLE VIII

STANDINGS OS THE AMERICAN LEAGUE TEAMS AT THE CLOSE OF THE 1956 AND 1957 SEASONS

1957 \ 1956		N.Y. 1	Cleve 2	Chi 3	Bos 4	Det 5	Balt 6	Wash 7	K.C. 8
N.Y.	1	×							
Chi	2			×					
Bos	3				×				
Det	4					×			
Zalt	5						×		
Cleve	6		×						
K.C.	7								×
Wash	8							×	

TABLE IX

STANDINGS OF THE NATIONAL LEAGUE TEAMS AT THE CLOSE OF THE 1956 AND 1957 SEASONS

1956 / 1957	Bkn. 1	Mil 2	Cin 3	St. L 4	Phil 5	N.Y. 6	Pitt 7	Chi 8
Mil 1		×						
St. L 2				×				
Bkn 3	×							
Cin 4			×					
Phil 5					×			
N.Y. 6						×		
Pitt 7							×	
Chi 8								×

APPENDIX II

TABLE X

TEAM STANDINGS OF THE AMERICAN LEAGUE TEAMS FOR THE YEARS 1917–1962

Teams	1	2	3	4	5	6	7	8
1	4	2	1	1	0	1	1	
2	3	1	4	0	1	1	0	0
3	0	2	1	5	1	1	0	0
4	1	1	1	0	2	4	1	0
5	0	1	0	0	4	2	2	1
6	2	1	1	2	0	1	3	0
7	0	2	2	2	1	0	1	2
8	0	0	0	0	1	0	2	7

TABLE XI

TEAM STANDINGS OF THE NATIONAL LEAGUE TEAMS FOR THE YEARS 1917–1926

Teams	1	2	3	4	5	6	7	8
1	3	1	3	1	2	0	0	0
2	3	3	1	1	0	2	0	0
3	3	0	2	3	1	1	0	0
4	0	2	0	3	1	1	1	2
5	1	2	2	1	1	0	2	1
6	0	2	1	0	2	3	2	0
7	0	0	0	0	2	2	2	4
8	0	0	1	1	1	1	3	3

TABLE XII

TEAM STANDINGS OF THE AMERICAN LEAGUE TEAMS FOR THE YEARS 1927–1936

Teams	1	2	3	4	5	6	7	8
1	5	3	1	0	1	0	0	0
2	4	4	1	0	1	0	0	0
3	0	3	3	1	1	0	2	0
4	0	0	3	4	1	1	1	0
5	0	0	2	1	2	3	1	1
6	0	0	0	4	1	1	2	2
7	1	0	0	0	0	2	2	3
8	0	0	0	0	1	3	2	4

TABLE XIII

TEAM STANDINGS OF THE NATIONAL LEAGUE TEAMS FOR THE YEARS 1927–1936

Teams	1	2	3	4	5	6	7	8
1	2	1	4	1	1	0	1	0
2	3	2	3	1	1	0	0	0
3	2	3	2	3	0	0	0	0
4	2	1	0	3	2	2	0	0
5	0	2	0	0	2	4	1	1
6	1	0	1	0	0	3	1	4
7	0	1	0	1	2	1	4	1
8	0	0	0	1	2	0	3	4

TABLE XIV

TEAM STANDINGS OF THE AMERICAN LEAGUE TEAMS FOR THE YEARS 1937–1946

Teams	1	2	3	4	5	6	7	8
1	4	1	2	0	1	1	1	0
2	1	3	1	0	3	0	1	1
3	4	0	1	4	0	1	0	0
4	1	2	1	1	1	3	1	0
5	0	2	1	2	2	2	0	1
6	0	0	3	0	3	1	1	2
7	0	1	1	3	0	1	2	2
8	0	1	0	0	0	1	4	4

TABLE XV

TEAM STANDINGS OF THE NATIONAL LEAGUE TEAMS FOR THE YEARS 1937–1946

Teams	1	2	3	4	5	6	7	8
1	3	5	0	2	0	0	0	0
2	3	0	4	2	0	1	0	0
3	3	3	0	1	1	0	2	0
4	1	1	1	1	2	2	0	2
5	0	0	1	2	2	3	0	2
6	0	1	1	1	2	3	2	0
7	0	0	2	1	2	1	3	1
8	0	0	1	0	1	0	3	5

TABLE XVI

TEAM STANDINGS OF THE AMERICAN LEAGUE TEAMS FOR THE YEARS 1947–1956

Teams	1	2	3	4	5	6	7	8
1	6	2	1	1	0	0	0	0
2	2	4	2	2	0	0	0	0
3	2	1	5	2	0	0	0	0
4	0	0	1	3	3	3	0	0
5	0	2	0	1	3	2	1	1
6	0	1	1	0	1	1	1	5
7	0	0	0	1	1	1	3	4
8	0	0	0	0	2	3	5	0

TABLE XVII

TEAM STANDINGS OF THE NATIONAL LEAGUE TEAMS FOR THE YEARS 1947–1956

Teams	1	2	3	4	5	6	7	8
1	2	3	4	0	1	0	0	0
2	3	4	1	1	0	0	1	0
3	3	1	1	1	3	1	0	0
4	1	0	3	3	1	0	1	1
5	1	2	0	2	3	1	0	1
6	0	0	1	2	0	4	3	0
7	0	0	0	1	2	1	3	3
8	0	0	0	0	0	3	2	5

APPENDIX III

TABLE XVIII

TEAM STANDINGS OF THE AMERICAN LEAGUE TEAMS FOR THE YEARS
1927–1936 AND 1937–1946

Teams	1	2	3	4	5	6	7	8
1	9	4	3	0	2	1	1	0
2	5	7	2	0	4	0	1	1
3	4	3	4	5	1	1	2	0
4	1	2	4	5	2	4	2	0
5	0	2	3	3	4	5	1	2
6	0	0	3	4	4	2	3	4
7	1	1	1	3	2	3	4	5
8	0	1	0	0	1	4	6	8

TABLE XIX

TEAM STANDINGS OF THE NATIONAL LEAGUE TEAMS FOR THE YEARS
1927–1936 AND 1937–1946

Teams	1	2	3	4	5	6	7	8
1	3	6	4	3	1	0	1	0
2	6	2	7	3	1	1	0	0
3	5	6	2	4	1	0	2	0
4	3	2	1	4	4	4	0	2
5	0	2	1	2	4	7	1	3
6	1	1	2	1	2	6	3	4
7	0	1	2	2	4	3	7	2
8	0	0	1	1	3	0	6	9

TABLE XX

TEAM STANDINGS OF THE AMERICAN LEAGUE TEAMS FOR THE YEARS
1917–1926 AND 1947–1956

Teams	1	2	3	4	5	6	7	8
1	10	4	2	2	0	1	1	0
2	5	5	6	2	1	1	0	0
3	2	3	6	7	1	1	0	0
4	1	1	2	3	5	7	1	0
5	0	3	0	1	7	4	3	1
6	2	2	2	2	1	2	4	5
7	0	2	2	3	2	1	4	6
8	0	0	0	0	3	3	7	7

TABLE XXI

TEAM STANDINGS OF THE NATIONAL LEAGUE TEAMS FOR THE YEARS
1917–1926 AND 1947–1956

Teams	1	2	3	4	5	6	7	8
1	5	4	7	1	3	0	0	0
2	6	7	2	2	0	2	1	0
3	6	1	3	4	4	2	0	0
4	1	2	3	6	2	1	2	3
5	2	4	2	3	4	1	2	2
6	0	2	2	2	2	7	5	0
7	0	0	0	1	4	3	5	7
8	0	0	1	1	1	4	5	8

APPENDIX IV

TABLE XXII

TEAM STANDINGS OF THE AMERICAN LEAGUE TEAMS FOR THE YEARS 1917–1956

Teams	1	2	3	4	5	6	7	8
1	19	8	5	2	2	2	2	0
2	10	12	8	2	5	1	1	1
3	6	6	12	12	2	2	2	0
4	2	3	6	8	7	11	3	0
5	0	5	3	4	11	9	4	4
6	2	2	5	6	5	4	7	9
7	1	3	3	6	4	4	8	11
8	0	1	0	0	4	7	13	15

TABLE XXIII

TEAM STANDINGS OF THE NATIONAL LEAGUE TEAMS FOR THE YEARS 1917–1956

Teams	1	2	3	4	5	6	7	8
1	10	10	11	4	4	0	1	0
2	12	9	9	5	1	3	1	0
3	11	7	5	8	5	2	2	0
4	4	4	4	10	6	5	2	5
5	2	6	3	5	8	8	3	5
6	1	3	4	3	4	13	8	4
7	0	1	2	3	8	5	12	9
8	0	0	2	2	4	4	11	17

CHAPTER 16

Market Evaluation through Transition Probabilities

Several approaches have thus far been used in the study of market trends and market potential. Some of these approaches are more or less mathematical, while others could easily be described as "largely subjective." In either case the objective of market research is to detect, as accurately as possible, the wishes of the human population that constitutes the "market." In turn, this means finding out the feelings of the buyer, and, if the buyer is a stochastic element in himself, his feelings are twice as stochastic.

The most obvious reason why mathematical analysis of the micro-event that takes place in a market has proved to be less dependable than market analysts were hoping for can be found in the fact that the singular psychological effect escapes mathematical thinking. A model of behavior becomes even more probabilistic when one wishes to integrate into it social and economic aspects—an area in which we have had thus far very few successes but a substantial variety of failures. This fact alone calls for more research.

For this reason, in the present chapter we will advance the hypothesis that if the micro-event defies mathematical analysis, at the present state of the art at least, the macro-event may be more amenable to the analytical approach. In studying the market behavior of human populations, we will use analogies from the behavior of colonies of insects. Our mathematical tool will be the matrices of transition probabilities. It is understood that this is not an exact model but an attempt to examine how Markoff chains can be applied to the study of macro-events, to obtain general market tendencies and drives.

It is understood that much more research is necessary if we are going to obtain transitional media capable of being used in "far-out planning." The whole field is yet in its infancy. Furthermore, the approach discussed in this chapter should not be considered an exclusive one. In Chapter 11 we have paid due consideration to mathematical studies oriented toward the discovery of rules that guide the structural behavior of a market.

Application of Markoff Chains in the Automotive Industry by Car Model

The information in Table I[1] indicates the relative position of the

TABLE I

COMPARATIVE POSITION OF AUTO MAKES BY YEAR, BASED ON NUMBER OF CARS SOLD

	1947	1948	49	50	51	52	53	54	55	56
1	Chev	Chev	Chev	Chev	Chev	Chev	Chev	Chev	Chev	Chev
2	Ford	Ford	Ford	Ford	Ford	Ford	Ford	Ford	Ford	Ford
3	Plym	Plym	Plym	Plym	Plym	Plym	Plym	Buick	Buick	Buick
4	Buick	Buick	Buick	Buick	Buick	Buick	Buick	Olds	Plym	Plym
5	Dodge	Pont	Pont	Pont	Pont	Pont	Pont	Plym	Olds	Olds
6	Pont	Dodge	Dodge	Olds	Dodge	Dodge	Olds	Pont	Pont	Pont
7	Olds	Olds	Olds	Merc	Olds	Olds	Merc	Merc	Merc	Merc
8	Merc	Stud	Stud	Dodge	Merc	Merc	Dodge	Dodge	Dodge	Dodge
9	Nash	Merc	Merc	Stud	Stud	Stud	Stud	Cad	Chrys	Cad
10	Stud	Hudson	Hudson	Nash	Chrys	Nash	Chrys	Chrys	Cad	DeSoto

various American automobiles, based on the number of cars sold each year. From these data we try to project on changes in position which may occur.

We start by analyzing this information to obtain a group of trajectories showing the transitions that take place from "relative position" to "relative position" in the automobile market. The trajectories are as in Table II, where the given numbers refer to the relative position.

TABLE II

Chevrolet	1	1	1	1	1	1	1	1	1	1
Ford	2	2	2	2	2	2	2	2	2	2
Plymouth	3	3	3	3	3	3	3	5	4	4
Buick	4	4	4	4	4	4	4	3	3	3
Dodge	5	6	6	8	6	6	8	8	8	8
Pontiac	6	5	5	5	5	5	5	6	6	6
Oldsmobile	7	7	7	6	7	7	6	4	5	5
Mercury	8	9	9	7	8	8	7	7	7	7
Nash	9	>10	>10	10	>10	10	>10	>10	>10	>10
Studebaker	10	8	8	9	9	9	9	>10	>10	>10
Hudson	>10	10	10	>10	>10	>10	>10	>10	>10	>10
Cadillac	>10	>10	>10	>10	>10	>10	>10	>9	10	9
Chrysler	>10	>10	>10	>10	>10	>10	10	10	9	>10
De Soto	>10	>10	>10	>10	>10	>10	>10	>10	>10	10

[1] From Ward's 1957 Automotive Yearbook.

A trajectory is easily obtained for each car under consideration simply by assigning a numerical value to its relative position, as for instance 1 for first, 2 for second, ... and > 10 for a car which ceases to appear in the table of the first ten places. Then, by counting the frequency of each individual change, for instance from 6 to 5, the probability of occurrence of that change can be established. These probabilities would then need to be assembled into a matrix, and, if the probabilities found for each transition are unchanged over long periods of time, the matrix may be considered to define a Markoff chain. From this matrix, we can determine the tendencies of the system.

The broad conclusions which can be derived from the relative positions in Table II are as follows: The cars on top of the matrix will stay on top, the cars on the bottom have a good chance of dropping off the list, and the cars in the middle will continue to interchange positions.

Based on these data, we will use a matrix of transition probabilities in studying the change in status effective within the "make-market" system, and will attempt to forecast its future status. However, it should be noted that this effort is based on the assumption that the data of Table II lead to a Markoff chain. In certain cases, the validity of this assumption may be questionable.

Conclusions drawn from such studies must be accepted within the limitations of explicitly stated considerations.

Markoff Chains by Car Manufacturer

Knowing from historical information the relative gains and losses for each of the major automobile manufacturing companies, it was possible to compute for every year the choice of the automobile-buying population among alternative makes. This population will hereafter be referred to as the "market."

For an example on how the data were treated we consider the year 1954. During that year, the following manufacturers showed an increase in the market:

(1) Ford Motor Company (5.68 %),

(2) General Motors (5.63 %),

(3) Overseas makes (0.09 %).[2]

Manufacturers showing a decrease during this same year, 1954, were Chrysler Motors Company (7.41 %) and all other American makes

---

[2] Taken in the commulative.

(3.99 %).[3] For manufacturers who showed a gain in the market, the portion of the total gain that each controlled can be expressed as a ratio:

$$\text{Ford Motors,} \quad \frac{5.68}{11.40} \ ;$$

$$\text{General Motors,} \quad \frac{5.63}{11.40} \ ;$$

$$\text{Overseas makes,} \quad \frac{0.09}{11.40} \ .$$

Hence, the portion of the market which Chrysler surrendered to each of the manufacturers "in the increase" is equal to

$$\text{Ford Motors,} \quad \frac{5.68}{11.40} \times 3.99\% = 1.99\% \ ;$$

$$\text{General Motors,} \quad \frac{5.63}{11.40} \times 3.99\% = 1.97\% \ ;$$

$$\text{Overseas makes,} \quad \frac{0.09}{11.40} \times 3.99\% = 0.03\% \ .$$

Similar calculations can be made for the remaining years under consideration, and such data can be tabulated as tables which show the transitions of the market percentages from one year to the next. Table III presents historical information on new passenger car registration

TABLE III

NEW PASSENGER CAR REGISTRATION BY THE MAJOR AUTO PRODUCERS, YEARS 1951–1957

Auto	Number of units						
manufacturer	1951	1952	1953	1954	1955	1956	1957
Chrysler Motors	1 103 330	884 667	1 165 357	713 347	1 206 195	922 043	1 096 359
Ford Motors	1 121 464	947 474	1 443 153	1 706 617	1 980 736	1 694 108	1 818 169
General Motors	2 167 713	1 735 694	2 586 697	2 006 595	3 639 120	3 024 286	2 683 365
All other U.S. models	646 758	561 260	514 821	282 520	292 199	223 769	177 622
Foreign models	20 828	29 299	28 961	25 385	51 658	91 042	206 827
Totals	5 060 093	4 158 394	5 738 989	5 535 464	7 169 908	5 955 248	5 982 342

[3] Also lumped together into one classification.

for years 1951 to 1957; Table IV gives the same information in percent of total new car registration; and Table V presents the percentage of gain or loss of new car registration for the major automobile manufacturers. The latter are based on the percentages in Table IV, taking 1951 as the starting year.

TABLE IV

Same Information as in Table III, Expressed in % of Total New Car Registrations

Auto	% of the total						
manufacturer	1951	1952	1953	1954	1955	1956	1957
Chrysler Motors	21.80	21.27	20.31	12.90	16.82	15.84	18.34
Ford Motors	22.16	22.78	25.15	30.83	27.63	28.45	30.39
General Motors	42.83	41.74	45.07	50.70	50.75	50.78	44.85
All other U.S. models	12.00	13.51	8.97	4.98	3.98	3.64	2.96
Foreign models	0.41	0.70	0.50	0.59	0.82	1.65	3.46
Totals	100.00	100.00	100.00	100.00	100.00	100.00	100.00

TABLE V

Percent of Gain or Loss of the New Car Registrations for Major Automobile Manufacturers (Based on Percentages in Table II with 1951 as the Starting Year)

Auto	Percent gain or loss with respect to preceding year						
manufacturer	1951	1952	1953	1954	1955	1956	1957
Chrysler Motors	0	—0.53	—0.96	—7.41	3.92	—1.34	2.86
Ford Motors	0	0.62	2.37	5.68	—3.20	0.82	1.94
General Motors	0	—1.09	3.33	5.63	0.05	0.03	—5.93
All other U.S. models	0	0.71	—4.54	—3.99	—1.00	—0.34	—0.68
Foreign models	0	0.29	—0.20	0.09	0.23	0.83	1.81
Total increase	0	1.62	5.70	11.40	4.20	1.68	6.61

Tables VI through XI offer information on the market transition for the major automobile manufacturers, expressed in percentage of the total market, on a year-to-year basis. In Table VI the market transition is from 1951 to 1952, in Table VII from 1952 to 1953, and so on to Table XI whose data correspond to the market transition from 1956 to 1957.

TABLE VI

MARKET TRANSITIONS (EXPRESSED IN PERCENTAGE OF TOTAL MARKET) FROM 1951 TO 1952[a]

	C	F	G	A	O	1952 Totals
C	21.27	0.00	0.00	0.00	0.00	21.27
F	0.20	22.16	0.42	0.00	0.00	22.78
G	0.00	0.00	41.75	0.00	0.00	41.74
A	0.24	0.00	0.47	12.00	0.00	13.51
O	0.09	0:00	0.20	0.00	0.41	0.41
1951 Totals	21.80	22.16	42.83	12.80	0.41	100.00%

[a] Key to symbols in this and following tables: C, Chrysler Motors; F, Ford Motors; G, General Motors; A, all other American makes; O, Overseas (foreign) makes.

TABLE VII

MARKET TRANSITIONS FROM 1952 TO 1953

	C	F	G	A	O	1953 Totals
C	20.31	0.00	0.00	0.00	0.00	20.31
F	0.40	22.78	0.00	1.89	0.08	25.15
G	0.56	0.00	41.74	2.65	0.12	45.07
A	0.00	0.00	0.00	8.97	0.00	8.97
O	0.00	0.00	0.00	0.00	0.50	0.50
1952 Totals	21.27	22.78	41.74	13.51	0.70	100.00%

TABLE VIII

MARKET TRANSITIONS FROM 1953 TO 1954

	C	F	G	A	O	1954 Totals
C	12.90	0.00	0.00	0.00	0	12.90
F	3.69	25.15	0.00	1.99	0	30.83
G	3.66	0.00	45.07	1.97	0	50.70
A	0.00	0.00	0.00	4.98	0	4.98
O	0.06	0.00	0.00	0.03	0.50	0.59
1953 Totals	20.31	25.15	45.07	8.97	0.50	100.00%

TABLE IX

MARKET TRANSITIONS FROM 1954 TO 1955

	C	F	G	A	O	1955 Totals
C	12.90	2.99	0.00	0.93	0.00	16.82
F	0.00	27.63	0.00	0.00	0.00	27.63
G	0.00	0.04	50.70	0.01	0.00	50.75
A	0.00	0.00	0.00	3.98	0.00	3.98
O	0.00	0.17	0.00	0.06	0.59	0.82
1954 Totals	12:90	30.83	50.70	4.98	0.59	100.00%

TABLE X

MARKET TRANSITIONS FROM 1955 TO 1956

	C	F	G	A	O	1956 Totals
C	15.48	0.00	0.00	0.00	0.00	15.48
F	0.66	27.63	0.00	0.16	0.00	28.45
G	0.02	0.00	50.75	0.01	0.00	50.78
A	0.00	0.00	0.00	3.64	0.00	3.64
O	0.66	0.00	0.00	0.17	0.82	1.65
1955 Totals	16.82	27.63	50.75	3.98	0.82	100.00%

TABLE XI

MARKET TRANSITIONS FROM 1956 TO 1957

	C	F	G	A	O	1957 Totals
C	15.48	0.00	2.57	0.29	0.00	18.33
F	0.00	28.45	1.74	0.20	0.00	30.39
G	0.00	0.00	44.85	0.00	0.00	44.85
A	0.00	0.00	0.00	2.96	0.00	2.96
O	0.00	0.00	1.62	0.19	1.65	3.47
1956 Totals	15.48	28.45	50.78	3.64	1.65	100.00%

On the hypothesis that the available sample of six years was representative enough of the corresponding population of transition, the experimenters tested various approaches to the continuation of the work. One of the approaches involved the use of the mode or the median as the "representative" value for a transition cell. Having obtained unsatisfactory results they tested certain other "values" derived from the available data. They finally decided to experiment with the sum-total of the transition values for the same cell. By summing up the corresponding values in Tables VI through XI, the data in Table XII were obtained.

TABLE XII

SUMMATION OF TABLES VI TO XI

	C	F	G	A	O
C	98.34	2.98	2.56	1.22	0.00
F	4.95	153.80	2.16	4.23	0.08
G	4.24	0.04	284.89	2.68	0.12
A	0.23	0.00	0.48	34.33	0.00
O	0.81	0.18	1.83	0.45	4.47
Totals	108.57	157.00	291.92	42.91	4.67

If we let Table XII represent the transition from the "present year" T to the next year $T + 1$, the summation of each of the columns gives a number representing the portion of the market that one automobile manufacturer had in relation to his four competitors. Taking year T as the reference for future years, $T + 1, T + 2, \cdots, T + n$, the columns of the Table in question can be expressed in a percent form. The transformated matrix is given in Table XIII.

TABLE XIII

TRANSFORMATION MATRIX FROM YEAR T TO YEAR $T + 1$

	C	F	G	A	O
C	0.905	0.019	0.009	0.028	0.000
F	0.046	0.980	0.007	0.099	0.017
G	0.039	0.000	0.976	0.062	0.026
A	0.002	0.000	0.002	0.801	0.000
O	0.008	0.001	0.006	0.010	0.957
Totals	1.000	1.000	1.000	1.000	1.000

The data in Table XIII can also be represented in a graphical form, as in Fig. 1. Arrows indicate the direction of the change, and the corresponding percentages are duly noted.

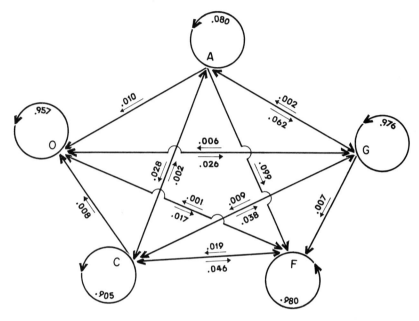

FIG. 1

Assuming that the information presented in Table XIII corresponds to a state of equilibrium,[4] from these same data we can derive a set of transition equations. For instance, let C', F', G', A', and O' represent the components of a vector resulting from the previous state (C, F, G, A, O). The equations derived from the information in the transition matrix, expressing the relation between the components of the two vector states, would be as follows:

$$C' = 0.905C + 0.019F + 0.009G + 0.028A,$$
$$F' = 0.046C + 0.980F + 0.007G + 0.099A + 0.017O,$$
$$G' = 0.039C + 0.976G + 0.062A + 0.026O,$$
$$A' = 0.002C + 0.002G + 0.801A,$$
$$O' = 0.008C + 0.001F + 0.006G + 0.010A + 0.957O;$$

or the resultant vector X_1 is derived by multiplying the transition matrix $[M]$ by the vector X, which is the state C, F, G, A, O of the system.

---

[4] A supposition.

If X_n represents the vector after n transformations, this could be expressed as $X_n = [M]X_{n-1}$.

Based on the same suppostion, the experimenters derived simulated data regarding the percent share of the market for the competing automobile manufacturers. They then compared this information against the available historical data. The results of the comparison are presented in Figs. 2 through 6. Three simulated data curves are plotted in each

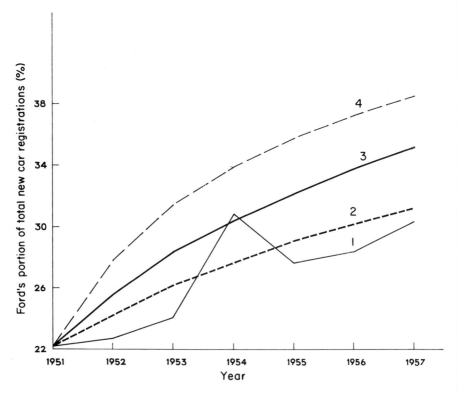

FIG. 2.   New Ford Motors cars registered in U.S. during years 1951–1957. Curve 1 is based on actual data, curve 2 on simulated data for 1-year cycles, curve 3 on simulated data for 2-year cycles, and curve 4 on simulated data for 3-year cycles.

figure. Each corresponds to a different cycling procedure. Namely, the hypothesis was made that if other things are kept equal and the cycle of transition is varied the resulting simulated curve may approximate more closely the historical data, which in every case are represented by curve 1.

Three alternative cycles have been considered, corresponding to curves 2, 3, and 4. Curve 2 is based on simulated data for a one-year cycle. For this curve the matrix of transition probabilities given in Table XIV was used. Curve 3 corresponds to simulated data for a two-year cycle, while curve 4 reflects the outcome of a simulation involving a three-year cycle. This reference to curves 1, 2, 3, and 4 is

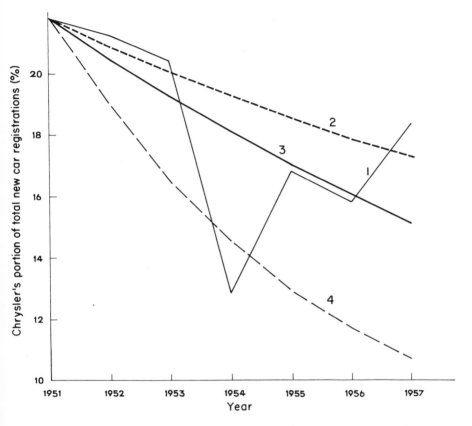

FIG. 3.   New Chrysler Motors cars registered in U.S. during years 1951–1957. Curve 1 is based on actual data, curve 2 on simulated data for 1-year cycles, curve 3 on simulated data for 2-year cycles, and curve 4 on simulated data for 3-year cycles.

valid for all figures under consideration. The rationale for the two-year and three-year cycle hypotheses was that the American market is getting into the habit of changing the low-priced cars on a two-to-three years basis.

The resulting graphical plot of the simulated data indicates that the year-to-year basis is the closest one to the actual. In Fig. 2 (Ford Motor

Company), curve 2 indicates with considerable accuracy the trend of the company with respect to percent share of the market. Curve 3 gives, generally, an overestimate and only once matches the actual data, while Ford cars sales were pick. Finally, curve 4 grossly overestimates market trends.

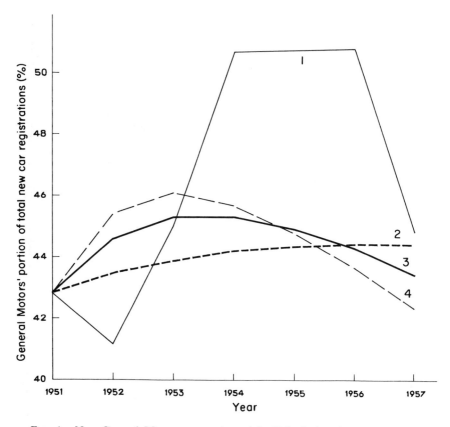

FIG. 4.   New General Motors cars registered in U.S. during the years 1951–1957. Curve 1 is based on actual data, curve 2 on simulated data for 1-year cycles, curve 3 on simulated data for 2-year cycles, and curve 4 on simulated data for 3-year cycles.

In the case of Chrysler Motors, curve 3 presents the best approximation of the trend in the company's percent share of the market. The approach represented by curve 2 seems to be "optimistic," while that of curve 4 deviates considerably from the actual data. Comparing the results for Ford and Chrysler of approach 4, we see that in both cases this three-year cycling has a tendency to go to extremes; when the percent share of the market is ascending it overestimates the gains, when it is descending it overestimates the losses. It should be noticed, however, that, as considered here, the approach of curve 4 is based on a smaller sample than either that of curve 2 or 3.

In the case of the General Motors, all three approaches failed to

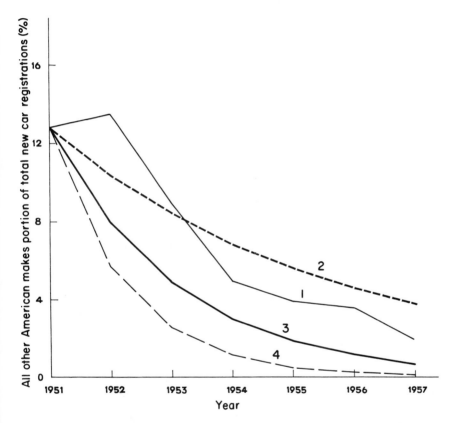

FIG. 5. All other new American-made cars registered in the U.S. during the years 1951–1957 (all those not produced by Ford, Chrysler, or General Motors). Curve 1 is based on actual data, curve 2 on simulated data for 1-year cycles, curve 3 on simulated data for 2-year cycles, and curve 4 on simulated data for 3-year cycles.

reflect the large increase in the company's share of the market for the years 1954, 1955, and 1956. Curve 2 still indicates the trend in percent share over the whole six-year span without the above-mentioned gains, while curves 3 and 4 present an off-phase increase in share, and they both are sensitive in the corresponding decrease during 1957.

Figure 5 presents actual and simulated data for the other American makes. While all three simulated curves reflect the trend in the market, curve 2 is the closest to the real data. With the overseas makes, as seen in Fig. 6, curve 2 gives the closest approximation. On the basis of the foregoing, it can reasonably be concluded that Markoff chains may eventually present good planning possibilities, but more research is necessary, both to establish its areas of best potential and to develop the sensitivity of the method.

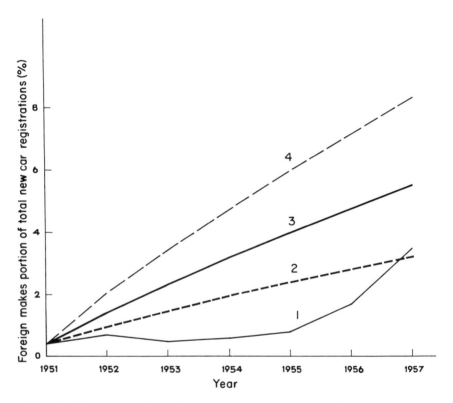

FIG. 6. New overseas (foreign) made cars registered in the U.S. during the years 1951–1957. Curve 1 is based on actual data, curve 2 on simulated data for 1-year cycles, curve 3 on simulated data for 2-year cycles, and curve 4 on simulated data for 3-year cycles.

A Used-Car Model

For another application of Markoff chains, an evaluation was made of the changes of automobile makes that take place when used cars are traded in for new cars. The obtained information is mostly from estimates made by car dealers in the Washington, D. C. area.

TABLE XIV

Car Trade-In Percentages

New car buy	Car traded in			
	Chevrolet	Ford	Plymouth	Others
Chevrolet	0.85	0.09	0.03	0.10
Ford	0.06	0.82	0.03	0.10
Plymouth	0.04	0.05	0.90	0.10
Others	0.05	0.04	0.04	0.70

The information in question is presented in Table XIV in the form of a matrix of transition probabilities. If we assume that 100 cars of each make: Chevrolet, Ford, Plymouth, and Others (lumped together) are traded in each year, the distribution of cars at the end of each year would be as shown in Table XV.

The results indicate that if the trade-in percentages do not change, and if the impact of first-time buyers is ignored, Chevrolet will have greatly improved its position, and the Other makes will have very reduced sales. These calculations are made on the basis of suppositions advanced by car dealers and reflect their way of thinking and of projecting into the future of their trade. The model was developed as a minor research project in 1957, and, since then, market evolution has generally tended to support the obtained results.

TABLE XV

Distribution of Cars after 1 to 15 Years

Years	Chevrolet	Ford	Plymouth	Others
0	100	100	100	100
1	107	101	109	83
2	111	101	115	73
3	113	100	120	67
4	115	100	123	62
5	117	99	125	59
6	118	98	128	56
7	119	97	130	54
8	119	95	133	53
9	118	95	135	52
10	117	94	137	52
11	116	93	138	53
12	115	92	139	54
13	114	91	140	55
14	114	91	140	55
15	114	91	140	55

Studying the Impact of the ABC Car on the American Economy

Over a number of years, considerable discussion has taken place in the United States on the rationale of the yearly change in model by all major American car manufacturers. The manufacturers have strongly maintained that the yearly change in model is the lifeblood of the growth in the automobile industry, and, therefore, both in the long and in the short run it is to the benefit of the nation.

To document their reports, car manufacturers have insisted that without the yearly change in design the automobile market would limit itself to the replacement of scrapped cars, or below the four-million-unit mark. In contrast, automobile sales for the last eight years varied in the range of five to seven and a half million units due to the artificial obsolescence or, in different terms, to the yearly change in model. On the other side of the fence, some economists argue that these yearly model changes with the corresponding retooling etc. are a kind of waste and that the American economy can do as well without them.

To test the validity of these arguments, we will assume that a "new" automobile company would design, produce, and market the American Basic Car, hereafter referred to as ABC, with a guaranteed no-change in model for a period of twelve years.[5] The engineering dependability of the car is also set at the same twelve-year level. By this token, a buyer of the ABC would have no inducement, either because of an artificial or real obsolescence, to trade in this car before the 12-year period is over. The objective is to study the effect of this policy on the American market.

Say that the ABC car is built in the size range of the Chevrolet-Ford-Plymouth lines with an economy engine. Say also, that because of its novelty the first year of being introduced into the market it captures somewhat over 54 % of the total car sales, dropping thereafter to 50 %. By the same token, a certain car market of (say) 5 500 000 cars would go up to 6 000 000 due to ABC's advent. Finally, it is assumed that the "other" cars are traded in every three years, as they used to up to now and that, in every trade-in model, ABC takes the 50 % of the buyers.

Some of the quantitative aspects of these assumptions may be regarded as unrealistic, yet the impact the compact cars had in the year of their introduction could help document that this is not so bad an estimate.

---

[5] To ease the questions which will automatically arise in regard to a marketing and servicing network, it is acceptable to assume that ABC represents the "Basic Cars" of all established manufacturers lumped together. The same twelve-year policy is assumed to prevail.

A second tentative statement must also be made. It concerns a static car market. With it, the result will be a major upheaval in the American economy. The upheaval would be reflected in the substantial shrinkage of the labor demand, a decline in the metals and other materials industries, a substantial reduction in numbers of dealers, advertisers, and auto service companies, and a decline in auto-parts manufacturing concerns. These changes would have an adverse affect on the purchasing power of the American public with an accompanying drastic shrinkage in all phases of the economy.

We will assume that the "present" market is divided as follows:

Northern Company	32%
Western Company	29%
Eastern Company	25%
Independents	14%

The owners of Big Three's cars, in 85 % of all cases, trade for the same car. The remaining 15 % go about even to the two other makes or to the independents. Owners of independent products stick, about 91 %, with their makes; the remaining 9 % distribute themselves about evenly among the big three makes. From these data, the following matrix of annual transformation can be developed:

	Northern (N)	Western (W)	Eastern (E)	Indep. (D)
Northern	0.85N	0.05W	0.05E	0.03D
Western	0.05N	0.85W	0.05E	0.03D
Eastern	0.05N	0.05W	0.85E	0.03D
Indep.	0.05N	0.05W	0.05E	0.91D

In the year "zero" based on the given percentages of the market,

Northern manufactures	1 760 000 Cars
Western manufactures	1 595 000 Cars
Eastern manufactures	1 375 000 Cars
Independents manufacturers	770 000 Cars
Total	5 500 000 Cars

In the ensuing years the market changes as follows:

	Year 1	Year 2
Northern	1 667 600	1 588 100
Western	1 535 000	1 484 700
Eastern	1 399 000	1 346 100
Indep.	937 200	1 081 100
	5 500 000	5 500 000

The big three are losing ground because of the hypothesis made that they command a lower customer loyalty than the independents.

Now say that into this market, at year "one," the new car is introduced by the ABC Company. This car guarantees the stated twelve-year life and no model change during the same period. We made reference to a market of 6 000 000 units the first year and some 54 % of the share would be gained by the ABC car the first year. For the subsequent years the matrix of transformation is

	Northern	Western	Eastern	Indep.
Northern	0.425N	0.005W	0.025E	0.015D
Western	0.025N	0.425W	0.025E	0.015D
Eastern	0.025N	0.025W	0.425E	0.015D
Indep.	0.025N	0.025W	0.025E	0.455D
ABC	0.500N	0.500W	0.500E	0.500D

After the first year, the hypothetical American market will continue for two more years as shown in the matrix for the pre-ABC period.

TABLE XVI

DISTRIBUTION OF CARS AT THE END OF EACH . YEAR

Company	Year			
	1	2	3	4
Northern	833 800	794 050	761 500	368 500
Western	767 800	742 350	720 000	350 300
Eastern	679 800	673 060	665 500	327 800
Indep.	468 600	540 550	620 000	328 400
ABC	3 250 000	2 750 000	2 750 000	1 375 000
Total	6 000 000	5 500 000	5 500 000	2 750 000
	5	6	7	8
Northern	357 000	347 300	169 600	166 200
Western	342 400	335 600	164 900	162 400
Eastern	324 400	321 300	159 200	157 900
Indep.	351 200	370 800	193 800	201 000
ABC	1 375 000	1 375 000	687 500	687 500
Total	2 750 000	2 750 000	1 375 000	1 375 000
	9	10	11	12
Northern	163 300	80 400	79 350	78 700
Western	160 300	79 200	78 450	77 700
Eastern	156 700	77 800	77 200	76 700
Indep.	207 200	106 300	108 750	110 750
ABC	687 500	343 750	343 750	343 750
Total	1 375 000	687 500	687 500	687 500

In the fourth year, however, the ABC owners will not trade their cars as they consider them good, engineering and designwise, for 12 years. This behavior will repeat itself to the twelfth year.

The effect of the super-durable car can be seen in Table XVI. The "old line" companies, which before the advent of the ABC had manufactured 5 500 000 cars per year, twelve years later are down to 343 750 cars. The ABC Company, while always maintaining at least 50 % of the market, drops from 3 250 000 cars in year "one" to 343 750 cars in the 12th year. The result, therefore, of this super-durable inovation would be a virtual collapse of the industry. Though this is just a hypothesis and the chosen percentages, such as 50%, might be considered as an exaggeration, it is nevertheless true that the same result would have been obtained with small, "more reasonable" percentages, the magnitude of this outcome becoming essentially a matter of time.

CHAPTER 17

Experimentation for the Military

The military has used to advantage computer processed mathematical models in simulating combat conditions. Although the idea of war gaming is not new, the processing of mathematical models through high speed electronic equipment for reasons of studying military warfare is one of the latest in the field. This is essentially a matter of competitive advantages presented by mathematical war gaming.

War gaming, which has been used in the military since the 19th century on a ground floor basis, can be vastly improved by simulation, using a computer-processed mathematical model. This in turn can be used to advantage in an advance evaluation of military equipment, tactics, and even strategy.

Large scale organizations have been developed in the United States for study and analysis of military problems, with the RAND Corporation as the pioneer. Other countries have been relatively slow in catching up with such "factories of gray matter." The German government, for instance, instituted in the early sixties a research center near Munich and called on an American aircraft manufacturer for its organization. The Japanese government is on the lookout for a similar operation, and in late 1962 the writer collaborated with the Finish Military Forces in a training program to that same end.

The synthesis of technological advances with the changing concepts and requirements of warfare has become far more complex and far more important than in the past. Twenty or thirty years ago it was handled by military officers on a judgement basis. In the years to come such decisions will no longer depend on the rule of thumb. The financial savings which may result through the usage of mathematical experimentation left aside, simulation is still the best tool for the reduction of time lags; decisions on weapons systems and equipment design made in 1964 will determine the characteristics of equipment in use in 1972 and later. Long-term evolution is another important factor in military simulation. In the age of atomic weapons, missiles, satellites, and other great technological developments, reasoning based on marginal improvement over existing facilities is no longer valid.

Simulating an Engagement of Tank Forces

Mathematical models can be constructed to simulate tactical situations which may arise in various types of military engagements. Such models might be studied by statistical methods based on estimated results over a large number of games; games played according to fixed rules but with random selection of individual moves. "Stupid" and "brilliant" moves can be simulated and plans and equipment can be tested in a reasonably efficient manner.

As a very simple example of simulation for the military, consider an engagement between two tank forces in a partially wooded flat country. Say that the battlefield is represented by a lattice of hexagonal fields which are selected so because they correspond to a higher degree of isotropy than the square lattice, as for instance that of a chessboard. Further, consider that a certain fraction of hexagons is tagged to represent the wooded areas, whereas other hexagons correspond to the open fields. The tagged hexagons can be clustered into groups representing wooded areas of different dimensions. The pattern may or may not be symetrical. In fact, it needs to be symetrical only in the case that no advantages are to be given to either tank force because of the specific terrain structure it occupies.

To proceed with a simulated battle, say that the two opposing tank forces, twenty units each, are orginally located at the rear lines of the battlefield, and "a move" on each side consists in displacement of each of the tanks to one of the adjoining hexagonal fields. Unlike the chess pattern, more than one element (tank) can move at a time, although not all tanks must necessarily be moved at each time.

Two opposing tanks coming to adjoining fields which are not in a wooded area engage in a "battle." Its outcome can be decided by a certain rule, as for example, by tossing a coin or throwing a die. When two possible outcomes exist, we determine which one by tossing a coin. For six possible outcomes, a die is used. Nevertheless, some complications may result, which neither rule could handle. An example is the case when a moving tank comes in contact with two enemy tanks simultaneously. Special rules can be provided for this and other particular cases, as, for instance, specifying that the single tank must engage in battle first with one of its opponent tanks and, if victorious, with the other. Or allowing an immediate battle with all three tanks but with a loaded outcome for those who are in plurality.

Rules should also cover particularities concerning the terrain and its structure. If a tank in a nonwooded area is in contact with an enemy tank in a wooded field, who has the competitive advantages? The tank in the wooded area might be considered as concealed, hence the first tank should be given a higher probability of being killed in the die-tossing process. If both tanks are next to each other in the woods, a battle could be announced only if some specific rule calls for it, for instance, the tanks remaining next to each other for at least two plays.

The objectives of the game may vary according to the subject under study. One such objective could be the destruction of a maximum number of enemy tanks with least losses for oneself. The destruction of some post located at the rear line of enemy forces, occupation of certain enemy territory, or the annihilation of the enemy force are other alternative objectives. Unlike chess, this game requires that the two opponents play facing their own copy of the battlefield showing only the position of their own tanks, hence that each opponent is unaware of the relative location of the enemy forces, with the exception of those it can immediately inspect.

Based on these fundamentals, one could evaluate combat conditions, alternative tactics, various degrees of armor, etc. An interesting research on simulated warfare was undertaken[1] with the objective of evaluating speed and armor protection in tank combat. For the purpose of this study, a traditional army organization was assembled with tank, infantry, and mortar units, equipped with conventional arms. A set of mathematical equations simulated terrain structure and fight conditions. Information was assembled from test firings, historical records, and other sources in order to evaluate the multipliers of the model. Assembling data and programming the electronic computer required about two man-years. The simulated warfare was repeated 100 times, and this required about 30 hours of machine time.[2]

The study proved of particular interest in the development of certain rules used to command the behavior of each tank force. Some of these rules can be put under the cumulative name of "random playing." This can be effected, for instance, if each tank of both forces is given a certain trajectory, while leaving the particular instantaneous actions to be decided in accord with certain "weights." While in "intelligent" playing different strategies will be used by the players themselves, the strategy in a random play must be "inbuilt" into the rules of the random tank movement—where, of course, the word "random" should not be interpreted as meaning without any rational pattern in the background.

In these simulators, the strategy of dispersing the tanks all over the field may be introduced by bringing in "repulsive" forces between the

---

[1] By the Operators Research Office, Johns Hopkins University, for the account of the U.S. Army.

[2] For the type of computer which has been used in the subject study.

tanks of the same tank force. This requires a modification of the simple die-tossing technique to the extent that the tanks have a preferential probability of moving away from the center of gravity of other tanks of the same force. Within this established pattern their movements can be kept stochastic.

Among a sufficiently large sample of such games played under the same rules and the same initial condition, there existed a fair percentage of even exchange, but there are also games in which one or the other side achieved a decisive victory. A plot of the results, selecting as a characteristic the marginal number of enemy losses over ours, could produce a probability distribution curve as shown in Fig. 1. The curve

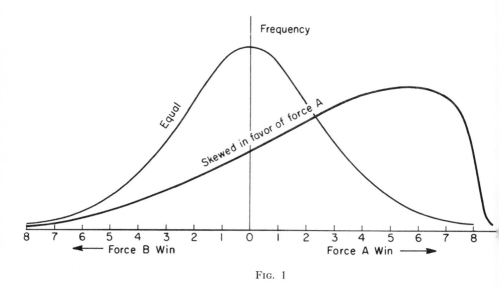

Fig. 1

will be symmetrical with respect to the center if both sides have exactly equal advantages and disadvantages, but in the case where one of the two sides has a competitive advantage over the other, the curve will become skew, and this skewness will be more pronounced the more pronounced is this competitive advantage. The skewness of the curve can be used as a criterion of success.

Say that the variable we wish to test is speed versus armor. We might change the parameters of the simulator so as to increase the speed of the tanks which belong to force A by e.g., twenty percent. This might be effected by giving them 12 moves per each 10 moves of the opposing forces. At the same time, we would decrease their armor by giving them, say, 40 against 60 chances in the battle. If the increase in speed exactly balances the increase in vulnerability, the resulting curve will remain symmetrical. If the advantages and disadvantages are not balanced up, the curve will become skewed, hence showing where the relative advantages lie.

In the same way, the experimenter can test out various strategies by giving, for example, a clustering tendency to one force and a dispersing tendency to the other. Assume that, after changing some crucial parameter of the system, we wish to study which of the two forces will have the greatest amount of remaining tanks after all the enemy force has been destroyed. A histogram plotted with data resulting from warfare can show whether or not the distributions of "killed tanks" approximate the normal, and whether they differ in respect to their central tendency and dispersion.

In this way a series of battle calculations for each tank design may be significant in identifying the superior tank design features under specified environmental and tactical conditions. Such "superiority" would be necessarily stated in terms of "battle result"; relative tank killing power can be used as indicating superiority. Other factors could be used equally well in its place. Variation in the criteria is no constraint since it has been established that the purpose of mathematical studies is not to formulate the criteria of superior performance but to provide the means for simulating battles so as to permit identification of superior performance once it has been defined.

Another interesting simulation study made on military warfare was that of a logistics system. Like other aspects of a large organization, the logistics system cannot be changed rapidly or frequently. In particular, in a military concern expanded over intercontinental distances, the logistics system is subject to special strains and to destruction by long-range weapons. This magnifies the need for advanced research. For the study under discussion, one of the U.S. Army's long lines of supply was examined in detail, particularly at the forward end. Actual data were collected on the location, size, and contents of all storage points, on the handling capacity and bottlenecks of transportation lines, and on the cost of operation. An evaluation was made concerning the probable wartime load and the likely damage from enemy attacks. The resulting losses were expressed in terms of reduced processing capacity and of net reduction in reserve stocks.

The mathematical model was processed many times to obtain significant results. These results gave an estimate of the weakest point in an actual logistics system and of the kinds of enemy attack that could be most successful. This led to a reevaluation and a redesign of the subject system.

Approaching the Model

We have made reference to the usefulness of a "battle simulator" in analyzing the effectiveness of new weapons, weapons systems, and tactical doctrines. With increasing numbers of new weapons (with radical or unproved capabilities) becoming available to all military forces, the problem of assessing their true worth becomes enormous. Tactical and organizational innovations which may appear desirable to fully exploit new weapons may cause unexpected chain reactions throughout the organization which could nullify the expected improvements. Also, as the tempo of battle steps up, the command-control-communication system becomes more critical than ever. As the weapons themselves become more complex the nature and degree of logistical support and training required acquire a crucial bearing on the selection of the best weapons systems. Finally, the potential violence of the initial stages of combat puts the most severe requirement on the thoroughness and accuracy of weapons tactical analysis.

Say that we wish to simulate a certain battle. A contour map may be marked to indicate the prebattle positions of two opposing armies. Suppose that one "general" directs one side and another directs the other through an imaginary combat. To organize the progress of this battle there could be established for the two men a set of rules, which we will examine as the discussion progresses.

This simulated combat action may involve any desired weapons, weapons systems, or other equipment; any specified tactical doctrines and mission; or any selected conditions of terrain, weather, and over-all situation. For computer processing, it is highly desirable that these factors be described in such a way that any variation of men, weapons, and terrain be merely a matter of changing certain parameters at the start of computation.

As with managerial and other problems one of the most difficult parameters to simulate in a military situation is that of human behavior. Human behavior against a set of rules necessarily brings into the picture a stochastic function. The outcome of a duel may not be specified as a certainty but as a weighted probability. To the extent that there are detailed tactical rules governing the progress of the battle, their effective modification will demonstrate their strength and weakness by counting their influence on the outcome of the battle.

Say that the rules of the game, taken together, specify the physical capabilities of the attacking force and the tactics it employs in the battle. Then comes the problem of establishing the form of the mathematical equations. Often, one of several alternative forms of an equation can be considered. It is then of advantage to select that form which is the least expensive in processing time.

In a certain mathematical simulator for military warfare, various approximations were considered in the interest of simplicity and saving of time. The exact calculation involved some multiplications. On the available (at that time) data processor, the delay for one multiplication was about 1.5 milliseconds, while a single addition (or subtraction) necessitated only 40 microseconds. Hence the researchers decided to reduce the number of multiplications required in the course of the experimentation. This is another way of saying that before setting up a simulator the researcher must deduce the limits imposed on the program by a computer's capacity for calculation. And, of course, much more important than the minimization of the computer processing time is the dependability of the results.

Apart from accuracy in the calculations, a factor which will also influence the dependability of the results is the "time scale" of the trial combat. This concerns the time which can be allowed for the computer to fight through a single battle. To a considerable extent, the time scale does not depend upon details of the methodology. It depends upon the way in which the methodology may be applied to the solution of military problems and upon the decision to use a very fine screen.

A most basic point to be made in developing an actual military simulator is that the model of a battle should refer directly to the individual participants in a combat action, at least so far as the major combat elements are concerned. If, for instance, we are concerned with a tank battle, it would be necessary to treat each tank individually; their movements, firing, and all other actions must be treated as individual and separate activities, they should not be averaged out over a platoon or other tactical unit.

This approach becomes necessary because the physical characteristics of weapons are usually best determined on an individual basis. Such characteristics are considered by many to be the most accurate information available. Furthermore, the proposed methodology will be more flexible the faster weapons and equipment are added, altered, or removed from the weapons systems. It is more convenient to evaluate a certain situation when the battle model includes the weapons and their characteristics explicitly than when weapons and equipment must be combined in some "average" way before insertion into the model of battle. Also, in a number of cases one of the primary purposes of constructing this new model is to render the interactions between weapons susceptible to calculation. Thus, to the extent that these interactions are "averaged out" prior to insertion into the model, they are not subject to analysis and part of the purpose of the methodology would remain uncovered.

When describing separate actions of an individual combat unit, probabilitistic notions are required. We have stated that, with a given round, a certain unit will either hit an enemy combat unit or it will fail to do so. The difference between various combat units in this regard can only be in the probability of a hit. The same is true if combat units are kept essentially the same and their tactics are varied. An experimental approach of this type may eventually lead to the discovery of new "regularities" in large military operations. There exist cases where the regularity of the existing laws of combat are clear enough to warrant the use of mathematical formulas; future analysis may well uncover even more extensive regularities in combat of a type which can be accurately described by convenient mathematical media.

Stochastic moves in a military situation, hence avoidance of using specific regularities, can be simulated through the Monte Carlo method. We have made reference to the use of the Monte Carlo method for the solution of certain complex systems of interest to the nuclear physicist. The command-control-communications decision process, necessarily included in a battle simulator, is a system which intimately involves human thought processes, whose reasoning appears to be best approximated through stochastic processes.

Some Additional Specifications

In the present section we are chiefly concerned with certain considerations relevant to firing conditions. The firing activity by an enemy combat unit should necessarily be represented by a systematic process. Such a process usually involves several steps, and each step needs to be specifically described for every combat unit on the battlefield. For instance, the first step may involve a tactical decision as to whether the particular combat unit was on a fire mission. This might be accomplished by a decision made in advance of the actual computations; it can be set that all combat units will fire, given a target, as soon it is physically possible to do so or this condition may be subject to certain constraints which would tend to reduce its occurrence.

The next step may involve those computations which list all potential enemy targets known at the time to the unit commander under consideration If it is so, then part of this step would necessarily involve the determination of which enemy units it is possible for the unit commander to see by reason of cover and concealment. Other factors involved might be treated in varying dregrees of completeness:

(i) Which enemy units have disclosed their position by fire or maneuver to any member of the opposing side?

(ii) What are the chances that all units of either side will share such knowledge through the ratio net?

(iii) Which enemy units have been actually noted by the unit commander?

(iv) Which enemy units are placing fire on the unit in question?

The next step would possibly concern selecting among the potential targets that one which has the highest priority. It obviously follows that a priority system has to be established by means of certain rules.

Some of the mechanics of a military simulator are relative to the particular battle being studied. For instance, a necessary step in a tank battle is that of establishing which gun has been reloaded and is laid on the target. Such calculation presumes that enough time has elapsed for the gun to have been reloaded and for minor adjustments of the gun's sighting before the tank was selected by the computer for processing. Nevertheless, if the selected target is a new one, then an additional time delay might be required while the gun is accurately laid on target.

To make the calculation realistic, a certain delay, for example 7 seconds, might be added onto the "firing clock" of the shooter. This would cause the machine to stop computations for this tank. When the tank is selected again for firing, it will then have its gun laid on target and will be able to fire immediately unless, in the meantime, the target has disappeared from sight, been killed, or if another target of higher priority has become known.

In every competitive situation the action of the opponent should be taken into serious consideration. The discussed course of the tank units would be unrealistic if we did not consider that the enemy would deploy elements able to effectively countermeasure the tank advance. A line of antitank guns may be set in a certain configuration. One way is to deploy it in depth and with no overlapping fields of fire. Then, the motion of the lead tank in an attacking column should be strongly weigthed with respect to the countermeasures with which it is faced. The tank column could be made to "follow the leader": the $(n + 1)$th tank always moving into the position just vacated by the nth tank.

As soon as a tank comes within range of an antitank gun, the antitank gun might get one shot at this tank. Random numbers then decide whether the tank was killed. If the tank was not killed it moves again, after which move the antitank gun gets another shot at it. The way in which this shooting takes place may vary. For instance, the antitank gun might get only one shot between each move and always shoot at the lead tank in that part of the tank column within range, or it might be otherwise. The rules may be so established that, if the antitank gun misses its second shot, the tank moves again, and the antitank gun shoots a third time. Then, immediately after this third shot, all surviving tanks within range of the antitank gun might get one shot at that gun. The odds may be either for or against the antitank gun depending on the case.

Obviously, a crucial step in the whole simulation involves the actual firing. The main problem at this point is to determine the correct kill probability for the particular set of circumstances. The kill probabilities can be stored in the computer's memory and depend upon a number of factors, among them the type of weapon, its movement, the type of target and its movement, the range of the target, its cover and concealment, etc. The distance of the shooter from its target should also be taken into account. For infantry units it is rather the "kill probabilities" which become the factor by which the effectiveness of their unit is degraded than the probability of their unit being destroyed.

Another set of conditions for a simulated warfare refers to the general factors which should influence the movement of a combat unit from point to point on the battlefield. Included in the factors to be considered should be terrain factors, enemy actions, and tactical decisions, since these are matters which influence the movement of the combat elements. One approach to this problem is to consider the over-all maneuver of the forces as resulting from a large number of a simple move decisions made repeatedly throughout the battle for each combat element.

Each elementary move decision would require that the computer determine which of the neighboring points in the simulated map shall be the next position of the combat element in question. This combat element would also have the option of remaining in its present position. Choice of "where to go" might effectively be made by the computer through the use of weighting factors for each of the respective points to simulate the decision-making process of the military commander. The combat action itself might be dissected into small pieces of terrain with minor combat actions in each piece. A series of precise calculations and decisions have to be established, such that when taken together they might provide systematic means for calculating the outcome of each separate elementary combat action of fire and maneuver.

On the whole, the detailed tactics employed may vary from one battle to another, but within limits this can be taken care of by altering the probability parameters which control the motion of the different units and degree of interaction with other units. Thus the call for help, the enveloping maneuver, a probing for a whole section of the front, the concentration of weapons, and the setting up of a stationary strong point are factors common (in varying degrees) in the employment of all weapons.

Using Transition Probabilities

Say that the air-defense commander of a certain country is faced with a problem of building underground field tank reservoirs. The major decision concerns their site and relative size.

Let's assume that this air-defense command consists of ten airfields which are active (I to X) and two obsolete airfields (XI and XII). Alternative plans for the country's defense have been developed with the objective of facing all probabilities of an attack. Airfields VIII, IX, and X have been developed to provide a protection to the country's southern shore, while airfields I to VII are the main base of the squadrons whose mission is to protect the country from an air attack coming from the north.

Airplanes leaving one of the subject airfields may return either to the base of their origin or to another one. Depending on the outcome of the battle, the probability also exists that some of these airplanes are shot down. No matter which airport they land in, these fighter planes must find available fuel in order to continue their task. The problem is to establish the best possible way of distributing the fuel tank installations, with due consideration to dispersion, security, and refueling requirements.

The research workers faced with this project started by examining the established plans for air defense, deducting from there the defense patterns this command had in mind to follow. Correspondingly, they deducted quantitative information for the fuel and service requirements which were imposed. This first step was followed by a rewriting of the strategic and tactical plans of the air-defense command in a mathematical form.

Proceeding with their work, the researchers established a grid (Fig. 2) covering the whole country from coast to coast. The grid was so selected that each square would include "one or none" military air force base. The tactics for the defense aircraft were once again considered. The research workers established the transition probabilities of aircraft leaving its base and landing on the same base, on another base, or being shot down. The appropriate matrices were developed.

The calculation of these probabilities was based on the cumulative judgment of the officers of the air-defense command, who had been assigned to the development of the alternative tactical plans. These officers readily established that the calculation of these probabilities was what

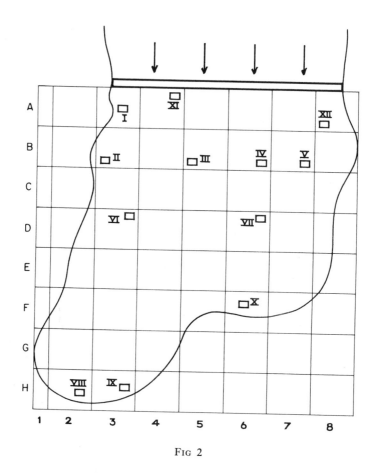

they were doing all the time; though not in a basically mathematical form. The difference was in the approach, and not in the basic nature of the calculations.

Once this scheme had been developed, it was easy for the research workers to proceed with a computer program which simulated the total range of an "air-attack-air defense" interplay. The subject program was run through a computer, a statistically significant number of times. It gave as an output fuel requirements at each one of the airports, as a function of alternative defense plans, of available aircraft, and of the hypothetical attack which was studied at that particular moment. This, in turn, oriented the decision of the military commander, who had asked about the investigation of matters concerning the allocation of funds and supplies.

PART V

Research on Traffic and Cargo Problems

CHAPTER 18

Studies in Cargo Handling

The objective of the study described in this chapter is the effecting of improvements in present-day cargo-handling methods and systems.[1] This is conceived as being feasible through the implementation of means for reducing the time and costs of handling, for reducing the damage to cargo, and for increasing the dependability of the over-all transportation process. The research workers proceeded by constructing a model of the system and subsequently analyzing its bottlenecks, wastes, and inefficiencies. From this study, certain improvements in cargo handling have resulted.

A major problem in describing an activity such as cargo handling is that of choosing a level of description which will yield to analysis and lead to useful results. The level selected in this investigation considers the cargo-handling system as a series of transporting links in which each of the links is the sum of all the movements required of a carrier in transferring a load of cargo from one point to another. This concept is sufficiently general, although limited in this particular application to the land-water-land sequence, to make it useful for the analysis of almost any similar system.

Formulating the Cargo-Handling Problem[2]

The study of the movement of goods must take into account all the activities which occur between the producer of a commodity and the consumer. These activities are the basis of a complex transportation system and must be treated as a series of distinct components:

(i) the facility,   (iv) the commodity,
(ii) the inland transport,   (v) the over-all control.
(iii) the sea transport,

---

[1] "An Engineering Analysis of Cargo Handling. II. The Field Study of 1953," Report 55-2, University of California, Department of Engineering, Los Angeles, November 1954.

[2] It is plainly understood that this is not simulation study within the framework of the description we have given in this work. Nevertheless, it constitutes an excellent example on a step-by-step approach to problem formulation and experimental investigation; it has been included to this end.

Another element, the process, is dependent upon the forementioned factors. The *process* is the path of the transporting agent and of the commodity. These six basic elements are presented in Fig. 1. The research workers postulated that they define the cargo-handling system.

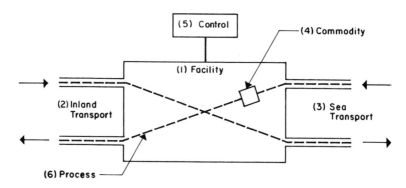

FIG. 1.   General process diagram of the activities involved in a cargo-handling system.

A knowledge of the six basic elements is a prerequisite to the understanding of the transfer of cargo between a land carrier and a ship. Yet their components and interactions are difficult to quantify, and for this reason it was decided that specific activities within a facility should be inspected. These activities can be viewed as a series of cyclic operations where each prime mover or transporting agent carries a commodity from one point to another and then returns to repeat the operation. A schematic diagram of a typical loading sequence is shown in Fig. 2.

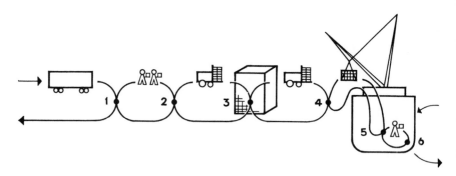

FIG. 2.   Cargo handling as a series of cyclic operations.

In general, the commodity arrives at point 1 by rail. It is unloaded, one carton at a time, to a pallet at point 2. A fork-lift truck picks up the pallet load and moves it to a position in the transit shed 3.[2] After a period of time in storage, the commodity is moved by fork-lift to the apron 4. The pallet is hoisted by the hook over the side of the ship and into the hold 5, where the pallet is unloaded by the hold men, one carton at a time, and stowed in the wings 6. Each separate operation is called a link. The term cycle has been reserved for a single performance of a link by a transporting agent.

The various activities which can occur during a cycle are grouped into four categories. These are pick-up (P), transport loaded (L), release (R), and transport empty (E). In addition to the productive activities, a cycle may also contain delays. A delay which results when a transporting agent is not able to pick up or set down a load because one of the connecting links is not in phase is called *an induced delay* (D). Any other delay, such as a breakdown or a stoppage within a link, is called *an internal delay* (A). Figure 3 shows a complete cycle

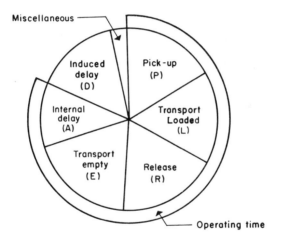

FIG. 3.   The total time of a cycle.

or the *total time* of a cycle for any link. The sum of the productive times plus the internal delays, which are inherent in a cycle, is called the *operating time*. In addition to these primary activity times, there are miscellaneous activities making up a relatively small percentage of the total time.

---

[2] While this is an almost "typical" situation in the United States, it is not necessarily so in most European ports, where this and the following elements may very well be completely manual.

The connecting points between links are called *nodes*. It is at a node that a commodity can be stored for a period of time or transferred directly to another transporting agent. It is also at a node that the characteristics of a commodity can be changed. For example, the commodity may enter as a single box and leave as a load of twenty boxes. The rate at which the commodity is moved from one node to the next is defined as the weight or volume of the commodity carried by one transporting agent per trip, times the number of transporting agents in the link, divided by the average time required to make one round trip. If, during an interval of time, the net change in the amount of storage at a node is zero, the average rates of flow in the preceding and succeeding links are equal. The operating rate of each link may be different. The "operating rate" is the weight or volume transported divided by the mean operating time. It is determined by the characteristics of the particular link only and is assumed not to be influenced by the adjacent links.

At the gross level, a port terminal can be thought of as a node; with a land carrier as the link on one side and a ship as the link of the other side. In this way, it is seen that the link-node concept may be used in a more generalized transportation system. However, for the purposes of this study, a limited number of operations within a terminal were considered. They are the links that connect the point of storage on the wharf and the point of storage in the hold of a ship. These links have certain general characteristics in common, for example, each is the round-trip path of a transporting agent. In their more specific characteristics, however, the links may be quite dissimilar. The following links have been studied:

Hook link. The transporting agent in the hook link is the combination of the hook, cables, booms, winches, and the operators of the equipment. This link is illustrated in Fig. 4(a), which is representative of the practices prevailing in the West Coast ports of the United States.

Wharf link. The operation in this link is the movement of a load between a point on the pier or quay, directly below the hook, and a point in the shed or storage area. The transporting agent is usually a tractor-trailer combination or a fork-lift truck and the driver [Fig. 4(b)].

Shed link. This link [Fig. 4(c)] connects the wharf link to the final point of rest in the transit shed or outside storage area. The transporting agent may be a fork-lift truck with driver or a crew of longshoremen who are loading a pallet which will in turn be picked up by a fork-lift truck in the wharf link. The shed link may not exist in all cargo-handling operations. For example, if a cargo is palletized by the supplier, all that is necessary is a fork-lift truck that can move the load from the storage point in the shed to the point below the hook (i.e., wharf link).

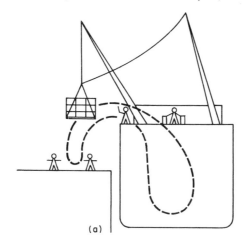

(a)

FIG. 4.   (a) The hook link.

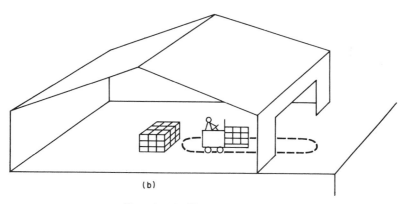

(b)

FIG. 4.   (b) The wharf link.

Hold intermediate link. In this link the load is moved between a point beneath the hook in the square of the hatch and some point in the wings. The transporting agent may be one or more men in combination with a hand trailer or a fork-lift truck. This link may exist during loading operations but it rarely exists during unloading. In many unloading operations the hook drags the cargo from the wings into the square of the hatch and then proceeds to lift the cargo out of the hold [Fig. 4(d)].

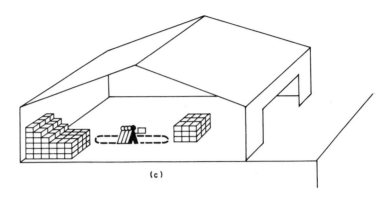

FIG. 4.   (c) The shed link.

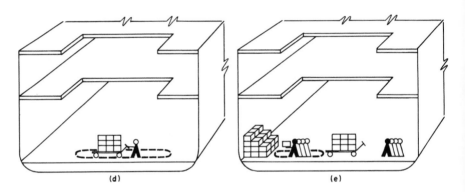

FIG. 4.   (d) The hold intermediate link. (e) The hold link.

Hold link. The hold link [Fig. 4(e)] includes the movement of a load between either a point directly beneath the hook or the end of the hold intermediate link and the storage position in the hold. The transporting agent is usually a group of men who may, for example, be unloading a pallet and placing the commodities into their final storage positions. In some specific instances the transporting agent may be a fork-lift truck which moves a unitized load into position.

Schematically, the described links fit together as in Fig. 5. The shed and hold intermediate links are shown as dotted lines because both or either of them may or may not occur during any particular cargo-handling operation. When a more general view of the link-node arrangement is considered, the rate of flow of the commodity through each of the links can be taken as equal. Nevertheless, in actual practice the operating rate for each of the links may be different. This difference may result because the links are unbalanced in their ability to keep the commodity flowing, and the difference is made up of the induced delay, i.e., the time that one link must wait for its connecting links to catch up.

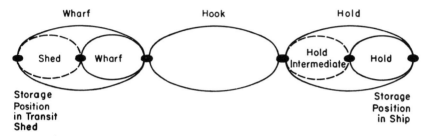

Fig. 5.   Observed relationship of the links.

The above discussion points to the fact that an improved system could be constructed by establishing a better balance between links. It is then necessary to find the slowest link in terms of the operating times and to increase its rate of movement in line with the others. The research workers wrote this interlink concept of the cargo-handling system in the form of a supposition: "If there is a group of transporting links connected in series, then there is one link which has the least mean induced delay and is the slowest link of the ensemble."[3]

The question now arises as to what can be done to the slowest (controlling) link to improve its performance. Basically, the performance times for the different activities of a link are relatively independent of each other and a function of the media used for their execution. As with every activity involving man-machine interactions, each operation would have a constant time (for instance, set-up time) usually independent of the magnitude of the operation, and a variable time depending on the operation. A knowledge of these times will enable decisions to be made which would improve the particular activity and, in turn, the performance of the link. The foregoing intralink relationship between the relevant factors which affect the mean activity time of a link can be formulated so as to make prediction possible. Both suppositions were used as the basis for the field study discussed in the following section.

---

[3] By the same token this is also the "controlling" link of the operation in the sense that it sets the pace for the activities in other links.

Considering the Field Study

In terms of the initial supposition, the data which would provide the maximum amount of usable information would consist of a complete time history of handling operations. For the collection of the necessary time data, the researchers decided to use work sampling. In the course of this study, time instants were randomly chosen on the basis of a table of random numbers. At each chosen instant, the operation being performed was observed and the link element in progress noted. The percentage of time required by each particular operation of the work cycle was estimated on the basis of the percentage of observations made when that cycle element was in progress. Some preliminary analyses were made of the required size of samples which would provide significant data. These analyses, as well as certain pilot studies, indicated that the data collected would be of greatest value if they represented the greatest diversity of possible operating conditions.

In order that any data collected may be considered as "typifying" the operations involved in cargo handling, the hypothesis must be made that the data are drawn from a collection of conceptually probable situations. This is equivalent to saying that the observed operations constitute a random process. Specifically, the source of the data presented in this report suggests the following: Under conditions of similar external determining factors (e. g., weather, ship type, commodity type, etc.), the extent of time required for each link activity is a random variable whose probability distribution is unknown. It is then desired to obtain an estimate through sampling of the mean value of this random variable.

For discussion purposes, attention will be focused on a single activity. Assume the time spent in that activity is a function of time $a(t)$ defined as

$$a(t) = 1 \quad \text{for those values of } t \text{ at which the activity is in process,}$$

$$= 0 \quad \text{for all other values of } t.$$

What is sought, then, is the mean value of the random function $a(t)$. A further hypothesis can be made which is not inconsistent with actual observation—that the probability that a single observation will reveal a particular "activity in progress" depends only on that activity and on the external determining factors. It does not depend on the specific time of observation. Hence, the mean value of $a(t)$, which may be denoted by μ, is independent of t.

Suppose observations are made at the instants t_1, t_2, ... $t_N = T = 0$.

This means N observations are recorded, $a(t_1)$, $a(t_2)$, ..., $a(t_N)$. A good estimate of the quantity μ is

$$\mathscr{E}(N_1 T) = \frac{1}{N} \sum_{1}^{N} a(t_i).$$

This is a "good estimate" in the sense that, if such estimates were made many times from repeated observations, the average of these estimates would approach very nearly the value sought, namely, μ the average value of $a(t)$. Further, as N increases and T increases, the probability that $\mathscr{E}$ is close in value to μ also increases.

Three possible schemes can be considered for choosing the instants t_i: (1) sampling at regularly spaced intervals of time; (2) sampling at instants chosen independent from a uniform distribution over a finite set of regularly spaced instants of time; (3) sampling at instants chosen independently from a uniform distribution over all possible instants in a fixed interval of time.

Consider case (1), that is, sampling at regularly spaced intervals of time; suppose that the process $a(t)$ can have one of two distinct values: one or zero. The intervals over which $a(t)$ is constantly equal to 1 have length α, which is random from interval to interval. These lengths are independent of each other and have identical probability densities:

$$p(\alpha) = A^{-1}e^{-\alpha/A} \quad \text{if} \quad \alpha \geqslant 0$$
$$= 0 \quad \text{if} \quad \alpha < 0,$$

where A is the mean length of an α interval. The intervals over which $a(t)$ is constantly equal to 0 have random length β and are independent from one interval to another. The probability density of β is

$$p(\beta) = B^{-1}e^{-\beta/B} \quad \text{if} \quad \beta \geqslant 0$$
$$= 0 \quad \text{if} \quad \beta < 0,$$

where B is the mean length of a β interval. Further, the α's and β's are mutually independent. In this case $\mu = A/(A + B)$ and

$$\rho(t, \tau) = \exp\left[\frac{-|t - \tau|}{t_0(\mu - \mu^2)}\right],$$

where $t_0 = A + B$ is the mean time per cycle. Suppose that T is very much larger than $t_0(\mu - \mu^2)$, and N is much larger than unity (i.e., sampling reasonably often over many cycles). Then, for the case of sampling at regularly spaced intervals of time and neglecting terms of second order of magnitude in $(1/T)$, we obtain

$$\sigma^2(\mathscr{E}) \cong [(\mu - \mu^2)/T][\delta(1 + e^{-x\delta})/(1 - e^{-x\delta})],$$

where $x = [t_0(\mu - \mu^2)]^{-1}$ and δ a function of T.

This formula can be used to determine the precision of a given sample or, if a required precision and sampling schedule is given, it can be used to determine the necessary time to acquire sufficient data. Sampling procedures (2) and (3) have been treated analytically in a similar manner, and the researchers arrived at the conclusion that regularly spaced sampling is preferable to the random sampling pattern for the timing of cargo-handling operations.

The types of data collected in the field study are limited to those which were believed necessary to test the hypotheses. The principal information required was the estimates of the operating and delay times for each of the links in order to test the first hypothesis that there is one link which is the slowest and therefore the controlling link. The researchers also required information concerning the variables that affect the element times (e.g., type of commodity, equipment used, distance traveled, etc.) These data could then be used to test the second hypothesis that the variables affect the time of link operation in some specific way.

After the decision had been made defining the types of data to be collected, it was necessary to devise data-collecting forms incorporating the listed factors and to determine the techniques of observation. Because the physical arrangement of a shed, wharf, and hold of a ship makes it impossible to observe an entire cargo-handling operation from one convenient point, a minimum of three observers were required during the data-collection study. The description of their specific functions and of the forms used for data recording is beyond the scope of the present discussion.

Tests and Evaluations

The first hypothesis we made stated that in a series link arrangement there is one link which "controls" the system. This link was defined as the one which has the slowest operating rate, and, consequently, its connecting links would wait during each cycle for this slow link to catch up. We called this waiting time "induced delay" and said that the slowest or controlling link itself should have very little or no induced delay.

A test of the hypothesis was made by comparing the percentage of time each of the three major links was in induced delay (Table I).

TABLE I

COMPARISON OF THE THREE MAJOR LINKS TO DETERMINE THE SLOWEST LINK

	Wharf	Hook	Hold
Pooled value of induced delay[a]	39.2	29.0	40.6
Upper and lower quarile points of the mean induced delay[a]	22–54	18–37	30–54
Slowest link[b]	19.0	53.0	28.0

[a] Percent of time.
[b] Percent of studies.

The data for this comparison are the pooled values obtained from all the studies that were made. Although neither the weight nor the volume appear explicitly in the determination of the mean operating time or mean induced delay, both were taken into consideration. For each loading and unloading operation, the average rate of flow was the same for all the links between the points of rest on the wharf and in the ship. In most cases, data were obtained simultaneously for all of the active links; thus for each study the mean activity times of the links may be compared directly.

The pool-induced delay values in Table I indicate that the hook was, on an over-all average, the slowest link. However, the values of the mean induced delay obtained for each of the studies of the hook are highly variable: 50 % of the weighted studies of the hook fell within the range 18–37 %. This makes it evident that the hook was not the slowest link in all studies. It "controlled" just the 53 % of the studies where comparisons could be made. Furthermore, a significant result obtained from the comparison of the induced delay is that the over-all average delay in even the slowest link is still very high. This was found equal to 29 %.

The finding of the hook link as the "controlling" element in more than half the studies is not unreasonable if consideration is given to the fact that the hook link, with its single transporting agent, is the most inflexible in the system. This is not necessarily inherent in all cargo-handling systems. In the system observed, that is, with a draft size approximating one long ton, and with the usual eighteen-man gang of West Coast ports, the hook link does tend to control.[4]

---

[4] With the hook operating at the same speed but with a different draft size, or with a different gang structure in the hold, another link may be found to control the system. The reader, therefore, should follow the method described here rather than trying to blindly apply to his own operations.

From Table I we also notice that the induced delay is relatively high in all links. One possible explanation is that it is caused by the cycle-to-cycle variation in the operating time of a link. An example of how this can occur is illustrated in Fig. 6. The operating time of the hook link is longer on the average than the operating time of the connecting

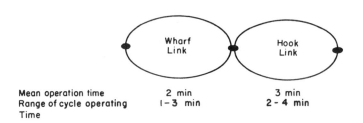

	Wharf Link	Hook Link
Mean operation time	2 min	3 min
Range of cycle operating Time	1 – 3 min	2 - 4 min

FIG. 6.   A hypothetical relationship between two links.

wharf link. The wharf link, therefore, will be expected to have a certain amount of induced delay. However, because of the wide range of cycle operating for each link, there will still be many specific cycles within, say, the hook link. The result, over a period of time, is that there is an appreciable mean induced delay in the hook as well as the wharf link.

The key to the foregoing discussion is the range of cycle operating times assumed in Fig. 6. Although the range chosen may seem large, all the evidence from actual observations has indicated very high cycle-to-cycle variability. One measure of this variability was obtained from the "cycle times" data, which were designed and used as a check on the work-sampling technique. It is also necessary to point out that another factor must be considered along with variability. In the example illustrated in Fig. 6, the transporting agent in the wharf link delivers a cargo to the node, and this cargo is picked up during the next trip of the hook. When the cargo is not delivered on time the hook must wait (i.e., induced delay). If a large stockpile of the cargo is maintained at the node, then the variability of the wharf link will not cause an induced delay in the hook. The amount of storage at the nodes must be taken into account in the study of system variability.

A possible explanation of the high induced delay in all links is that the work arrangement or pattern inherently causes induced delays in connecting links during the same cycle. An example of this occurs when the hook link operating time during a certain cycle is shorter than that for the hold link it is feeding. Because of the resulting unbalance there will be a certain amount of induced delay during each of these hook cycles as it waits for the hold cycle to be completed. For reasons of safety, the hook does its waiting on the deck of the vessel. Only after the hold cycle has been completed may the hook begin to descend into the hold of the ship. During this period of time, the hold link is inoperative or in a state of induced delay. Thus, the situation occurs in which two connecting links both have induced delay during the same cycle.

In summary, from tests of the first hypothesis, it was found that the hook link generally was the controlling link in the system studied. It was also found that there is high induced delay in all links of the system, which probably is caused by the cycle-to-cycle variations of the system and also by the adopted work patterns. The second hypothesis states that the relationship between the relevant factors which affect the mean activity time of a link can be formulated. The knowledge of these relationships should then make it possible to improve the system by improving the performance of the controlling or slowest link. The type of relationship that is desired is a simple equation in which the mean activity time is a function of certain factors. For example,

$$\text{mean activity time} = f\,(\text{commodity weight, commodity volume, distince moved, etc.}).$$

The technique used to obtain this functional relationship was to test one or two of the factors individually against the criterion, the activity time. Although the hook link has been singled out as generally being the controlling link in this study, analysis has been made of the factors in each of the links. Information relating to any of these factors is useful in obtaining a better understanding of the entire cargo-handling system. The following discussion considers the effect of these factors in the three major links.

Wharf Link Results

From the information recorded for the wharf link the following factors were expected to affect the acitivity times:

(1) type of transporting agent: fork-lift truck or tractor-trailor;

(2) commodity variables: weight, volume, and dimensions;

(3) distance the commodity is moved.

The prime factor in the wharf link is the transporting agent. The relationship between the type of transporting agent and the direction of movement has been found highly significant, with the tractor-trailor used mainly for unloading operations and the fork-lift truck used for loading operations. There is also some evidence to indicate that the distance the commodity is moved is related to the direction of movement: goods to be loaded on a ship generally need to be stored close to the pier and then moved to the hook by a fork-lift truck, while the commodities that are unloaded from a ship need to be stored further away and moved by tractor-trailor.

Certain other factors in the wharf link were tested. The travel times, both "loaded" and "empty," were correlated with the distance of travel, the weight of the commodity, and the volume of the commodity. To keep the transporting agent constant, this relationship was calculated only for studies using a fork-lift truck. The distance traveled was found to have a high correlation with the travel times both loaded and empty. The relationship of the weight and volume to this travel time is, however, negligible. The following is a brief description of the data-reduction procedures.

A chi-square test of independence was made between the direction of movement (loading or unloading) and the type of transporting agent in the wharf link. Also, a chi-square test was made between direction of movement and the distance the commodity is moved. The level of significance was selected at 0.05. All the data samples were taken from studies made in the Los Angeles area. The types of transporting agents were divided into two groups: fork-lift trucks and tractor-trailer combinations. The distances the commodity was moved were divided into two groups: distances of less than 200 feet and distances of more than 200 feet. Contingency tables were constructed from the number of studies obtained in each category and the number expected (shown in parentheses).

Type of transporting agent	Type of operation		Totals
	Loading	Unloading	
Fork-lift truck	10 (5.5)	1 (5.5)	11
Tractor-trailer	3 (7.5)	12 (7.5)	15
	13	13	26

The adjusted χ^2 is 10.09, with 1 degree of freedom. This result is significant at the 0.05 level and indicates that the tractor-trailer combinations are used predominantly in unloading operations, while fork-lift trucks are used mainly in loading operations.

Distance moved (feet)	Type of operation		Totals
	Loading	Unloading	
Less than 200	10 (7.5)	5 (7.5)	15
More than 200	3 (5.5)	8 (5.5)	11
	13	13	26

The adjusted χ^2 is 3.12, with 1 degree of freedom. This result is not significant at the 0.05 level of confidence.

A multiple regression equation and the multiple correlation were computed between the sum of the mean transport loaded and empty times of the wharf link, the distance of travel, and the weight and volume of the commodity. The samples consisted of all studies of fork-lift truck operations in Los Angeles. The multiple regression equation was found to be

$$\hat{Y} = 1.237 + 0.00232X_1 - 0.000034X_2 - 0.00173X_3,$$

where $\hat{Y}$ is the mean transport loaded and empty time, and X_1, X_2, and X_3 are the distance of travel, weight, and volume, respectively.

HOOK LINK RESULTS

The following factors were expected to have an effect on the activity times of the hook link:

(1) type of vessel and characteristics;

(2) position in the vessel that the commodity is moved to or from;

(3) auxiliary equipment such as slings, cant hooks, cargo boards;

(4) commodity factors such as weight, volume, and dimensions.

The first relationship sought was the multiple correlation between the weight and volume of a commodity and the operating time of the hook link. Within the range of variation observed, the result obtained was not significant, and therefore the weight and volume of a commodity are considered unrelated to the operating time of the hook link. Another factor of the commodity, which was expected to have an effect on the hook operating time, was the maximum dimension. To make this test, the operating time was normalized, to a certain extent, by using the operating time per measurement ton. Within the range of variation observed, this factor was also found unrelated to the operating time.

Since quantitative measures of the commodity were all apparently uncorrelated with operating time, qualitative measures were investigated. One such qualitative test considered the type of auxiliary equipment used in handling the commodity. The equipment was divided into two categories; the first group included pallets, clamps, cant hooks, and cargo boards; and the second included the rope slings and wire slings. In this investigation the results showed that the first group was handled faster than the second, but the difference was not significant.

The influence of the storage position was also tested. The factors relating to the commodity were kept constant by using only those studies in which a single commodity, coffee, was being unloaded. The actual variables tested were the storage deck (i.e., upper "tween deck," lower "tween deck," and lower hold) and the operating time per measurement ton for the unloading operation. Here again, the operating time was found to be greater for the greater depths, but the difference was not significant. More explicitly, the mathematical analysis was as follows.

The multiple regression equation and the multiple correlation were computed between the mean operating time of the hook link and the weight and volume of the commodity. The samples consisted of all studies of loading operations in Los Angeles and San Francisco. The multiple regression equation was found to be

$$\hat{Y} = 1.2807 + 0.0000996X_1 - 0.0000153X_2,$$

where $\hat{Y}$ is the mean operating time and X_1 and X_2 are the weight and volume of the commodity, respectively. A chi-square test of independence between the mean operating time per measurement ton of the hook link and the maximum dimension of the commodity samples consisted of all studies made in Los Angeles and San Francisco. The maximum dimensions and the mean operating times per measurement ton were both divided into two groups of high and low values. The expected numbers from each class are shown in parentheses.

Maximum dimension (inch)	Mean operating time per measurement ton (min/measurement ton)		Totals
	Low 0 to 1.25	High >1.26	
Low 0–70	13 (16)	17 (14)	30
High >71	29 (26)	20 (23)	49
	42	37	79

The adjusted χ^2 is 1.35, with 1 degree of freedom. This result is not significant and indicates that the mean operating time per measurement ton of the hook link is unrelated to the maximum dimension of the commodity.

Another chi-square test of independence was made between the mean operating time per measurement ton of the hook link and the type of auxiliary equipment used. Samples consisted of all studies made in Los Angeles and San Francisco. The types of auxiliary equipment were divided into two groups: group I included pallets, clamps, hooks, and cargo boards; group II included rope slings and wire slings. The mean operating times per measurement ton were divided into two groups of high and low values. A contingency table was constructed from the number of studies obtained in each category and the number expected (shown in parentheses).

Auxiliary equipment	Mean operating time per measurement ton (min/measurement ton)		Totals
	Low 0–1.25	High >1.26	
Group I	27 (23.1)	16 (19.9)	43
Group II	16 (19.9)	21 (17.1)	37
	43	37	80

The adjusted χ^2 is 2.27, with 1 degree of degree of freedom. This result is not significant at the 0.05 level of confidence.

An analysis of variance was made of the relationship between mean operating time per measurement ton of the hook link and the deck level of the ship in which the commodity is stored. The samples consisted of all studies of the unloading of coffee in San Francisco. The storage decks in the ship fell into three categories: lower hold, lower "tween deck," and upper "tween deck." The summary of the analysis of variance is shown below:

Source of variation	Degrees of freedom	Sum of squares	Mean squares
Deck means	2	0.18	0.0900
Individual studies	14	1.03	0.0735
Total	16	1.21	

$v^2 = 0.0900/0.0735 = 1.22$, with 2 and 14 degrees of freedom. This result is not significant and indicates that the mean operating time per measurement ton is independent of the deck level at which the commodity is stored.

HOLD LINK RESULTS

The factors tested for the hold link are

(1) vessel characteristics;

(2) type of transporting agent such as man or fork-lift truck;

(3) commodity factors such as weight, volume, and dimensions.

The tabulated data showed that the fork-lift truck had been used only to a limited extent during the field studies. This reduced the validity of any analysis of the difference between the two types of transporting agents. A single measure of the distance of travel, which was expected to be related to operating time, was also found to be inadequate because the commodity was moving either to or from a constantly changing storage position. Therefore, the distance of travel was not included in the tests made. The computed correlation was between the weight and volume of the commodity and the operating time of the transporting agent. The result was a high multiple correlation, with the volume being a little more important than the weight.

The multiple regression equation and the multiple correlation were calculated between the mean operating time of the hold link and the weight and volume of the commodity. The samples consisted of all studies in Los Angeles and San Francisco. The multiple regression equation was found to be

$$\hat{Y} = 0.07698 + 0.000228X_1 + 0.01386X_2,$$

where $\hat{Y}$ is the mean operating time and X_1 and X_2 are the weight and volume of the commodity, respectively.

In evaluating hold link results, the most statistically significant relationship was the high positive correlation in the hold link between the weight and volume of a commodity and the operating time of the transporting agent (i.e., men). The values to be noted are the percentages of time for transport loaded (L) and transport empty (E) for the wharf, hook, and hold links. The failure to obtain a relationship between the weight, volume, and dimensions of a commodity and the hook operating time can probably be explained by the small range of variation that was observed. This small range is due to the fairly constant draft size of one long ton which is moved by the hook.

In all, very few relationships have been found between factors of the system and the criterion measure: time. The recommendations advanced by the researchers can be grouped into two categories: those dealing with relationships among the links of the system, and those dealing with relationships within an individual link. Among the former, the most significant finding at the interlink level is that the hook, which was generally the slowest link, still has a large delay induced by the other links. This large delay has been attributed to the variability of the system and the particular work patterns that were used.

In attacking the problem of "variability" certain recommendations can be made. One is to synchronize some of the activities in the different links of the system. For example, a short repetitive rest period could be set up for the longshoremen which would occur in all links at the same time. In this way, some of the allowable internal delays in each link would occur simultaneously and would thus prevent an internal delay from causing an induced delay in an adjacent link. Similarly, it would be advantageous to use mechanized equipment in the controlling and other links provided the effect of the usage of this equipment is carefully considered in relation to the prevailing realities in each particular case.

One effective way of reducing the consequences of cycle-to-cycle variability would be an increase in the amount of storage at the various nodes in the system. It is, nevertheless, necessary to determine how much storage is required to offset a given amount of variability, and also how this storage can be established at the nodes within the physical restrictions of the system. The other reason for high induced delay in all links has been ascribed to the work patterns used in the system. Recommendations for changes in this area are not made, because it was difficult to generalize on the effects of different work patterns.

The findings and recommendations presented above are all based on the assumption that the cargo-handling system is to be improved by gradual changes. As a further step, this same analysis could serve as the basis for the design and evaluation of radical systems in which the present restrictions are removed. The findings of this and similar would enable further study of the cargo-handling process and subsequent simulation of its related activities.

CHAPTER 19

Simulation for Motor Traffic

Traffic studies can be broadly divided into two major classes. One involves the processing of a great deal of data, the other design work. We will be concerned with simulation for traffic studies, and in particular with data generation and data reduction.

In the course of the last few years, analytic studies in the transportation industry have revealed some of the fundamental characteristics of traffic problems. Other studies resulted in the development of certain formulas which help in the analysis of transportation links, flows, and bottlenecks. An example is an equation for the number of cars N entering an intersection, per hour, from a given intersection approach:

$$N = \frac{G + A - MD}{S},$$

where

G = the total number of seconds of "green" allowed to that approach per hour;

A = the total number of seconds of "amber" allowed to that approach, per hour;

M = the number of signal cycles per hour;

D = the average starting delay of vehicles, i.e., the time required for the first vehicle to enter the intersection after the display of the green light;

S = the average time spacing of the vehicles entering the intersection.

For the purpose of estimating intersection capacity (in a study made in Los Angeles) D was assumed to be equal to 3.8 seconds. Estimates for S are shown in Fig. 1. The total capacity of an intersection per hour was taken equal to the summation of the capacities of all the approaches to that intersection. But applications studies can only be effective when we have on hand a significant amount of theoretical knowledge along with experimental verifications. With our rapidly accelerating technological accomplishments, in certain domains of endeavor we are now searching the bottom of our theoretical background.

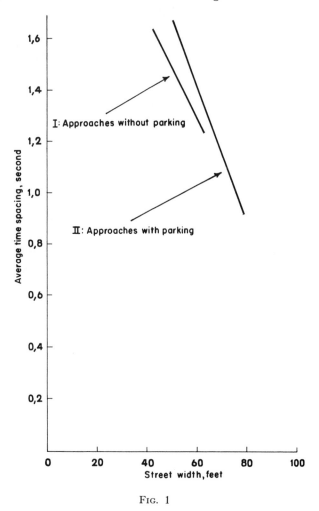

FIG. 1

The Planning Phase

Before starting to plan a highway, the designer has to do a thorough traffic survey in the area where the highway is going to be built. The first stage of this work is the determination of present traffic volumes in the existing route systems in order to establish the roads which have the heaviest traffic. Historical data must be collected by counting this traffic. Since it is unfeasible to count the traffic in each section of the route system, some representative counting points must be selected for the count. Information available on that basis will later be used for inference purposes, in an attempt to compute the traffic volumes of the whole system through statistical media.

There exist three main methods of counting. The first is to question the drivers—where do they come from and where do they want to go—the second is to glue a label on the windshield of the car, and the third is to note the vehicle numbers.[1] When beginning to analyze the counting results, the area under survey is divided into zones, a zone being a city, a group of cities, or a certain part of a city. The traffic relations between zones must also be considered. If a road map is divided into a number of zones (Fig. 2) one zone would be used as the origin of a

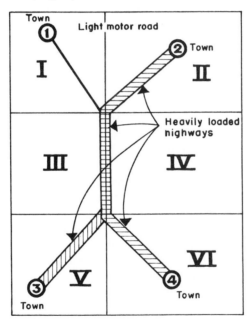

FIG. 2

trip and another as the destination. The combinations of these zones gives a "traffic relation."

---

[1] Recording the numbers of vehicles is meaningless in the United States but meaningful in certain European countries. In France, for instance, the last two digits on the plate indicate the city; for example, 75 would indicate Paris and 69 Lyon.

Consider the case where a certain city is divided into 200 zones.[2] This is a very simple subdivision, since, normally, subdivisions are done in a more complex way. Even so, the subdivision in question will give approximately 40,000 traffic relations. It is necessary to process all traffic relations in order to develop a chart of traffic volumes on the road system. These traffic analysis studies can be classified into (i) freeway assignment and (ii) interroad movement.

With both, the aim is to foresee developments of traffic with respect to a newly built highway and with respect to the future. The former, namely, traffic forecasting with respect to a new highway, is what we mean by "freeway-assignment." It is a method for appraisal of a proposed freeway route. What we usually wish to know is the percentage of traffic volume attracted by the new highway.[3]

For traffic relations, the gain, "shorter distance" and "less time" necessary to drive, may vary. There exist negative differences or losses. For instance, the traveling distance may increase when using the new highway. Also the necessary time may increase. In a number of traffic studies recently performed by processing statistical traffic data before and after construction of a new highway, the critical relations were found between distance- and time-gains, and percentages of traffic attraction to a new highway. These relations are expressed in Fig. 3. On the abcissa of this graph are plotted the values of the time ratio. T_F is the time spent driving on the freeway, T_B the time necessary on the basic route system. On the ordinate is plotted the value D, equivalent to the ratio of distances. The indices have the same meaning as for the time ratio.

The curves of Fig. 3 give the percentage of traffic attracted by the new highway. The evaluation of this diagram for each traffic relation is a routine affair which can be done automatically, i.e., by means of a computer. The results can be plotted in a new traffic volume chart, displaying now the distribution of traffic volumes for the present time, but simulating the existence of the new highway. Using this procedure, several variants of a proposed highway can be studied in an able manner.

Another important activity to consider is traffic analysis with respect to the future, or, otherwise, forecasts of zonal traffic movements. It is an objective of any traffic study to provide information to help decide where highway improvements should be made and what their traffic-carrying capacity should be. Survey data, reflecting the present traffic situation, must be projected into the future by some means. If this is

---

[2] Credit for the example presented in this section must be given to Mr. H. Schulz.
[3] See also the model presented in Chapter 20.

not done, traffic analysis can only have historical value, reflecting what happened in the past.

Various methods have been proposed for carrying through traffic forecasting. One of the first was to apply a uniform growth factor to all traffic-generating zones. This method has proved to be inadequate because the growth factors of the different zones are actually not equal. The suburban areas of large cities are growing very rapidly, while other

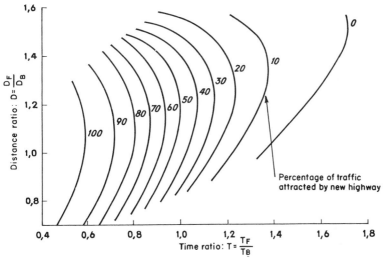

Fig. 3

parts of the city, mainly the older ones in the center, remain static or even decline as far as traffic-generating potential is concerned.

Traffic-generating potential can be expressed as the number of cars belonging to the people resident in that area. Applying to each zone a special growth factor of generated traffic creates the problem of distribution of the generated traffic in such a way that no zone imports more traffic than it exports and vice versa. The solution to this problem can be obtained by applying a series of successive approximations to project present interzonal traffic volumes to some future time, based on separate growth factors for each zone.

For an example, assume that we have four traffic-generating zones. The numbers in Fig. 4(a) give the respective traffic volumes, i.e., the number of trips in this traffic relation. The four circles at the corners of the graph represent the traffic zones. The numbers of trips within this zone, or the so-called "intrazonal traffic relation," are 5, 25, 40, and 50 for zones 1, 2, 3, and 4, respectively. Say that we want to develop the same schematical representation of the traffic volumes for the

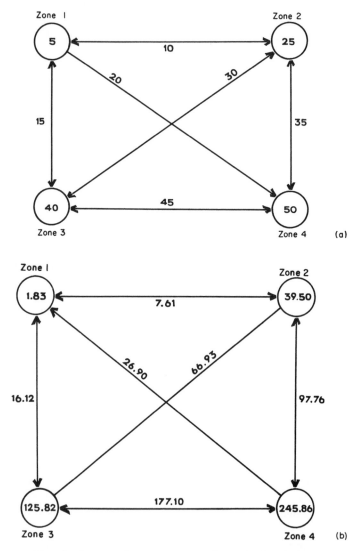

FIG. 4.   Intrazonal movements are shown in the circles.

twenty years to come. The assumed growth factors of traffic generation for the four different zones are:

Zone	Growth factor
1	1.00
2	2.00
3	3.00
4	4.00

The necessary calculations consist of matrix multiplications. One factor is the matrix of traffic volumes, the indices of which are the zone numbers. The other factor is a matrix with all elements being zero except the elements in the diagonal, which represent the growth factors. After three approximations, the developed traffic volumes are as shown in Fig. 4(b).

Having developed the traffic volumes for the future, one restarts the procedure of freeway assignment with new input data. Thus, it is possible to get some ideas of how effective the construction of a new highway will be some years ahead, provided the necessary media for experimentation are available. We have already made reference to the interaction which exists between a simulator and the computational media employed for its processing. A discussion about calculation and simulation in traffic studies necessarily involves a consideration of electronic computation. High speed computational media usually offer the possibility of applying methods which render results far more accurate, not only by providing more significant digits in the output figures, but also by making it possible to include variables which result in a more accurate approach to the problem itself and, of course, by allowing experimentation on a compressed time basis, as with all studies concerning systems and simulation.

Through electronic computation, traffic engineers are able to examine many additional trial designs in detail. They can more accurately establish the most economical location of highways, are relieved of tedious computations, and can more profitably employ their skills in establishing pure engineering details associated with highway design. The design work can be completed in less time than is necessary with manual methods, which is very important as there are in most cases fixed time limits for its completion. In a similar manner, more accurate estimates of costs can be made with little effort in the preliminary states of design, while unusual topographical and geological conditions can be brought to light very early.

Other highway design studies focus on survey computations for preparing terrain data (including aerotriangulation and the determination of automatic plotter settings, triangulation, traversing, leveling, and distance measurements); horizontal alignment; vertical alignment; cut and full; earthwork data check; preliminary earthwork program. Most of these areas offer interesting possibilities for mathematical experimentation.

Certain Theoretical Aspects

An essential step in forecasting and in planning for future traffic are analytic studies of a theoretical or semitheoretical nature on present traffic conditions, including traffic congestion. As discussed by R. J. Smeed,[4] the fundamental objective of traffic engineering studies is to assist in devising means of lowering transport costs in money and accidents. To achieve this object it has been found necessary to discover how the traffic is distributed over the road system in time and space, how the speeds of vehicles are related to the prevailing road and traffic conditions, and how much traffic a road or a road intersection can carry per time unit. It has also been found necessary to investigate the factors which cause changes in accident frequencies.

Apart from studies on the distribution of traffic on the road system as a whole, it is often desirable to consider how the traffic is distributed along a particular road, realizing that the distances between vehicles probably form a random distribution and that time intervals between vehicles passing a point behaved like a random series. Adams showed that under normal conditions, freely flowing traffic corresponds very closely to a series of events which are random in time. Wardrop demonstrated that traffic randomly distributed in time could also be randomly distributed in space along the road. Some typical time and distance distributions between vehicles are given in Fig. 5, which show conditions when traffic is partly flowing freely and partly prohibited from overtaking by the presence of other vehicles.

It is often advantageous to use the concept of a mean speed when considering questions of traffic flow. When doing so, one has the choice of taking

(i) *the time-mean speed* $\bar{v}_t$, or the mean of the instantaneous speeds of vehicles passing a point on the road in a period of time,

(ii) *the space-mean speed* $\bar{v}_s$, or the mean of the instantaneous speeds of vehicles along a stretch of road.

---

[4] R. J. Smeed, Director of Road Research, Road Research Laboratory, Department of Scientific and Industrial Research, Great Britain. This section is a condensed extract from his article: "Theoretical Studies and Operational Research on Traffic and Traffic Congestion," published here by permission of the author.

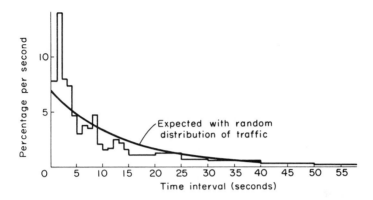

FIG. 5. (a) Example of time distribution of time intervals. Specifications are as
follows:

Road	Straight level section of A5
Width	24 ft
Flow	245 vehicles/hr in direction studied
Total flow	550 vehicles/hr
Sample size	765 vehicles
Average interval	14.7 sec.

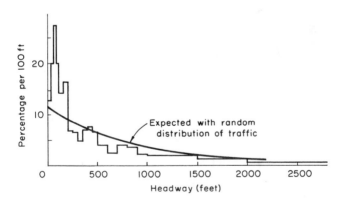

FIG. 5. (b) Space distribution of headways. Specifications are as follows:

Road	Straight level section of A5
Width	24 ft
Flow	245 vehicles/hr in direction studied
Total flow	580 vehicles
Sample size	765 vehicles
Average headway	890 ft
Average concentration	5.95 vehicles/mile.

These mean speeds are connected by the equation

$$\bar{v}_t = \bar{v}_s + \sigma_s{}^2 \bar{v}_s ,$$

σ_s being the standard deviation of the space-mean speed distribution. An important advantage of $\bar{v}_s$ is that it is simply related to the flow q (the number of vehicles passing a point per unit time) and the concentration k (the number of vehicles per unit length of road). These three quantities are connected by the relation

$$q = k\bar{v}_s .$$

Using (1) the equation $q = k\bar{v}_s$, (2) the experimentally determined relation between $\bar{v}_s$ and q, and (3) the equation of continuity expressing the fact that the difference in the numbers of vehicles passing two points on a road in any period of time is equal to the difference in the numbers of vehicles between those points at the beginning and end of that time, Lighthill and Whitham have produced a theory which shows how changes in traffic distribution are propagated down the stream at a speed dq/dk, i.e.,

$$v + k \left(\frac{dv}{dk}\right) .$$

Since dv/dk is always negative, the changes are always propagated backwards relative to the vehicles on the road.

The theory, however, in its present form, takes no account of the finite deceleration and acceleration of vehicles, nor does it take full account of the variation in speeds between vehicles. Some observations were carried out to throw light on these omitted factors, and the results are given in Fig. 6. Observations of the numbers of vehicles passing in periods of 2.5 seconds were made at two points, one just beyond a traffic light and the other 600 yards beyond. The expected flows at the second point were deducted from those at the first point on two separate assumptions: (1) that the Lighthill-Whitham theory was applicable, and (2) that the differences between the flow-time curves at the two points were entirely due to random differences in the speeds of vehicles (diffusion theory).

As shown in Fig. 6(a), under conditions of moderate flow, Smeed experimentally found that the diffusion theory fitted the results much better than the Lighthill-Whitham theory. Under heavy flow conditions, however, the Lighthall-Whitham theory fitted the results quite well, but the diffusion theory was not satisfactory.

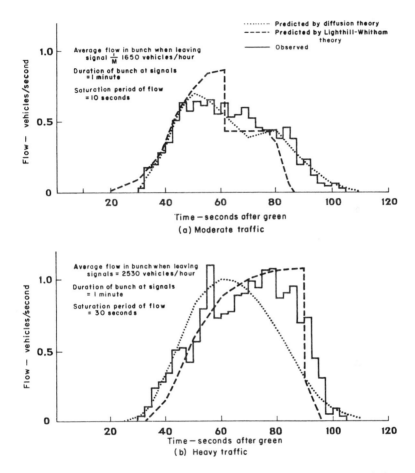

FIG. 6. Predicted shapes of bunch at second observation point (600 yards beyond signals); Great West Road (3-lane dual carriageway 30 ft wide); eastbound traffic from Vicarage Farm Road signals.

Research work in this field is confronted with major problems arising from the fact that the traffic is unevenly distributed over the road system. There also exist large variations in the average speed of traffic on different roads and in the speeds of individual vehicles on the same road. Research workers have established that the distribution of instantaneous speeds of motor vehicles on three important main roads are of the form given in Fig. 7. These distributions are approximately "normal" over the greater part of their speed range, the main discrepancy

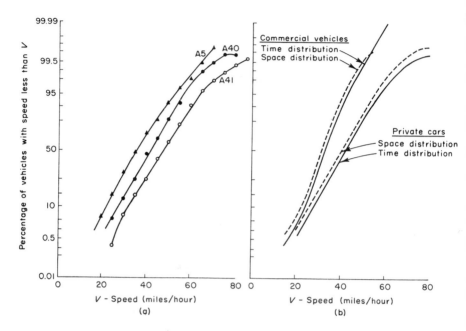

FIG. 7.   (a) Speeds of private cars on straight rural roads. Specifications are given in the following tabulation.

Road	Time mean speed (mile/hr)	Standard deviation (mile/hr)	Flow (vehicles/hr)	Width of road (feet)	Sample size
A41	47.9	10.1	150	20	370
A40	42.2	8.8	370	21	363
A5	36.2	7.9	690	24	727

FIG. 7.   (b) Speeds on a level section of road A40. Specifications are given in the following tabulation.

Type of vehicle	Space mean speed (mile/hr)	Time mean speed (mile/hr)	Standard deviation of time mean speeds (mile/hr)	Sample size
Private cars	40.2	42.2	8.8	363
Commercial vehicles	31.7	32.8	5.9	330

being that the upper tail is longer than it would be for a normal distribution.

In this particular example, while the average speeds of cars on the three roads differ (being lower the more heavily trafficked the road) the standard deviation of the speeds was found to be about the same on all three roads. Information on the effect of traffic flow on mean speed is given in Fig. 8. This figure presents the results of a number

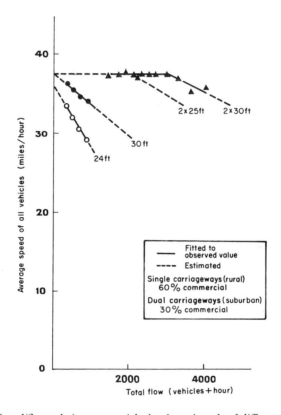

Fig. 8.   Speed/flow relations on straight level rural roads of different widths.

of sets of observations of traffic speeds on four rural roads at different levels of flow. The data were obtained by making observations at different times of the day. They can be expressed approximately, over the range of the variables shown in the graphs, by the formula

$$v = 29{,}5 + 0.271w - 0.00232\,q\left(\frac{w - 17.79}{w - 22.22}\right)$$

or

$$v = 37.6,$$

whichever is the lower, where w is the total width of the road, q is the flow over the whole road in vehicles per hour, and v is the average speed of trafic on the road in question.

This formula cannot be of general application since a number of factors, such as the composition of the traffic, are left out of account, but it does approximately describe the nature of the variation of v with q and w in many circumstances. The formula shows that on narrow roads even a small increase in flow has an immediate effect in lowering average speed. On wider roads, the average speed does not tend to decrease until a certain flow is reached. The formula also shows that an increase in average speed on the road with given flow due to a given increase in width is less on wide than on narrow roads.

It has been found that there is a close relation between the average speeds of different classes of vehicles on level rural roads. This is illustrated in Fig. 9. When speeds are low, the average speeds of all classes of

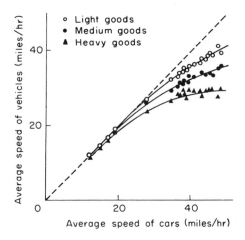

Fig. 9.   Relations between average speeds of goods vehicles and of cars on level roads.

vehicles are the same. The higher the average speed of cars the higher the average speed of other classes of vehicles but the greater the differences between the average speeds of the various classes.

Regarding the effect of road curvature and gradient on vehicle speeds on rural roads, an investigation was carried out on this subject on the rural roads of Buckinghamshire, England. Thirty-four sections of road of average length 1.3 miles were selected and records taken of the horizontal and vertical profile, carriageway width, and the number of access points. Measurements of journey speeds were made in daylight in fine clear weather. The data used were

v = average journey speed of all types of motor vehicles in both directions (mile/hour);

q = flow of motor vehicles in both directions at the time of making speed measurments (hundreds of vehicles per hour);

w = average carriageway width (feet);

c = average curvature, defined as the numerical sum of the deflections of all the horizontal curves divided by the length of section (hundreds of degrees per mile);

s = average steepness, defined as the numerical sum of the vertical distances between successive crests and troughs divided by the length of section (hundreds of feet per mile);

n = number of access points per mile.

A multiple regression formula

$$v = b_0 + b_1 + b_2 w + b_3 c + b_4 s + b_5 n$$

was fitted to the data. The values of the regression coefficients found by this method are given in Table I. b_1 and b_2 are not, statistically,

TABLE I

RURAL ROAD REGRESSION ANALYSIS

	b_1	b_2	b_3	b_4	b_5
Coefficient	—0.083	0.13	—2.12	—1.68	—0.047
Standard error	0.34	0.14	0.40	0.56	0.027

significantly different from zero; b_2 and b_4 are highly significant; b_5 is statistically significant at the $\alpha = 0.10$ significance level but not at the "usual" 0.05 level. The standard deviation of the original distribution of mean speeds was 3.74 miles/hr while the residual standard deviation was 2.02 miles/hr.

Hence, over the range of flow and width for which data were available, there is no evidence of correlation between v and either q or w. This was perhaps to be expected because the flows were light. There is strong negative correlation between v and each of c and s. The result for b_5 would not usually be taken as good evidence of correlation between v and n, but it nevertheless points in an expected direction.

New regression equations of the form

$$v = b_0 + b_3 c + b_4 s$$

were then fitted to the data in three consecutive experiments conserving v. The dependent variable was taken (a) equal to the average speed of all vehicles, (b) the average speed of private vehicles, and (c) the average speed of commercial vehicles. The results are given in Table II.

TABLE II

<small>REGRESSION ANALYSIS OF AVERAGE SPEED ON AVERAGE CURVATURE AND STEEPNESS</small>

	b_0	b_3	b_4	Standard error of b_3	Standard error of b_4	Orig. stand. dev. of v	Residual stand. dev. of v
All vehicles	36.3	−2.31	−1.49	0.38	0.54	3.7	2.1
Private cars	39.3	−3.07	−0.86	0.53	0.77	4.7	2.9
Commercial vehicles	33.3	−1.67	−2.22	0.40	0.55	3.6	2.1

All the coefficients are significant at the 0.05, or a more stringent level, except b_4 in the case of private cars. Thus each 100 degrees of average curvature per mile apparently reduces the average speed of private cars by about 3 miles/hr and commercial vehicle speeds by about 1.7 miles/hr. Each 100 ft per mile of average steepness reduces the average speed of private cars by about 0.9 mile/hr and commercial vehicle speeds by about 2.2 miles/hr. It follows that gradients have more effect on commercial vehicles than on cars, but the reverse is true of road curvature.

On the Impact of Road Traffic Signals[5]

In this section we describe an experimental project concerning traffic signals. Traffic signals are set on a road network to perform a given

---

[5] This section is based on an article by Dr. F. V. Webster, also of the Road Research Laboratory, Great Britain, on road traffic signals, abstracted and published here by permission of the author.

function. Hence, it is quite important to obtain quantitative data on the manner in which this function is performed and to evaluate the effects of alternative designs and approaches.

Since the introduction of automatic traffic signals, several investigations have been made into methods for setting them. Almost all this work was devoted to fixed-time signals, and semi-empirical formulas for cycle time and green times were deduced. With regard to delay, however, none of the formulas was really applicable to practical conditions, being based on the assumption that traffic arrives at an intersection at a uniform rate. Observations have shown that the arrival times of vehicles at an interesection deviate widely from uniformity and in many cases are distributed at random. Until recently, therefore, it was very difficult to make a realistic economic assessment of any road improvements at signaled junctions or of changes brought about by prohibiting waiting vehicles, right-turning vehicles, and the like.

In the following, we are concerned with the results of research conducted by the Road Research Laboratory into the delays to vehicles at traffic signals and into the settings of signals which give minimum delay to all vehicles. The results obtained provide a more definite basis for setting fixed-time signals. They are of practical importance also for vehicle-actuated signals that are acting virtually as fixed-time signals in periods of heavy traffic. In such periods it is necessary to have correct signal settings to give minimum delay to all vehicles. At other times of the day, it can be shown that vehicle-actuated signals will, to some extent, look after themselves.

For fixed-time operation of traffic signals, the delay to traffic using a single approach to an intersection controlled by such signals was computed over a range of values of green time, cycle time, random traffic flow, and saturation flow[6] covering most practical possibilities. The computations were carried out by simulating the events of the road by means of a computer.

In this investigation, the research workers assumed that the saturation flow was constant over the period of time considered. In practice the saturation flow may vary within a cycle and between cycles, but the effect of these variations is not likely to be very great. It was found that the results of the computation could be expressed by the equation

$$d = \frac{c(1-\lambda)^2}{2(1-\lambda x)} + \frac{x^2}{2q(1-x)} - 0.65 \left[\frac{c}{q^2}\right]^{\frac{1}{3}} x^{(2+5\lambda)},$$

---

[6] Saturation flow is the rate of flow past the stop line during the green period, while there is a continuous stream of vehicles. It is usually measured in vehicles per hour of green time.

where

d = average delay per vehicle on the particular arm of the intersection,

c = cycle time,

λ = proportion of the cycle which is effectively green for the phase under consideration,

q = flow,

s = saturation flow,

x = the degree of saturation. This is the ratio of actual flow q to the maximum possible flow under the given settings of the signals λs. Thus, $x = q/\lambda s$.

In applying this equation, the same units of time must be used throughout. The first term is, in fact, the expression for delay when the traffic can be considered to be arriving at a uniform rate. The second and third terms account for the irregularity of traffic. Figure 10 shows that

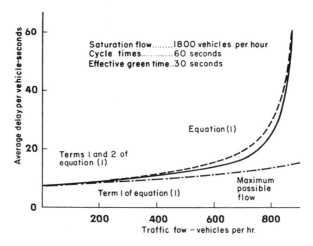

FIG. 10. Typical delay/flow curve obtained from computations in fixed-time traffic signals.

the "uniform flow" expression (term 1) is sufficiently accurate at low levels of flow but not at higher flows. Terms 1 and 2 together give a reasonable fit at all levels of flow, although they overestimate the computed results. The last term of the equation has a value in the range 5 to 15 percent of d in most cases. A rough approximation to the delay may therefore be given by

$$d = \frac{9}{10}\left[\frac{c(1-\lambda)^2}{2(1-\lambda x)} + \frac{x^2}{2q(1-x)}\right].$$

The delay formula has been tested under actual road conditions at several fixed-time and vehicle-actuated intersections and the variation between observed, and calculated values was no greater than would be expected due to random fluctuations (see Fig. 11).

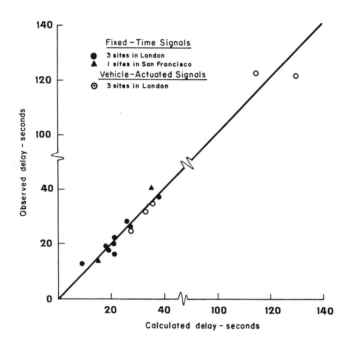

FIG. 11. Observed and calculated average delays at traffic signals.

In deducing an expression for the cycle time which gives the least delay to all traffic, it has been found to be sufficiently accurate to select one arm only from each phase to represent that phase. The arm with the highest ratio of flow to saturation flow is selected, and in the following this value is denoted by the symbol y. By differentiating the equation for the over-all delay at an intersection it was found that the cycle time for which the delay is a minimum could be represented by

$$c_0 = \frac{1.5L + 5}{1 - y_1 - y_2 - \ldots y_n} \text{ sec,}$$

where $y_1, y_2, \ldots, y_n$ are the maximum ratios of actual flow to saturation flow for phase 1, 2, ... n and L is the total lost time per cycle (in seconds), i.e., it is the sum of the starting delays (usually about 2 sec per phase) and any all-red periods. This cycle time will be referred to as the "optimum cycle time."

As an example of the calculation of lost time L, suppose there are all-red periods of 3 sec, and that the duration of a red/amber is also 3 sec. Then, the total time when red (including red/amber) signals are common to both phases is 6 sec at each change of right-of-way (see Fig. 12). The total lost time per cycle is therefore equal to $2 + 6 + 2$

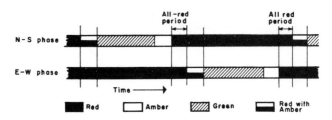

FIG. 12.   Aspects of traffic signals where all-red periods are included in the cycle.

$+ 6 = 16$ sec. Constant saturation flow has been assumed in the derivation of the cycle-time formula. If the saturation flow falls off with green time, e.g., owing to heavy right-turning movements, this formula does not hold. The variation of delay with cycle time is shown in Fig. 13 for a few hypothetical cases.

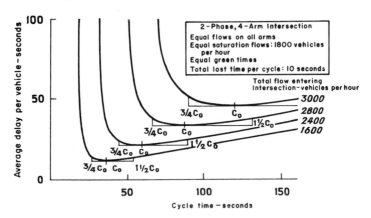

FIG. 13.   Effect on delay of variation of the cycle length.

In most practical cases it has been found that, for cycle times within the range $\frac{3}{4}$ to $1\frac{1}{2}$ times the optimum value, the delay is never more than 10 to 20% greater than that given by the optimum cycle. This fact can be used in deducing a compromise cycle time when the level of flow varies considerably throughout the day. It would of course be better either to change the cycle time to take account of this or, as is more common, to use vehicle-actuated signals. However, if it is desired to use a single setting of fixed-time signals, a simple approximate method may be used. This involves three steps:

(i) Calculate the optimum cycle for each hour of the day when the traffic flow is medium or heavy, for instance, between the hours of 8 A.M. and 7 P.M., and average it over the day.

(ii) Evaluate three-quarters of the optimum cycle calculated for the heaviest peak-hour.

(iii) Select whichever is greater for the cycle time.

A simple rule for setting the green times to give the least over-all delay to all traffic using the intersection was derived from the delay equation. It was found that the ratio of the effective green times should equal the ratio of the y values, that is,

$$\frac{g_1}{g_2} = \frac{y_1}{y_2},$$

where g_1 and g_2 are the effective green times of phases 1 and 2, respectively. This rule can be extended to three or more phase operations. Where the two arms of a single phase have different values of the ratio q/s, approximately minimum over-all delay is still obtained by dividing the cycle according to the y values as given above, even though the q/s ratio of other arms may vary between zero and y.

Where the level of traffic flow is varying throughout the day and a single value of green time is required for each phase, it is suggested that the total effective green time in the cycle $(c_0 - L)$ be divided in proportion to the average y values (for each phase) for peak periods only:

$$\frac{g_1}{g_2} = \frac{(\bar{y}_1)_{peak}}{(\bar{y}_2)_{peak}},$$

where $(\bar{y}_1)_{peak}$ is the average y value during peak periods for phase 1 and $(\bar{y}_2)_{peak}$ that for phase 2.

If other junctions are close-by it is desirable to know how far the queue is likely to extend, and a formula has been derived for predicting the average queue at the beginning of the green period (N). This is generally the maximum queue in the cycle and is given approximately by

$$N = q\left[\frac{r}{2} + d\right]$$

or

$$N = qr,$$

whichever is larger, where r is the red time, q is flow, and d is the average delay per vehicle. Important also is the extent of the queue in certain infrequent cases, as for instance the queue which will be exceeded only once in twenty cycles and the queue which will be exceeded only once in a hundred cycles.[7]

The foregoing studies refer to fixed-time signals or to vehicle-actuated signals which are operating on a fixed cycle because of heavy traffic demands. In the following, we will be concerned briefly with vehicle-actuated operations. A computer was used to simulate traffic conditions at an intersection controlled by vehicle-actuated signals, assuming that traffic was random and that saturation flow was constant. The variation

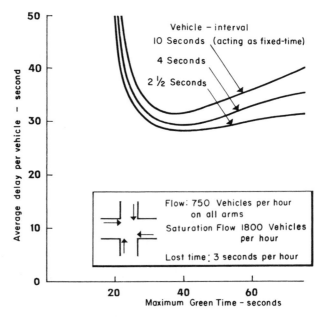

FIG. 14.   Calculated effect of the vehicle interval and the maximum period on delay at vehicle-actuated signals.

of calculated delay with vehicle interval[8] and maximum period[9] is shown for a particular case in Fig. 14.

---

[7] Tables of these are given in "Traffic Signal Setup," Reed Research Laboratory Technical Paper No. 39 (HMSO), London.

[8] Vehicle interval (now called vehicle-extension period) is the green time extension granted each time a vehicle crosses the detector in the "running" phase.

[9] Maximum period is the time from the vehicle crossing the detector on the "closed" phase to the right-of-way being arbitrarily terminated on the "running" phase.

The data given in Fig. 14 seem to indicate that for minimum delay the vehicle interval should be as short as is practicable, so that the signals just allow the queue to disperse before changing to the other phase if there is waiting traffic. This is difficult to attain in practice because, unlike the theoretical model assumed so far, the discharge rate varies within a cycle and between cycles, and the vehicle interval which is just greater than the average discharge interval would under actual conditions frequently cut off part of the queue. This would have an adverse effect on delay. Because safety requirements demand that a vehicle interval be not too short (say at least 4 sec), this state of affairs is not likely to arise in practice.

A computer has also been used to compare vehicle-actuated and fixed-time operation in a particular case, and the results are shown in Fig. 15. The maximum green periods were chosen to suit high-flow

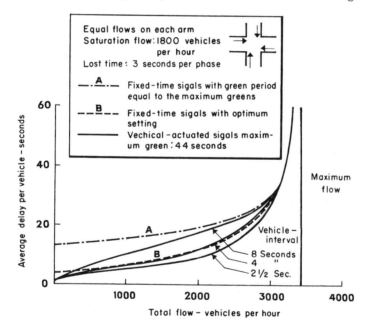

FIG. 15. Comparison of vehicle-actuated with fixed-time signals (4-way intersection)

conditions. It can be seen that under light-flow conditions the delay is much lower with vehicle-actuated signals, although the absolute value of delay, even with fixed-time signals, is not excessive. At higher flows the vehicle-actuated signal is running to maximum more often, and the two types of curves converge. The point at which this occurs depends largely on the value of the vehicle interval. In this example the saturation flow is assumed to be constant at 1800 vehicles/hr, corresponding to a discharge interval of 2 sec, so that when the vehicle interval is $2\frac{1}{2}$ sec the signals change soon after the queue has dispersed. With a longer vehicle interval the signals run to maximum at much lower flows.

In the fixed-time case (curve A) the green periods were equal to the maximum green periods of the vehicle-actuated signal. When the green periods have optimum values[10] at each value of flow, the delay curve, represented in Fig. 15 by curve B, is practically identical to the vehicle-actuated curve corresponding to a vehicle interval of 4 sec. Only one setting of the vehicle-actuated signal is necessary to cater to the whole range of flows shown in the subject figure.

A comparison of vehicle-actuated and fixed-time working has also been made for cases where the total flow entering the junction is assumed to be constant, but the ratio of the flows on the two phases varies from 1:1 to $2\frac{1}{2}$:1. In the course of these studies it was found that the fixed-time signal becomes overloaded with the $2\frac{1}{2}$: 1 flow ratio. If the fixed-time controller could provide optimum settings for each flow ratio chosen (either with a program or being altered manually to suit the traffic) then the delays would be comparable to those of the vehicle-actuated signal working with a short vehicle interval.

It follows from the foregoing discussion that the real value of a vehicle-actuated signal is not that it caters to the random variations in traffic, i.e., variations in flow from cycle to cycle, but that it can deal satisfactorily with long-term variations both in total flow and in the flow ratio of the phases, provided the vehicle interval is sufficiently short. Under steady flow conditions, as in the case when variations from hour to hour are small, the fixed-time signal has been shown to give delays comparable to a vehicle-actuated signal operating on a short vehicle interval. The simulation work we have discussed has shown that the fixed-time signal is less able to cope with variable traffic conditions, particularly when the flow ratio of the phases changes, than the vehicle-actuated signal.

---

[10] According to rules given in this presentation.

CHAPTER 20

Research on Highway Planning

The purpose of the research project to be discussed in this chapter is to develop a mathematical model for the study of the growing motor traffic on the modern highways. This "traffic data generator" should describe vehicle miles in all roads and streets of a nation as a function of the population growth, the number of motor vehicle registrations, and the changes in "necessary" travel distance, time, and cost.

To focus attention on some of the points that have been presented and supported many times throughout the present work, about pitfalls in simulation, due emphasis will be given on how a mathematical model that starts in a reasonably sound manner can end in trivialities. The cases experienced thus far in analytical work, in a variety of projects observed both in Europe and in America, show an incredible tendency toward that direction. Not only is skill in mathematical simulation still a rather rare commodity around the world, but, even where skill is exercised, minor absent-mindness on the part of the researcher is enough to throw the simulator out of control.

Since a study on motor vehicle traffic would necessarily require historical data to test the obtained simulated information, the United States has been selected as a sample country for the purpose of utilizing available motor traffic data. A set of relevent traffic information from any other country might have served the purpose just as well.

Forcasting the Need for Traffic Facilities

Traffic planners can use to advantage a mathematical simulator in determining needs, in time and place, for additions, betterments, and new facilities and for the optimization of design, operation, and maintenance of a highway network. A close-to-reality simulator can assist planners in determining justification, priority, scheduling, and phasing of improvements, and apportionment of funds.

As we know it today, a highway network is a dynamic entity. It is affected by such variables as shifts in population, industry, and commercial centers; variations in the degree of saturation of existing highway

371

facilities; changes in the mode of competition; and increase or decrease in the level of the economy. However, forecasting is not foretelling, and forecast involves risks. A sound approach will, then, require two estimates: one of high traffic volume, for design and cost evaluation, and another of low traffic volume, as a source of revenue, on the supposition of a pay-as-you-go system.

Since the best time for provision of increased traffic load is in the designing stage, the high estimate should take into full account the probable traffic growth. This means that the essential first step in the making of a "highway needs" study is to estimate what future travel will be.

This is exactly the approach taken in the making of the present mathematical model. The first part is concerned with data generation for future requirements. But mere figures on traffic growth are not enough. Not only is it necessary to determine the number of travel lanes necessary to handle traffic flow between two populated areas, but the designer must decide upon whether or not all of these lanes should be incorporated into one large highway (for instance, six lanes of traffic) or two or more "narrower" highways (e.g., two three-lane highways or three two-lane highways), each destined to special traffic categories. The economics of the situation must also be studied along with the needs of location and serving.

Traveling any distance over a congested road costs money. Inadequate highways and the resultant congestion cost directly in wasted time, wasted gasoline, and increased wear and tear. The inadequacies of the American highway system, for one, raise average vehicle operating cost by one cent a mile, which means over five billion dollars a year at the current volume of travel. Hidden costs, higher accident rates, and the like bring this figure much higher.

Some figures may help to show the magnitude of the highway problem. In 1900 there were only 144 miles of first-class surfaced rural "intercity" roads in the United States and 8000 motor vehicles to use these and all other roads. By 1920 these figures were brought up to 9 million motor vehicles traveling about 50 billion miles. In 1955, over 3 400 000 miles of rural and urban roadways were in existence, and the automotive industry had produced 125 million motor vehicles. Over 52 million passenger automobiles were in operation and traveled almost 500 billion miles during that year (Table I). By 1965, there will be, conservatively estimated, 81 million automobiles on the nation's roadways, traveling 800 billion vehicle miles each year (Fig. 1).[1]

---

[1] The subject study was conducted in the form of term projects in Graduate Courses in Applied Mathematics and System Engineering taught by the writer during the years 1957–1958. Hence, reference to the 1965 data was based on seven-year forecasts.

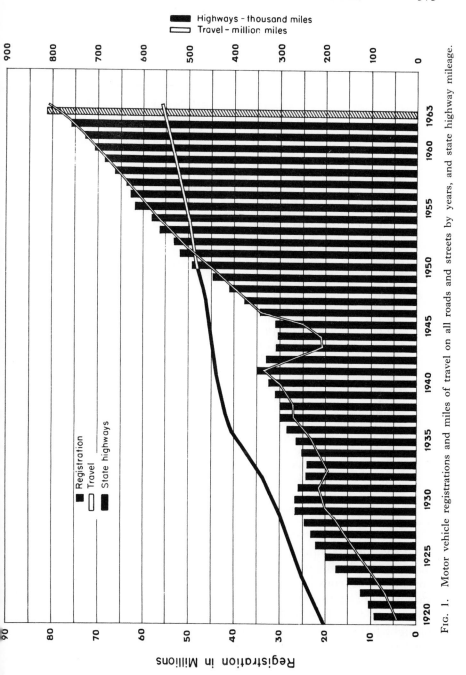

FIG. 1. Motor vehicle registrations and miles of travel on all roads and streets by years, and state highway mileage.

TABLE I

SUMMARY NUMBER OF AUTOMOBILES REGISTERED, AUTOMOBILE VEHICLE MILES TRAVELED,
AND STATE HIGHWAY MILEAGE IN THE UNITED STATES FOR SELECTED YEARS

Years	Automobiles	Estimated travel by automobiles (in millions of vehicle miles)	State highway mileage[a] (in thousands of miles)
1900	8 000		
1910	458 377		
1920	8 131 522		200
1930	23 034 753		324
1936	24 182 662	208 654	421
1937	25 467 229	223 467	424
1938	25 250 477	224 174	430
1939	26 226 371	235 629	435
1940	27 465 826	249 600	437
1941	29 624 269	275 839	444
1942	27 972 837	219 303	449
1943	26 009 073	163 169	448
1944	25 566 464	167 144	450
1945	25 793 493	200 398	456
1946	28 213 336	280 597	461
1947	30 845 350	300 444	462
1948	33 350 894	319 665	470
1949	36 453 351	342 478	478
1950	40 333 591	363 613	487
1951	42 282 591	392 131	496
1952	43 817 580	410 187	502
1953	46 460 094	435 351	503
1954	48 498 870	450 605	509
1955	52 173 234	487 540	520

[a] Includes municipal extensions of state highway systems. Also includes both primary and secondary highways.

Of the 3 400 000 miles of roadways in 1965, some 520 000 were state highways, including municipal extensions. Of these, 387 000 miles were considered to constitute the nation's primary highway system. This vast network of roadways connecting the various areas of the country and the spiderweb of roads that has developed in every urban area has brought forth many problems of traffic congestion, a subject of major concern for all state highway departments. Throughways, expressways, parkways, and bypasses have become important facilities, developed to relieve this congestion.

However, before such remedial measures can be put into effect, the areas of major congestion must be accurately located and a determination made of the traffic patterns of all trips, the relative amounts of "local" and "through" trips, and the types of vehicles making these trips. In turn, in order to evaluate these various factors, a traffic survey must be effected for all major control points.

The motor highway problem is further magnified by the tremendous cost involved in land acquisition, engineering, and construction. In a certain sense, the way to decide what highway construction the nation needs would be to balance these costs with the various benefits to be derived from an expansion and improvement of the highway network. Figure 2 presents cumulative data on highway construction expenditures.

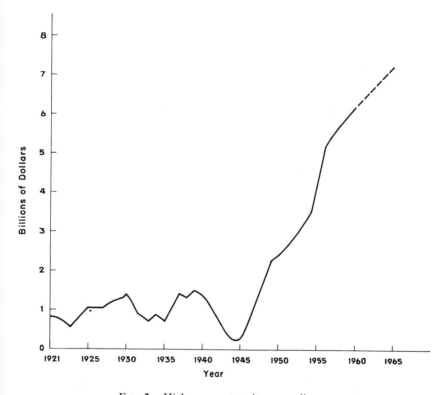

Fig. 2.   Highway construction expenditure.

Table I gives statistics on the increase in the number of passenger vehicles, miles traveled, and the state highway mileage through 1965. This situation is scheduled for major changes, since both the Federal

Government and the States have undertaken a program for the construction of a national system of interstate and defense highways.

The subject highway program, spanning over thirteen years, is supposed to be the most ambitious peacetime public works program ever undertaken. It will connect 90 % of all cities of over 50 000 population with 41 000 miles of expressways. For the most part the roads will be four-lane divided highways, expanding to six and eight lanes in and near metropolitan areas. In sparsely settled areas, where two-lane roads are to be built, provisions will be made for expansion to four-lane divided highways, if future traffic warrants.

Although the interstate system, as presently designed, will constitute only a little more than 1 % of the nation's total road and street mileage, it will carry 20 % of all traffic. These roadways are being planned to handle the traffic volumes of 1975, when an excess of 100 million motor vehicles are anticipated.

The whole network will cost somewhat in excess of $40 billion with 90 % of the funds provided by the Federal Government and 10 % by the States. To finance the program the average motorist will pay about $9 a year, but he will gain in return new traffic freedom, speed, and safety. As presently planned, the points of critical congestion are being relieved first. This brings us back to the primary purpose of the present project: establishing a mathematical formula which can be used to advantage for generating data on future motor traffic and for determining the relative adequacy or inadequacy of existing roads to handle the anticipated flow.

Some Basic Definitions

In order to avoid useless duplication of work the study of the data generator started with a systematic survey for the determination of techniques and approaches traditionally used by researchers for the solution of problems along the line established by the present research. As a result of the survey, it was found that traffic engineers who have been studying traffic patterns and trends for years have never developed a simple, universal model.

Even by restricting their formula to certain areas of the country (U.S.A.) and by considering only the flow of traffic on major highways between homogenous, highly populated areas, they still have not come up with any working mathematical formulas that can be used without gross inaccuracies. This initial survey disclosed a list of variables having a direct or indirect bearing on the density of traffic flow between areas. These were

(i) population,

(ii) number of motor-vehicle registrations,

(iii) distance between populated areas,

(iv) travel time from one area to another,

(v) cost of travel,

(vi) gross national product.

Considering traffic volume, then, as the dependent variable and the six variables given above as the independent variables, we can write the function

$$\text{Traffic volume} = f(\text{population, registrations, distance, travel time, cost,}$$
$$\text{gross national product}).$$

The fluctuation of motor-vehicular traffic volumes was found to depend upon dimensionless numbers determined from surveys and, sometimes, listed in statistical handbooks. Such are seasonal, hourly, and daily travel data, factors taking into account the influence of other types of travel conveyances, and factors which measure the characteristic differences between certain areas. For the purpose of this study "characteristic differences" are taken as

(a) the diversification of the area;

(b) the type of area, such as industrial, resort, agricultural;

(c) the location of the area within the continental United States.

It is often difficult to determine the relative influences of each of these factors due to lack of complete knowledge about the situation and the prevailing conditions. This is where the most difficulty usually arises and where most traffic analysts are willing to place the blame of the shortcomings of their particular model.

Furthermore, the confusion that has existed concerning the meaning and the shades of meaning of many terms used in traffic engineering practices has contributed, in some measure at least, to the wide differences of opinion regarding the capacity of various highway facilities. To cite but one of the many examples it is not uncommon to find the terms "high traffic density" and "high traffic volume" used synonymously or interchangeably. Yet, the traffic volume is a product of the traffic density and the traffic speed. It is possible to have a very low traffic volume with high traffic density. In fact, the highest traffic densities occur when vehicles are practically at a standstill, in which case the traffic volume would approach zero.[2]

The term which is perhaps most widely misunderstood and improperly used in the field of highway studies is "capacity." This term, without modification, is simply a generic expression pertaining to the ability of a roadway to accomodate traffic. Like the power of an engine, the capacity of a roadway must be rated by some standard before it can be expressed intelligibly. There exist three levels of roadway capacity that are of utmost importance in any discussion of the subject:

(i) *basic capacity* or the maximum number of passenger cars that can pass a given point on a lane or roadway during one hour under the most ideal roadway and traffic conditions which can be obtained,

(ii) *possible capacity* or the maximum number of vehicles that can pass a given point on a lane or roadway during one hour under the prevailing roadway and traffic conditions.

(iii) *practical capacity* or the maximum number of vehicles that can pass a given point on a roadway or in a designated lane during one hour without the traffic density being so great as to arouse unreasonable delay or hazard to traffic conditions.

Prevailing roadway conditions include roadway alignment, number, and width of lanes. From a practical standpoint, speed should be included in any definition of traffic capacity, since the driver is interested primarily in the amount of time it takes him to arrive at his destination. Composition of traffic, roadway alignment, number and width of lanes, and vehicular speeds are some of the conditions to which we referred collectively as the "prevailing" conditions. They may be divided into two groups:

(1) those determined by the physical feature of the roadway,

(2) those that are dependent upon the traffic using the roadway.

The first group of conditions, none of which changes unless some construction or reconstruction work is performed, is referred to as the "prevailing roadway conditions." The conditions of the second group, any of which may change or be changed from hour to hour, day to day, month to month, or over the years, are referred to as the "prevailing

---

[2] It is therefore necessary that certain terms be defined. The definitions given here are selected so as to be descriptive and widely used in engineering practice. Most of them are based on current usage or are definitions already adopted by various organizations doing work in the field of traffic analysis.

traffic conditions." The researchers decided that the second group is the one which lends itself better to as systematic analysis with the objective of data generation regarding vehicular traffic. It is this second group, therefore, with which we shall be concerned in this part.

Also, we shall use the word volume[3] and define it as the number of vehicles passing a given point per unit of time. *Density* refers to the number of vehicles in a given length of lane. Hence, *average volume* equals *average density* times *average speed*.

The Problem and the Model

Say that we wish to study analytically the volume of vehicular traffic which can be expected to traverse any major highway between cities of 0.5 million population or more in the United States. The model shall be expected to hold for vehicular traffic which exists either at present or in the near future.

Based on the definitions given about capacity, volume, speed, and density, if we wish to know the "theoretical maximum volume" we can readily compute it with historical data since the amount of traffic per unit of time depends on the speed and the spacing between vehicles. The greater the speed the larger the volume, and the greater the spacing the less the volume.[4] Therefore,

$$\text{volume} = \frac{\text{speed}}{\text{spacing}} \, .$$

For a given type of highway, figures pertaining to average speeds of motor vehicles are generally available. Likewise, knowing the time that it takes a driver to initiate a reflex which "tells" him to stop, and the lag time for his foot to be applied to the brake pedal, researchers have been able to apply these "reaction times" and calculate the minimum stopping distances for vehicles moving at various speeds. Minimum spacing distances can thus be prescribed between moving vehicles on a highway. As a result, a highway's theoretical maximum capacity may be determined. Tables II and III give the minimum driver stopping distance for various speeds.

---

[3] In order to avoid the ambiguities attached to the word "capacity."

[4] This should not be interpreted in absolute terms since, beyond a certain saturation point, greater spacing has adverse effects on speed with the net result of a reduction in volume per unit of time.

TABLE II

APPROXIMATE MINIMUM DRIVER STOPPING DISTANCE FROM VARIOUS INITIAL SPEEDS[a]

Speed (mph)	Dry concrete (ft)	Oil gravel (ft)	Gravel (ft)	Packed snow (ft)	Glare ice (ft)
20	45	45	55	90	190
30	75	85	85	180	290
40	120	140	140	310	500
50	180	220	200	470	750
60	250	310	280	670	1100

[a] The data in this table were the results of tests performed at test grounds. A $\frac{3}{4}$-sec time, driver, and good brakes are assumed.

TABLE III

DRIVER STOPPING DISTANCES USED FOR DESIGN PURPOSES

Initial speed (mph)	Distance (ft)
30	160
40	250
50	360
60	480
70	610

One of the quantities that is usually available in statistical abstracts is the amount of total motor-vehicle travel in the United States. This is generally expressed in motor-vehicle miles. *One vehicle mile* is defined as the movement of one vehicle over the distance of one mile. If one could predict the size of this quantity for any future year, he has a fairly good estimate of what the over-all travel trend, whether heavy or light, will be during that year.

In estimating vehicle miles of travel, areawise, interest was stressed in relating travel to trends in growth of other items, in order to obtain a relatively simple index for use in traffic estimates. The correlation between vehicular travel and gross national product provided a very good correlation coefficient. With both the gross national product and the motor traffic expressed with 1940 as the base year, their trend lines were found nearly coincident, with the only exception being the war years (Fig. 3).

FIG. 3. Index of gross national product and vehicle miles of motor vehicle travel (1940 = 100).

Let

  n be the base year for our derivations,

  P the gross national product,

  M the total vehicle of motor-vehicle travel in the United States in one year,

  R the total number of motor-vehicle registrations in the United States,

  u the purchasing power of 1940's dollar in the year n (based on comparison of consumer prices).

Then, P_n, M_n, and R_n would simply refer to the gross national product, the total vehicle miles, and the number of motor-vehicle registrations, respectively, during the year which we will consider as the base n.

We can express the total vehicle miles of travel, M, as a function of P, where P is based on the value of the 1940 dollar:

$$M = f(u, P).$$

But since, except for the war years,[5] it was found that M and P are directly proportional, we can write

$$M = auP,$$

where a is a constant of proportionality. As of 1955, the figure for total vehicle miles in the United States was equal to about three times the figure for gross national product (1940 dollar). Therefore, $a = 3$, and the equation becomes

$$M = 3uP$$

or

$$M_n = 3uP_n. \tag{1}$$

Both traffic and the gross national product increased at an average rate of about 4 % a year compounded from 1936 to 1951. If the prediction that the gross national product will continue to grow until 1970 at a rate of about 4 % a year compounded annually holds true, then it can be said that, except for any major upset such as a world war, vehicular traffic will increase at the same rate of 4 % per year. Hence,

$$P_{n+1} = 1.04P_n,$$

or

$$P_{n+2} = 1.04P_{n+1} = (1.04)^2 P_n,$$

and

$$P_{n+3} = 1.04P_{n+2} = (1.04)^2 P_n.$$

In general,

$$P_{n+k} = (1.04)^k P_n, \tag{2}$$

where k represents the numbers of years, following the base year n, for which calculations may be made. Knowing P_{n+k}, we may now solve for M_{n+k}. If Eq. (1) holds, then there exists a value M_{n+k}, such that

$$M_{n+k} = 3uP_{n+k}. \tag{3}$$

From Eqs. (2) and (3),

$$M_{n+k} = 3u(1.04)^k P_n. \tag{3a}$$

Historical data indicate that the average yearly mileage per vehicle is 10 500 miles. This figure is based on the years 1940, 1945, 1950, and

---

[5] This can be considered as one of the limitations of the model, and it is discussed later on.

1955. M_n may be related to the average vehicle mile for one year and the total vehicular registrations R_n as follows:

$$M_n = 10\,500R_n\,,$$

or assuming the above average mileage to hold for a certain time span (1970) for which our equation holds, we obtain

$$M_{n+k} = 10\,500R_{n+k}\,. \tag{4}$$

Substituting into (3a) and solving for R_{n+k}, we obtain

$$R_{n+k} = \frac{3u(1.04)^k P_n}{10\,500}\,, \tag{4a}$$

from which the total number of vehicle registrations may be projected, knowing the value of the gross national product and the value of the 1940 dollar in the base year.

A comparison between actual and simulated data might illustrate the use of this formula in calculating future numbers of motor vehicles registrated in the United States. Such comparison indicates a rather close agreement. This lack of major discrepancies between the actual statistical values and the calculated values can be seen in Fig. 4. The difference between the two sets of data is constant, and it can be accounted for in the equation, so that the simulated curve will shift toward the curve of actual data.

So far so good, though, of course, the simulator would need major improvements still, and an adaptation to prevailing condition, wherever it is to be applied.[6] Exactly at this point of the specialization or "personalization" of a mathematical model to the prevailing conditions, to the case under investigation, lie the great opportunities for pitfalls and mistaken paths. In the following, we will examine some of the pitfalls into which researchers have fallen in the past.

Vicious Cycles Around a Model

To make our example on what can happen in "model deviations" complete, we will advance the hypothesis that the sponsor of the project presses for what he considers to be "the most necessary additions."

We need to determine what relationship the number of registrations during any one year has on the volume of traffic. At first glance, it

---

[6] The reader should keep in mind that this was a graduate student project and it was done at no cost, through the time-honored and University-practiced method of "slave labor." And yet, with regard to rationality, it could compare well with other projects, which could easily cost one million dollars to their sponsor.

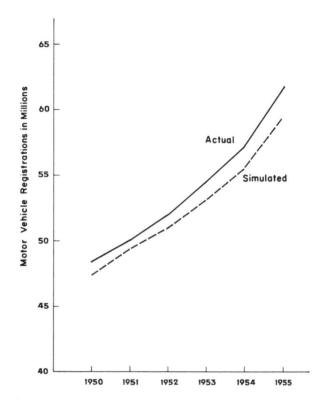

FIG. 4.   Number of motor vehicle registrations in the U.S.

might seem rather obvious that the volume of traffic is directly proportional to the number of registrations. Unanswered questions still remain, however, such as: Is the relationship linear? What other constants also come into the picture? With what other variables are the registrations tied to in equating them to traffic volume?

One relationship which has proved to be fairly reliable, for computing inter-area traffic volumes in the state of New Jersey, is the following:

$$V_{12} = \frac{r_1 f_2}{T_{12}}, \tag{5}$$

where

V_{12} = volume of traffic from area 1 to area 2,

r_1 = the number of motor vehicles registered in area 1,

f_2 = the force of attraction which area 2 exerts on area 1,

T_{12} = total elapsed time to travel from area 1 to area 2.

Notice the striking similarity of Eq. (5) to Eq. (1) of Chapter 11. Needless to say, this is given with all reservation in order to allow the continuation of the discussion on the subject project. As a matter of fundamental principle the reader should question everything he is told. He should accept nothing as "true" unless he can prove its merits, in the case he is concerned with, and set its relationship to the other variables of the system and to its environment. This is the "spirit of analysis."

In this particular case, for instance, the various so-called "attraction factors" widely used in the U.S.A., completely fail to account for business traffic, which has nothing to do with general attraction and with through-traffic, which is independent both of the "unspecified attraction reasons" and of the population density in each considered area, as such. For the sake of this discussion, we will continue, nevertheless, the subject example. Hence, in a similar manner,

$$V_{21} = \frac{r_2 f_1}{T_{21}} , \tag{5'}$$

where

V_{21} = volume of traffic from area 2 to area 1,

r_2 = the number of registrations in area 2,

f_1 = the force of attraction which area 1 exerts on area 2,

T_{21} = the total elapsed time to travel from area 2 to area 1.

In order to account for round trips, the preceding expressions must be multiplied by 2. Thus the total traffic volume V between the two areas becomes

$$V = 2V_{12} + 2V_{21} ,$$

which may be expressed as

$$V = 2 \frac{r_1 f_2 + r_2 f_1}{T} , \tag{6}$$

on the supposition that $T_{12} = T_{21}$ which, of course, does not need to hold always because of the particularity a certain area may present in respect to through-traffic.

The validity of this equation has first to be proven in general terms and, also, as a function of the hour of the day. This is a very critical factor, which most traffic models fail to account for. In certain big cities, Paris and New York being excellent examples, the end of the working day is accompanied by monster bottlenecks where in several main streets all traffic comes to a standstill. Just try to drive along the Champs Elysées, or the Quai Rive Droite along the River Seine, between 5.30 P.M. and 6.30 P.M., and next day you will be highly tempted to leave your car at home. Where is this fatigue and discourage-ment factor reflected in the "magic" general attraction equation? And what about the relative position a driver has within a big city and his access to through-city arteries?

Another factor, which could easily escape the attention of an analyst conducting a highway research project, are the monster jams created because of accidents and their aftermath. This omission starts by forgetting to account for a lot of relevant but not immediately apparant factors, like the prevailing weather conditions, exceptional weather situations and their probability, fog, ice, and the population's driving habits. Within these driving habits should obviously be considered the driver's reaction and capability of coping with exceptional cases. Such data usually evade current available statistics, and their determination constitutes in itself a sizable work. But let's continue with this study in full understanding of the involved pitfalls.

The factor f, determined by results of traffic surveys and other studies, is equated to the following:

$$f = 0.001 \frac{r_1 r_2}{\underset{\sim}{Q}} \gamma \qquad (7)$$

where Q is the population of an area and γ is a multiplier expressing the attraction which one area has for another. For many areas its value is one. For highly industrialized or for resort areas, both of which seem to attract a greater volume of traffic, $\gamma > 1.0$. Likewise, for rural-type areas, where the traffic volume is light, $\gamma < 1.0$.

Using the relationship expressed in (7), Eqs. (5) and (5') now take the form

$$f_1 = 0.001 \frac{r_1 r_2}{Q_2} \gamma_2, \qquad (5a)$$

$$f_2 = 0.001 \frac{r_2 r_1}{Q_1} \gamma_1. \qquad (5a')$$

Substituting (5a) and (5a′) into (6) we obtain

$$V = \frac{r_1 r_2}{T} \left(0.002 \frac{r_1}{Q_1} \gamma_1 + 0.002 \frac{r_2}{Q_2} \gamma_2 \right), \tag{6a}$$

where V is the number of vehicles per day, r is the number of registrations, Q the number of persons and, T the time in minutes.

From a study made in 1956 by the Bureau of Public Roads, Department of Commerce, the average vehicle speed measured on rural highways during off-peak hours was 50.5 mph. Since speed $=$ distance/time, we may express T as,

$$T = \frac{D}{50.5} \frac{60 \text{ m n}}{\text{hr}} = 1.19D, \tag{8}$$

where D is distance in miles. By substituting (8) into (6a), we obtain

$$V = \frac{r_1 r_2}{(1.19D)^2} \left[0.002 \frac{r_1}{Q_1} \gamma_1 + 0.002 \frac{r_2}{Q_2} \gamma_2 \right]$$

or

$$V = \frac{1.4123 \times 10^{-3}}{D^2} r_1 r_2 \left(\frac{r_1 \gamma_1}{Q_1} \frac{r_2 \gamma_2}{Q_2} \right).$$

Weighting factors could be used to adjust the calculated average daily traffic volume for various hours of the day and months of the year. Relative factors are given in Tables IV, V, and VI. Anyway, this model

TABLE IV

DAILY VARIATIONS OF TRAFFIC VOLUME ON A STATE HIGHWAY SYSTEM

Day	Percent of total weekly volume	Percent of average day	Weekly factor
Sunday	18.10	126.73	0.789
Monday	13.32	93.25	1.072
Tuesday	12.75	89.14	1.121
Wednesday	12.89	90.22	1.108
Thursday	13.00	91.04	1.198
Friday	14.06	98.44	1.015
Saturday	15.88	111.18	0.899

TABLE V

SEASONAL VARIATION BY MONTHS

Month	Percent of average month	Monthly factor
Jan.	82.24	1.215
Feb.	83.94	1.191
March	90.94	1.100
April	100.79	0.992
May	105.29	0.949
June	108.89	0.918
July	109.51	0.913
Aug.	113.38	0.882
Sept.	113.10	0.884
Oct.	107.46	0.931
Nov.	97.38	1.026
Dec.	87.13	1.114

TABLE VI

HOURLY VARIATIONS OF TRAFFIC VOLUME ON A STATE HIGHWAY SYSTEM

Hour	Percent of total 24-hr volume	Hour	Percent of total 24-hr volume
12:00–1:00 A.M.	1.89	12:00–1:00 P.M.	5.34
1:00–2:00 A.M.	1.32	1:00–2:00 P.M.	6.18
2:00–0:00 A.M.	0.90	2:00–3:00 P.M.	6.56
3:00–4:00 A.M.	0.76	3:00–4:00 P.M.	6.88
4:00–5:00 A.M.	0.76	4:00–5:00 P.M.	7.71
5:00–6:00 A.M.	1.05	5:00–6:00 P.M.	7.30
6:00–7:00 A.M.	2.53	6:00–7:00 P.M.	6.12
7:00–8:00 A.M.	3.69	9:00–8:00 P.M.	5.72
8:00–9:00 A.M.	4.42	8:00–9:00 P.M.	4.74
9:00–10:00 A.M.	5.34	9:00–10:00 P.M.	3.85
10:00–11:00 A.M.	5.73	10:00–11:00 P.M.	3.18
11:00–12:00 Noon	5.42		

is suitable only as an example and not as a "working simulator."[7] It was developed for population centers (city clusters or major cities)

---

[7] It was most thoughtful of the researchers to make at least this reservation.

equal to or exceeding the 500 000-people level. These population areas must be homogeneous. This model also has other inherent constraints:

(i) Arterial routes are the only roads that can be considered.

(ii) Happenings of an extraordinary nature, and their effects on motor traffic have not been taken into account.

(iii) It has been assumed that states, municipalities, etc. have uniform traffic laws.

(iv) Some of the constants which were used in the model were calculated for an expected useful life of the simulator of about twelve years, starting at 1958.

And, of course, to these should be added all the reservations that were noted in the course of the discussion on the model's development. A host of other factors, often forgotten and not accounted for, could be told. Not among the least are parking facilities the object area can offer for the traffic it attracts. Though this can be taken as part of the attraction factor γ, this factor is so general that its uninterrupted and unqualified use can make the application of any model perfectly invalid.

PART VI
Hydrological Applications

CHAPTER 21

Simulation in Hydrological Works

In developing river regulation schemes for hydroelectric works and for irrigation projects it is necessary to test the contemplated improvements and their operations against actual or simulated flow data. To evaluate alternative schemes, hydraulic engineers have traditionally used scale models, that is, simulation through a physical analog. Quite similarly, power networks have been studied by means of network analyzers. It was the advent of the electronic computer which helped shift the emphasis to experimentation through mathematical model-making.

The objective of this and the following two chapters is to present and describe approaches to mathematical experimentation for hydraulic and hydroelectric works. We will follow the background method and present examples of model-making for controlling a river or a power network. Through mathematical equations we will specify the amounts of water to be released from individual reservoirs, during each month, as functions of the contents of certain other reservoirs and of the discharges flowing at certain other points on the river at the end of the previous month.

Once a mathematical model has been developed and tested, an electronic computer can be used to evaluate the behavior of a system, obeying the forementioned equations, and subject to the external conditions of rainfall and evaporation which held for the river in question during a certain period of years, for which the resulting hydrological data are available. Although there is no unique sample size for these hydraulic data, it can be said that a 50-year period is quite satisfactory, with 25-year data constituting a minimal dependable sample size.

One approach, with an actual river simulator, calls for each calculation to start at the head of the furthest branch of the main river and to proceed downstream, reservoir by reservoir, along each branch in succession, and along the main river. For each reservoir the appropriate control equation is used to compute the discharge to be released. The mathematical computation takes into account the contents at the end of the previous month, the inflows, the volumes to be used for power and irrigation, and the evaporation losses.

The amount of discharge from each reservoir minus the amount lost in transmission in the next reach of the river and minus the amount abstracted for local irrigation requirements gives the amount of river flow reaching the next reservoir downstream. When the calculations for one month have been completed the same cycle is repeated for the next month, and the process is continued until the full period of sample years has been covered. The calculated discharges, end-of-month contents, reservoir losses, and other relevant quantities are presented in a variety of forms, depending on their final destination.

Fundamental Data for Hydrological Simulation

Say that irrigation is the main concern of a river control scheme to be designed at this stage. An important but subsidiary consideration is the provision of hydroelectric power. Navigation interests are relatively minor. Flood control is of importance, but it can be incorporated in a scheme designed primarily for irrigation. Other local factors may have an effect. For example, the preservation of antique structures on islands in the river, or in the lakes connected with the river, restricts the maximum level at which these lakes may be operated.

There are also geological considerations to be kept in mind. Prolonged storage of silt-lade water results in a lesser or greater reduction in the silt content of the water passing downstream. Along the river bed, and at its mouth, a natural balance is maintained between the processes of erosion and sedimentation. The storage of water in reservoirs can, therefore, affect the rate of sedimentation downstream disturbing this balance.

Another factor distinguishes this plan from other river-control projects. It provides for over-year storage on a very large scale, with the objective of making the maximum possible use of the water available for irrigation, and eliminating, as far as possible, the wastage which results from the passage of surplus water to the sea. Annual storage methods, used frequently in irrigation schemes up till now, merely store water during the flood season of a year for use during the dry season of the same year. Over-year storage, which has found relatively little application in the past, involves the accumulation of water during a succession of rainy years and its retention for use during subsequent years of drought. Over-year storage is maintained as close as possible to a value that varies very slowly, being held proportional to a long-term mean of natural conditions.

As with most mathematical simulators, the great number of the equations which would form the basis of the study need to have a fairly simple origin. The river system can be regarded as a set of reservoir sites, which may be natural or artificial lakes, and in which water may be accumlated or released by the control of gates in a dam. These reservoirs are connected by reaches, in which water flows freely. In any time interval, the change in contents at a reservoir site can be obtained arithmetically by combining the inflows from upstream along the main river course, from rainfall and from subsidiary streams running into the reservoir, and subtracting the combined losses from outflow downstream along the river course and by evaporation from the surface of the reservoir.[1]

The reaches of the main river between reservoirs can be further divided at the points of confluence with tributaries. In any time interval, the amount of water leaving a confluence would be simply the sum of the amounts arriving there along the main stream and the tributary. In some cases, it might be assumed that at any point on the river the rate of flow remains constant with time, so that the "lag" of time taken by water to flow along any particular reach of the river remains unchanged throughout the period of which the calculations are being made.

From the amount of water which flows in at the upstream end of the river during a certain period of time, it is possible to find the amount which takes the same time to flow out at the downstream end. This outflow will occur, in fact, after a period of time equal to the appropriate lag. Allowance must be made for the water lost by seepage through the banks and by evaporation, and the water removed for irrigation.

The accuracy of the calculations depends in part on the length of the time interval chosen as the basis of computation. In practice the settings of dam gates are controlled at intervals ranging from a few hours to several days, depending on circumstances. For the purpose of these computations, however, a time interval of a certain constant number of days can be chosen as providing sufficient accuracy. In some cases, the meteorological records which list rainfalls and so forth by periods ranging from one to several days would not warrant the use of a time interval shorter than the longest of these periods.

Although the data and other information needed for a simulation study of hydraulic works may vary from one case to another, in general such data should include

---

[1] Depending on the nature of the model, the provided data might consist of monthly values of the recorded inflows entering the main river system, or a computation thereoff In a certain experimentation with a river model, these values were taken "net," that is, they allowed, where necessary, for local evaporation losses which occur naturally.

  (i) reservoir capacities and control equations,
 (ii) reservoir contents at the start of the simulation period,
(iii) rainfall and "sidestream" inflows at the reservoir sites,
(iv) evaporation losses from the surface of the reservoirs,
 (v) losses by seepage and evaporation along reaches of the main river, and any local inflows from catchments,
(vi) irrigation off-takes for each reach of the river,
(vii) inflows from tributaries at points of confluence,
(viii) time "lags" for flow of water along each reach of the river.

Nevertheless, this classification is not unique and it might be argued that, in specific cases, different sets of data are necessary. For instance, a hydrological research project in the United States considered as crucial data dead storage, flood storage, and conservation storage. The target of this developmental project was maximum yield. Hence, all dams were designed for the maximum height economically achievable at the site. The storage volume was divided as follows:

(a) dead storage, to allow for 50 years of estimated siltation;
(b) flood storage, to reduce the design flood to approximate channel capacity; and
(c) conservation storage, to compensate for all other available storage.

In this particular project, the site configuration determined the type of dam and spillway. Two sites were found to be most suitable for earth dams with free-flowing saddle spillways. The third dam site appeared most favorable for a concrete dam with gated over-all spillway. The size of the spillways was based on the spillway design for probable maximum flood. Detailed hydrological studies based on past records, particularly the drought period of 1930–1931 and the floods of 1924, influenced the way of facing record drought conditions and the choice of the maximum safe flood permissible.

Other criteria were also used to determine certain discharges specified in the operational studies. Fish propagation and the associated recreation values of fishing also were given due weight. So was the estimate of the over-all effect of this project on the local economy. Then, to test the efficiency of the projected reservoir system, the operation was simulated using historical flow data. The operation of each reservoir, therefore, had to be described, rule curves had to be established, and standard notations had to be adapted.

A certain research project was confronted with a substantial number of natural lakes. For each of these lakes which were to be used as reservoirs, the researchers had to have available data on the combined rainfall plus inflow from side streams, less evaporation. The sum of these data gave the "net natural inflows."

For the calculation of the evaporation losses the researchers had to formulate a number of hypotheses, since these losses also depend on climatic conditions and on the free surface area of the water. Similarly, for the reservoirs which were to be made, an estimated fraction of the contents had to be taken for the monthly evaporation. These estimates were based on the corresponding free-surface areas, the local topography, and the observed rates of evaporation per unit surface area in other, similar operations within the same region.

To allow for the loss by seepage through the banks and evaporation along the course of the successive reaches of the river, the inflow at the upstream was multipled by a constant "transmission factor" to give a value for the outflow at the downstream end. Use of transmission factors in this way is equivalent to the removal of the entire irrigation off-take for any particular reach of the river at the downstream end. The error introduced by this approximation was considered to be not serious. The values of the transmission losses were obtained experimentally by comparing the natural inflows and outflows for each reach of the river, assuming that the losses are proportional to inflow, and averaging the monthly values for the transmission factors. The scatter of individual results over a quite considerable period of observation was found to be relatively insignificant.

The foregoing discussion brings into proper perspective the amount of calculation involved in an experimental method of investigation for hydrologic works. We have followed this process through a succession of phases. The routine calculations involved document the increasing need of automatic computational media to test the relative merits of alternative values of parameters and methods of control. As the mathematical simulation study progresses, it becomes apparent that limited sets of results would not provide accurate indications of the more general trends. A large amount of data is usually necessary, and this leads to the need for statistical data-reduction techniques and automatic data calculators.

A Multipurpose Water-Resource System

A research group in a major University simulated a river basin on a large scale computer. The program was completed, debugged, and tested within one year from the day this work started. The research workers set as their objective the improvement of the current methodology for the planning and designing of multiunit, multipurpose water-resource systems.

We have already stated how and why planning techniques can be improved by providing design engineers with means enabling them to take into account and compare alternatives, and to experiment on an optimal combination of different system components. To estimate the largest positive difference between benefits and costs, a "production function" has to be described. Hence, this work began with the development of such a function.

In the simple case of a single reservoir–single output, the mass curve may serve adequately to establish the relationship between input (reservoir capacity) and output (irrigation water, hydroelectric force, or water supply). But, as more units and purposes are added to the system, this technique becomes unworkable. For a complex system drafts from the several reservoirs can be varied in many ways to meet a specified output. Conversely, the quantity of output depends upon the manner in which the reservoir system is operated. Complementarity and competition among purposes are usually present to complicate the problem. For instance, within certain limits, the same acre foot of water may be put to more than one use, for example, for irrigation and for electric energy generation. Also, the same reservoir capacity may be used for more than one purpose, for flood control in winter and spring and electric energy generation or irrigation in the summer and autumn.

To help examine these problems the research workers developed a prototype river basin system sufficiently complex to present the most significant aspects of a multipurpose, multiunit design, yet not so complex as to raise insuperable barriers to solution for the optimum. Included are three basic factors:

  (i) irrigation (representing consumpting uses),
  (ii) power production,
  (iii) flood control

and eight physical units, namely: four storage dams, one diversion dam, two power plants, and one system of irrigation distribution works. These physical units were taken as the variables in the system. Storage dam or power plant sizes or levels of outputs could be varied within rather wide ranges.

Records from river studies in the United States were used for the basic hydrology of the system. Capital, operation, and maintenance cost functions for all physical units and benefit functions for all outputs were assumed as given. Other given data included the head-capacity relationship for the variable head power plant and the consumption-return flow pattern for irrigation water.

Three methods were examined:

(a) selecting and analyzing, through engineering judgment and experience, a limited number of combinations;

(b) constructing simple mathematical models by abstracting the problem, so that much of the analysis could be handled by standard mathematical or statistical methods;

(c) simulating the system on electronic digital computers.

The researchers proceeded by building up an optimum system, step by step, from individual components. In this way, first the most important units and purposes were identified by making rough estimates of a cost and benefit function and of the input-output relationships. The maximum limits of outputs were approximated from the given hydrology. Short cuts, such as analysis of critical periods rather than the entire period of hydrologic record, were used to reduce the volume of work. Special attention was given to points where benefits, costs, or input-output relationships change abruptly, since it is likely that optimal combinations are located at such points.

Next the most important variables were analyzed in greater detail, on an incremental basis, and in the order of their importance. For example, the most important output and the principal unit or units which supply that output were analyzed as a single-purpose system. Alternatively, the most important unit and the principal output or outputs therefrom were analyzed as a single-unit system. In this way, a first approximation was established. Other components and outputs were added on an incremental basis.

Although theoretically this method was developed in a satisfactory manner, it was found to have practical limitations. Such limitations led the research workers to the conclusion that the method should not be relied upon alone. Their next step was to examine a computerization of the method, which in itself brought about the use of simulation techniques and of mathematical models. In this study, the experimenters considered

(i) the natural flow hydrology;

(ii) the levels and time patterns of outputs;

(iii) the sizes of reservoirs, power plants, canals, and other system units;

(iv) the operating policy and the benefit and cost functions.

For each "combination of inputs," for instance, levels of reservoir capacity, the machine computed by time periods (usually month by month) the quantitity of water required to meet a "combination of outputs." These were feet of water for irrigation and kilowatt-hours. The data processor calculated the natural flow and the resultant addition to, or subtraction from, storage. In this manner the compatability of a selected combination of inputs and outputs was determined, and above all the net benefits produced by this combination.[2]

Three methods for handling operating procedures have been investigated in the course of this project. One involves formulating a relatively small number of separate operating procedures, each with a distinctive logic. In this way, a specific operating procedure is developed and programmed, and a set of studies is run to determine the results of using this operating procedure over a range of combinations of specified inputs and outputs. Then, a second operating procedure is coded, as a separate machine program, and the same set of inputs and outputs is analyzed in order to examine the influence of the operating procedure on compatibility of the various combinations in the set. The process is repeated for different input-output combinations, and the results compared.

To some extent, the value of this method depends upon the number of separate operating procedures which must be used to produce optimal or near-optimal results, and upon the ease with which operating procedures can be programmed for the machine. If, for example, there are relatively few operating procedures that together will give near-optimum results over almost the entire range of combinations, and if these procedures can be identified readily by a skilled technician, then the method would seem to have promise.

The alternative method tested by the experimenters was the development of a very generalized master operating procedure, which, within the detailed rules, could be varied within certain limits. Using this approach, the operating procedure was treated more directly, as an input variable, in the same manner that reservoir and power plant generating capacities are treated. The master operating procedure needs to be programmed in a manner flexible enough to permit a number of detailed operating procedures to be incorporated. The advantage of this method is that many operating procedures can be tested quickly. The approximate shape of the production function and the net benefit can be determined with a single machine program—

---

[2] It is interesting to note certain similarities between the research project currently under discussion and the TVA simulator (Chapter 23).

provided the general conditions allow the development of the program.

A third alternative is to write the optimum operating procedure as an integral part of the machine program. General rules have to be formulated initially, assuming a knowledge of future flows or degrees of forecastability. These rules must then be refined as they are applied progressively to time increments. The University team developed a procedure of this type. It apportions storage and releases among the various reservoirs so as to minimize waste of water, power head, and storage space. In this way, it tried to optimize the available water supplies with given sizes of inputs-reservoirs, power plants, and the like.

Experimenting for Water Control

In one of the research projects for hydrological works, the mathematical procedure for calculating the change in the condition of the river combines two sets of equations. The first set consists of the "contents change" and the "transmission" equations.

Each of the "contents change" equations relates the change in contents of a reservoir to the appropriate inflows, evaporation loss, and discharge. Correspondingly, the "transmission" equations relate the quantity of water leaving a reach of the river to the quantities entering (along the main stream and from tributaries), the amount removed for irrigation, and the transmission loss. These equations result from the conservation of matter, from the natural structure of the river, and from basic hydrological considerations.

The equations of the second set relate the controlled discharges at dam sites to the reservoir contents and other factors that determine the quantities of water to be released in different circumstances. They have been worked out with the aim of meeting, as successfully as possible, the objective of highest priority to irrigation. This can be achieved by reducing to a minimum the wastage of water, and by the maintenance of the annual water supply as close as possible to some mean value.

The control equations have to provide for local requirements of different degrees of stringency. These range from absolute necessities, such as the restriction of discharges within well-defined limits at certain points of the river's course, to more qualitative objectives, such as the avoidance, if possible, of departures of the level in a lake from a prescribed value. The control equations incorporate also local procedures that may be expected, from general experience, to contribute to the achievement of the over-all objectives of the scheme.

In what regards local necessities, the most obvious arise from physical or contractual limits imposed on the discharges from individual dam sites. Such restrictions were first included in the calculations for dams below which channel dimensions imposed an upper limit on the discharge that could be tolerated or at which hydroelectric power requirements imposed a lower limit. It was found, however, that the full implications of a changed form of control equation could not always be gaged in advance, and that new equations sometimes led to calculated values that were negative for the discharges.

It also proved useful to impose temporary limits on particular discharges, for particular simulation runs. An "absolute minimum discharge" was therefore associated with each reservoir, as a parameter that could be set without affecting the rest of the program. For most reservoirs, this parameter was normally set equal to zero. For each reservoir, the discharge found by direct application of the control equation each month was checked against the appropriate absolute minimum value.

Any discharge that fell below the "absolute minimum" was increased to the necessary value, and the reservoir contents modified accordingly. Any discharge that resulted from direct application of a control equation and that was in excess of a preset limit was reduced to the appropriate value, again with a corresponding modification to the calculated reservoir contents. In general, the control equations strove to prevent reservoirs from emptying or filling completely, but negative contents or spilling were accepted in preference to discharges that fell outside prescribed limits.

Considering the procedures that affect combinations of adjacent sites jointly it was found that one involves just an "upstream supplement," in different terms, a return in the computational loop to an upstream reservoir to provide a modified discharge. This became necessary when the value, which had been calculated according to the normal rules, together with the other conditions at the lower reservoir, failed to meet the downstream requirements.

Additional considerations had to be given in determining the form of the equations which would integrate the entire river valley as a single control system. The simulator was developed to provide mathematical connections between the control procedures adopted for the head waters with the state of the various reservoirs which were located some thousands of miles distant. As a basis for determining the control action to be applied on the head waters according to the condition of the reservoirs, the idea of supplementary reservoirs was introduced at one stage. A certain constant reserve was held near the sources, to be drawn upon only when there was a serious shortage of water in middle and lower river. Water accumulating during the wet season, in excess of the "supplementary reserve," was apportioned between the different months and utilized completely during the dry season of the same year. These procedures can be effectively described by means of mathematical equations.

The total irrigation off-take was kept constant throughout each of the earlier runs. Nevertheless, as a final measure to maximize the irrigation supplies, it was assumed that the mannual irrigation abstraction, for the entire river, should be linked to the water actually available from natural inflows over some previous period of time. The total abstraction in any one year was taken as the running average of the combined natural inflows. This, in turn, was converted to the resulting discharges which they would have produced at a predetermined point, if allowed to flow freely down the river. Consideration was given to natural transmission losses and to evaporation losses in all reservoirs. By using a relatively long-term mean, the fluctuations in total water supply from year to year were found to be relatively small.

CHAPTER 22

Mathematical Models for Hydroelectric Studies

A Twofold Model-Making Procedure

Research on mathematical models for hydraulic works has used two distinct approaches to model-making, one deterministic and the other probabilistic.

For an example of the deterministic class, we consider a mathematical model using sinusoidal functions to simulate the natural flow hydrology and the time pattern of flows for various specified uses. This model proceeds from two basic concepts:

(1) The main function of a reservoir is to distribute the natural flow of a stream in a time pattern that will be desirable for a particular use or set of uses.

(2) In any sufficiently long time period, reservoir inflows and outflows must balance, and thus a direct solution to the storage-yield relationship can be derived from mathematical equations of continuity.

Curves of this type can be expressed as sinusoidal functions with parameters relating to frequency, amplitude, and phase angle with respect to time. In this way, the natural flow can be expressed as a function of time:

$$f = \bar{f}[1 + K \sin(2\pi t)],$$

where

$\bar{f}$ = mean inflow;

K = parameter representing variation of flow during the year; it measures the amplitude of the curve;

t = time.

For some rivers it is necessary to use additional higher order sine terms in a Fourier series to fit the inflow hydrograph closely. In the same manner, the time pattern of output can be expressed by the equation

$$g = \bar{g}[1 + C \sin(2\pi t - \Phi)],$$

where

$\bar{g}$ = mean outflow
C = distribution factor for mean outflow use. It measures the amplitude of the curve.
Φ = phase angle of g.

If total reservoir outflow is assumed to equal total inflow, the rate of change of reservoir storage can be stated as

$$\frac{dV}{dt} = f - g$$

or

$$\frac{dV}{dt} = \bar{f}[1 + K \sin(2\pi t)] - \bar{g}[1 + C \sin(2\pi t - \Phi)],$$

and, from continuity, $\bar{f} = \bar{g}$.
Thus,

$$\frac{dV}{dt} = K\bar{g} \sin(2\pi t) - C\bar{g} \sin(2\pi t - \Phi).$$

By treating the right-hand term as a vector, it is possible to solve the equation to obtain the maximum storage required to convert the natural flow to the regulated flow. To this calculated maximum storage are applied benefit functions, indicating the value of each use as a function of the volume of flow allocated to it. Cost functions, relating the over-all capacities of the reservoirs to construction, operation, maintenance, and replacement costs, can also be considered.

This method can be effectively applied to simple cases of one or two reservoirs and two or three purposes, where the hydrology and time pattern of flows for specified uses can be expressed in simple mathematical functions as above. In these cases, the method can provide a quick approximation of the optimum reservoir size, allocation of water among uses, and operating policy.

Nevertheless, this method has important limitations arising from assumptions that must be made in application. For instance, the time period for which the mathematical functions apply must necessarily be short, a year is usually selected for convenience because use patterns ordinarily follow an annual cycle. Another limitation is the problem of over-year storage. The method calculates the size of reservoir needed to store the excess flow in the selected year and to release it as needed throughout the year, but it allows no carry-overs. Furthermore, complementarity, that is, the joint use of flow to produce more than one output, is not easily handled by the model.

These limitations of the deterministic approach led the research workers at a major university to develop a stochastic model through the use of queuing theory.[1] With this approach, random inflows during successive time periods are approximated by a binomial probability density function. Drafts during each time period are specified constants, except when reservoirs are overflowing or empty. The formulation relates means and variances of inflows, volumes of reservoirs, specified drafts, and probabilities of draft shortages and overflows.

The model determines the relative frequencies of spills and exhaustion of contents for particular reservoir sizes and levels of draft with given time distributions. Spills occur when the reservoir capacities are insufficient to hold inflows, under the conditions imposed by the specified drafts. Reservoir contents are exhausted when the specified drafts for any time period exceed the inflows during that period plus contents available at the beginning of the period. The queuing equation may be written as

$$R_i = R_{i-1} + (\bar{f}_1 + ds_{f_i}) - L_i,$$

where

R_i = storage at end of period 1,

R_{i-1} = holdover storage from preceding period,

$(\bar{f}_i + ds_{f_i})$ = inflow of current period,

$\bar{f}_i$ = mean inflow during period,

s_{f_i} = the standard deviation of the inflow of the current period,

d = a stochastic normal deviate with zero mean and unit variance,

L_i = draft for the current period.

As both the reservoir storage capacities and the levels of draft are selected or specified for each run or try with the model, the results of

---

[1] See "Statistical Process and Reliability Engineering."

each run can be interpreted as a "sample" of the physical response surface of the system. By using the cost of each reservoir size and the benefits of each level of output, or losses of each shortage, it is possible to transform the "physical" response surface into an "economic," or "net benefit," response surface and calculate the net benefits associated with different combinations of reservoir sizes and levels of draft.

Stochastic models of this type may presumably handle the problem of over-year storage and avoid the question of which hydrologic year to use by using all of the available hydrologic record. Nevertheless, other problems still remain unsolved, such as the complementarity among uses and reservoirs. Also, the method requires an unambigious statement of permissible shortage rules in terms of frequency, intensity, and extent of serial correlation. Such data may not be obtainable in every case.

Developing Equations for Hydrologic Works

For an example of the application of mathematical experimentation to hydroelectric works, consider a mathematical model written for a network of dams. The problem was the design of a flood control system of three reservoirs on a river and its tributaries, on which one dam had already been built. As can be seen in Fig. 1, two areas, towns A and B, can be fully or partially protected by the joint effect of the already built

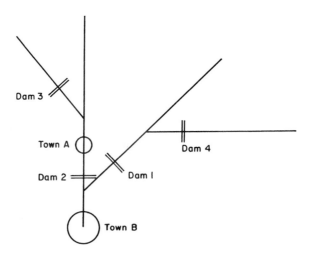

FIG. 1

reservoir (dam 1) and the three planned dams, 2, 3, and 4. The question to be answered was whether all three new dams should be built and, if yes, to what size.

At the beginning of this study, a basic supposition was made that the use of linear equations would not cause an appreciable deviation from the actual conditions. This supposition was tested and found acceptable before proceeding further with the construction of the model.[2] The following functions can be deduced:

(1) $Q_n = Q_n(F, BD)$,

(2) $Q_m = Q_m(Q_n, S)$,

(3) $S = S(Q_n, Q_m, SD[\text{limit only}])$,

(4) $C = C(S, SD)$,

(5) $B = B(Q_n, Q_m, DD)$,

(6) $P = P(C, B)$,

where

F = frequency,
Q_n = natural peak flow,
Q_m = modified peak flow,
S = storage,
C = cost,
B = benefit,
SD = site data,
DD = drainage data,
BD = basin data,
P = profit.

Since the exact form of these functions is, for the time being, unknown, it is evidently necessary to make some fundamental assumptions that would enable us to visualize the general form of the equations. The first of these assumptions has to do with a simulation of the model.

First, the researcher decided to eliminate "frequency" F as a variable. While normally, in an analysis of this type, the entire range of frequencies is considered, here only one value (the 1 % frequency) was used. This in turn made Q_n a constant. The researcher studied once more the

---

[2] This model is the result of the research done as a term project by H. E. Schwarz, in a graduate course in System Engineering, given by the writer during the Spring semester of 1957, at the Catholic University of America.

effect of his initial hypothesis about linearity. Actual data satisfied him that, within the range and accuracy of the considered application, the supposition of linearity could be accepted.

The second major assumption was that the effects of flood reduction from various dams could be added to each other. This means $Q_n - Q_m = R$, or flow difference equals the reduction R. It also means that $R_j = \Sigma_i R_{ij}$, where the suscript i represents the number of the dam and j the letter of the town. The third assumption was that if the 1 % storm occurs once in a hundred years, it will occur 0.5 times in any year economical life of a flood control project. Finally it was assumed that the annual cost of such a project, including interest, amortization, and maintenance is about 1/20 of the capital cost. Therefore, the determination of the profit function P from the project is the following difference between the 50 % of the "benefits" and 5 % of the "costs":

$$P = 0.5B - 0.05C.$$

In a general manner, reservoir releases can be determined as functions of the storage content of the reservoir (or of the reservoir system) at the end of the preceding time period and of the inflow-outflow activity of the period under consideration. Obviously, inflow — outflow = change in storage. This equation holds for reservoirs as well as for natural reaches of the river, or free-overflow spillways. As the accuracy of high flow is considered of little importance in this study compared with the need for accurate volume accounting on a day-by-day basis, the normal difference equation of routing with free outflow can be simplified to a form in which inflows are distributed over a specified outflow time period by distribution coefficients. These coefficients can be computed from a study of actual flood flows.

The next step in this study was to develop a certain number of preliminary alternative designs for the three planned dams. This was done along with a study of flood flows and their damages and a study involving synthetic storms and their regulation by dams of various sizes. This required mathematical analysis, the results of which are given in very simplified terms by the following equations:

Cost:

$$C_2 = 4500 + 133\,S_2\,,$$
$$C_3 = 2900 + 135\,S_3\,,$$
$$C_4 = 2000 + 246\,S_4\,;$$

Damages:

$$D_a = -395 + 16Q\,,$$
$$D_b = -6200 + 200Q\,;$$

Flood reduction:

$$
\begin{aligned}
R_{3a} &= -20.60 + 0.646\, Q_n + 1.90\, S_3 , \\
R_{1b} &= 6.98 + 0.054\, Q_n + 0.82\, S_1 , \\
R_{2b} &= -15.30 + 0.240\, Q_b + 0.47\, S_2 , \\
R_{3b} &= -7.31 + 0.082\, Q_n + 0.25\, S_3 , \\
R_{4b} &= 3.97 + 0.021\, Q_n + 0.68\, S_4 ;
\end{aligned}
$$

Frequency:

$$1\% \text{ natural flow} = 52\,000 \text{ cfs.}$$

In all these equations, the units of flow are given in 100 cfs, the storage in 100 acre feet, and cost and damages in thousands of dollars. C_i, D_j, and R_{ij} should become zero when S_i or Q becomes zero. The large constant terms in the equations are due to the assumption of linearity, which is far off in the vicinity of zero.

Benefits can be expressed as the damages due to the natural flow less the residual damages after the flood reduction due to the dams. Therefore,

$$B_a = D_a(Q_n) - D_a(Q_n - R),$$

and

$$B_b = D_b(Q_n) - D_b(Q_n - R).$$

Substituting the values of D_a and D_b, we obtain $B_a = 16R_a$ and $B_b = 200R_b$, where again $R_j = \Sigma_i\, R_{ij}$. Substituting further the values of R_{ij} and neglecting the constant terms, as they do not enter into the calculations of maximization, we obtain

$$
\begin{aligned}
B_a &= 30.4 S_3 , \\
B_b &= 164 S_1 + 96 S_2 + 50 S_3 + 136 S_4 .
\end{aligned}
$$

As dam 1 has already been built and its storage is unchangable, the term containing S_1 in the latter equation becomes a constant, and may not be considered further. The complete profit equation would be equal to

$$P = 41.4 S_2 + 33.4 S_3 + 55.7 S_4 .$$

The limiting factors of the study need also to be considered. Three of these are obvious: S_2, S_3, and S_4 must be equal to or greater than zero. Three other limits were imposed by the physical conditions of the area: (1) The storage in all three dams together should not exceed 50 000 acre-feet. (2) The storage in dam 2 should not exceed 40 000 acre-feet. (3) The storage in dam 2 should be at least five times that in dam 4. Expressed as inequalities these relationships can be written in the following manner:

$$S_2 \geqslant 0,$$
$$S_3 \geqslant 0,$$
$$S_4 \geqslant 0,$$
$$S_2 + S_3 + S_4 \leqslant 50,$$
$$S_2 \leqslant 40,$$
$$S_2 - 5S_4 \geqslant 0.$$

An examination of the profit equation shows that, for maximization, S_4 must be made as large as limitations allow. Hence S_2 should be made as large as its respective limitations permit, and S_3 should take what is the difference. This indicates an optimum solution of

$$S_2 = 40 \times 10^3 \text{ acre-feet,}$$
$$S_3 = \ 2 \times 10^3 \text{ acre-feet,}$$
$$S_4 = \ 8 \times 10^3 \text{ acre-feet.}$$

As only three key variables are part of this system, a three-dimensional graphical solution for optimization is possible and is presented in Fig. 2.

Using Interpolation Theory

One of the most frequently occurring handicaps in a hydroelectric study is the lack of complete data which will allow, in an able manner, the development of a simulator for predictive purposes. In the present section, we consider three examples of data generation through use of the interpolation theory.

EXAMPLE 1

To operate electric power utilities, the time and size of the peak demand on the system must be estimable. These data are necessary so that the system will be prepared to absorb the maximum load in the most economical manner as discussed in Chapter 23.

The largest demands have, in the past, occurred during the Christmas season, when the days are shortest; cold weather is present, and much

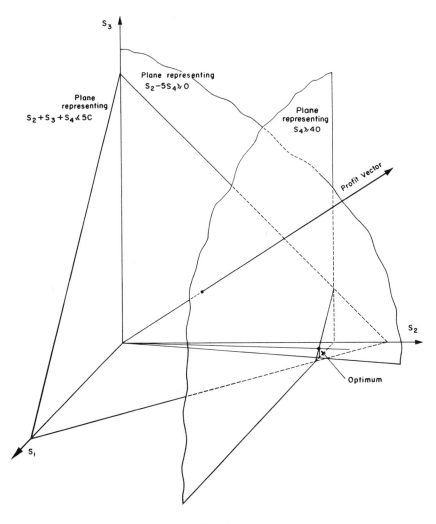

FIG. 2

decorative lighting is used. A demand sample for a certain city served
by a particular utility company is listed below:

	Dec. 3	Dec. 13	Dec. 23	Jan. 2
Maximum demand (MW)	10	13	19	12
Time of peak demand (P.M.)	6:40	6:10	6:13	6:21

It is required to find

1. Amount and time of maximum demand on December 20.
2. Day, time, and amount of maximum demand.
3. The number of, and dates of, the days on which the normal maximum of the system (15 MW) is exceeded.
4. Day and time of earliest peak.

1(a). *Demand on December 20* :

Dates	Demand	Δ	Δ^2	Δ^3
Dec. 3	10	3	3	—12
Dec. 13	13	6	—9	—
Dec. 23	19	—3	—	—
Jan. 2	16	—	—	—

$$D_x = D_0 + C_1 \Delta + C_2 \Delta^2 + C_3 \Delta^3 ,$$

$$C_1 = \frac{17}{10} = 1.7, \qquad C_2 = \frac{\left(\frac{17}{10}\right)\left(\frac{17}{10} - 1\right)}{2 \cdot 1} = \frac{(1.7)(0.7)}{2} = 0.595,$$

$$C_3 = \frac{\left(\frac{17}{10}\right)\left(\frac{17}{10} - 1\right)\left(\frac{17}{10} - 2\right)}{3 \cdot 2 \cdot 1} = \frac{(1.7)(0.7)(-0.3)}{6} = -0.03,$$

$$D_{20} = 10 + 1.7(3) + (0.595)(3) + (-12)(-0.03)$$
$$= 10 + 5.1 + 1.8 + 0.36 = 17.26 \text{ MW}.$$

1(b). *Time*:

Date	Time[3]	Δ	Δ^2	Δ^3
Dec. 3	400	—30	+33	—28
Dec. 13	370	+ 3	+ 5	—
Decl 23	373	+ 8	—	—
Jan. 2	381	—	—	—

$$T_{20} = 400 - 30(1.7) + 33(0.595) - 28(-0.03)$$
$$= 400 - 51 + 19.8 + 0.84$$
$$= 369.64$$

Time $= 6{:}10$ P.M.

---

[3] Noon reference, $T_{\text{noon}} = 0$.

2(a). *Day of maximum demand*:

$$D_x = 10 + \frac{3x}{10} + \left(\frac{3}{2}\right)\left(\frac{x}{10}\right)\left(\frac{x}{10} - 1\right) - \left(\frac{12}{6}\right)\left(\frac{x}{10}\right)\left(\frac{x}{10} - 1\right)\left(\frac{x}{10} - 2\right),$$

$$D_x = 10 + \frac{3x}{10} + \frac{3}{2}\left(\frac{x^2}{100} - \frac{x}{10}\right) - 2\left(\frac{x^2}{100} - \frac{x}{10}\right)\left(\frac{x}{10} - 2\right),$$

$$\frac{dD_x}{dx} = \frac{3}{10} + \frac{3x}{100} - 0.15 - \frac{6x^2}{1000} + \frac{12x}{100} - 0.4,$$

$$6x^2 - 150x + 250 = 0,$$

$x = 23.2$, or approximately 23 days. Thus the maximum demand results on December 26.

2(b). *Amount*:

$$D_{26} = 10 + \frac{23}{10}(3) + \frac{23}{10}\left(\frac{23}{10} - 1\right)\frac{3}{2} - 2\left(\frac{23}{10}\right)\left(\frac{23}{10} - 1\right)\left(\frac{23}{10} - 2\right),$$

$$D_{26} = 10 + 6.9 + 4.5 - 1.8,$$

$$D_{26} = 19.6 \text{ MW}.$$

2(c). *Time*:

$$T_{26} = 400 - 30(2.3) + 33(1.5) - 28(1.5)$$
$$= 400 - 69 + 49.5 - 4.2,$$
$$= 376.3 = 6{:}16 \text{ P.M.}$$

3. *Range of days load exceeds* 15 MW:

$$15 = 10 + \frac{x}{10}(3) + \left(\frac{x}{10}\right)\left(\frac{x}{10} - 1\right)\frac{3}{2} - 2\left(\frac{x}{10}\right)\left(\frac{x}{10} - 1\right)\left(\frac{x}{10} - 2\right),$$

$$5 = \frac{3x}{10} + \frac{3}{2}\frac{x^2}{100} - \frac{3}{2}\frac{x}{10} - 2\left(\frac{x^3}{1000} - \frac{x^2}{100} - \frac{2x^2}{100} + \frac{2x}{10}\right),$$

$$2x^3 - 75x^2 + 250x + 5000 = 0,$$
$$x^3 - 37.5x^2 + 125x + 2500 = 0.$$

The last equation can be written in the form

$$(x + c)(x^2 + ax + b) = 0,$$

where $c = -(37.5 + a)$, $b = 125 - ac$, and $cb - 2500 - 0$ (see Table I). For $a = -6.68$, $b = -81.0$, and $c = -30.82$, the equation

TABLE I

For a	c	b	$cb-2500$
0	−37.5	125	−7400
−10	−27.5	−150	+1630
−5	−32.5	−37.5	1280
−7	−30.5	−111	+ 190
−6.68	−30.82	−81.0	0

becomes

$$(x - 30.82)(x^2 - 6.68x - 81.0) = 0,$$

$x_1 = 30.82$; $x_2 = 12.9$; $x_3 =$ negative, thus rejected. Therefore, the time range during which consumption is greater than the system's normal peak of 15 MW is equal to 18 total days, from December 16 to January 3.

4(a). *Earliest peak day*:

$$T_x = 400 - 30 \frac{\left(\frac{x}{10}\right) + 33 \left(\frac{x}{10}\right)\left(\frac{x}{10} - 1\right)}{2} - \frac{28}{6}\left(\frac{x}{10}\right)\left(\frac{x}{10} - 1\right)\left(\frac{x}{10} - 2\right),$$

$$\frac{dT_x}{dx} = -3 + 0.33x - 1.65 - \frac{14}{1000}x^2 + \frac{28}{100}x - 0.933 = 0,$$

$$14x^2 - 610x + 5583 = 0,$$

$$x = \frac{610 \pm \sqrt{372100 - 312648}}{28} = \frac{610 \pm 243.8}{28}.$$

Of the two roots, $x \cong 13$ and $x = 30.5$, only the first is acceptable, and therefore the date is December 16.

4(b). *Time of earliest peak*:

$$T_{16} = 400 - 30(1.3) + \frac{33}{2}(1.3)(3) + (-0.7)(0.3)(1.3)\left(-\frac{28}{6}\right)$$

$$T_{16} = 400 - 39 + 6.42 + 1.27$$

$$= 368.7 \text{ or } 6:09 \text{ P.M.}$$

Thus the earliest peak results on December 16 at 6:09 P.M.

Using this information the power company would know that additional generating power would be needed from December 16 to January 3; also that the maximum peak would be 19.6 MW on December 26 at 6:16 P.M. The company knows the time and amount of peak for any given day (part 1); and it knows the earliest that the extra generators must be ready (from part 4) as December 16 at 6:09 P.M.

EXAMPLE 2

The data recorded at a residential electric power substation over the summer months are listed in Table II.

TABLE II

Date	Peak power load (watts $\times 10^5$)	Time of peak P.M.	Time expressed in minutes from 8:00 P.M
May 1	8.20	8:15	15
June 1	6.85	9:00	60
July 1	7.25	9:50	110
August 1	8.90	8:45	45

The following quantities need to be determined (Tables III and IV).

(1) the time that the peak occurred on June 16th;
(2) the peak power load that occurred on June 16th;
(3) the date, time, and peak power load of the minimum peak power load for the summer.[4]

TABLE III

POWER DIFFERENCE

Date	Power $\times 10^5$	Δ_1^1	Δ_1^2	Δ_1^3
May 1	8.00	—1.35	+1.75	—0:90
June 1	6.85	+0.00	+0.85	—
July 1	7.25	+1.25	—	—
Aug. 1	8.50	—	—	—

[4] See also Chapter 7.

TABLE IV

TIME DIFFERENCE

Date	Time	$\Delta_2{}^1$	$\Delta_2{}^2$	$\Delta_2{}^3$
May 1	15	+45	+5	−120
June 1	60	+50	−115	—
July 1	110	−65	—	—
Aug. 1	45	—	—	—

$$f(t) = t + C_1 \Delta^1 + C_2 \Delta^2 + C_3 \Delta^3,$$

$$C_1 = \frac{\gamma_1}{\gamma_0}, \qquad C_2 = \frac{C_1(C_1 - 1)}{2!}, \qquad C_3 = \frac{C_1(C_1 - 1)(C_1 - 2)}{3!}.$$

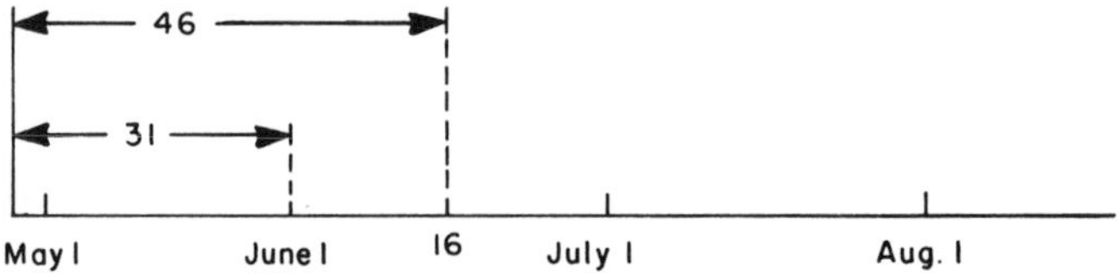

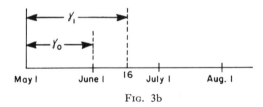

FIG. 3a

1. *Time of peak load on June 16th, for* $\gamma_0 = 31$, $\gamma_1 = 46$:

FIG. 3b

$$t_{\text{June 16}} = 15 + \frac{46}{31}(+45)$$

$$+ \frac{\left(\frac{46}{31}\right)\left(\frac{46}{31} - 1\right)(+5)}{2!} + \frac{\left(\frac{46}{31}\right)\left(\frac{46}{31} - 1\right)\left(\frac{46}{31} - 2\right)(-120)}{3!}$$

$$= 15 + 65.7 + 1.781 + 7.4,$$

$$t_{\text{June 16}} = 89.88,$$

$$t_{\text{June 16}} = 9{:}30 \text{ P.M.}$$

The time of peak load on June 16th was 9:30 P. M.

2. *Amount of peak power load on June 16th:*

$$P_{\text{June 16}} = 8.2 + \left(\frac{46}{31}\right)(-1.35)$$

$$+ \frac{\left(\frac{46}{31}\right)\left(\frac{46}{31} - 1\right)(+1.75)}{2!} + \frac{\left(\frac{46}{31}\right)\left(\frac{46}{31} - 1\right)\left(\frac{46}{31} - 2\right)(-0.9)}{3!}$$

$$= 8.2 - 2.0 + 0.625 + 0.0555 = 6.88$$

$$P_{\text{June 16}} = 6.88 \times 10^5 \text{ watts.}$$

The amount of peak power load on June 16th was 6.88×10^5 watts.

3. *Date, time, and peak power load of minimum peak for the summer:*

$$f(t) = 8.20 + \frac{t}{31}(-1.35)$$

$$+ \frac{\left(\frac{t}{31}\right)\left(\frac{t}{31} - 1\right)(1.75)}{2!} + \frac{\left(\frac{t}{31}\right)\left(\frac{t}{31} - 1\right)\left(\frac{t}{31} - 2\right)(-0.9)}{3!},$$

$$3! \, f(t) = (6)(8.20) - (6)(1.35)\frac{t}{31}$$

$$+ (3)(1.75)\left(\frac{t^2}{31^2} - \frac{t2}{31}\right) - 0.9\left(\frac{t^3}{31^3} - \frac{3t^2}{31^2} + \frac{2t}{31}\right),$$

$$(3!)31^3 f(t) = (49.2)(31^3) - (8.1)31^2 t + (5.25)31t^2 - (5.25)31^2 t - 0.9t^3$$
$$+ (2.7)31t^2 - (1.8)31^2 t,$$

$$(3!)31^3 f(t) = (49.2)(31^3) - (15.15)31^2 t + (7.95)31t^2 - 0.9t^3,$$

$f(t)$ is a minimum when $d/dt \, f(t) = 0$

$$(3!)31^3 f^1(t) = -(15.15)31^2 + (2)(7.95)31t - 2.7t^2,$$
$$t = 37.$$

Thus, the date of the minimum peak is June 7th.

4(a). *Time of minimum peak:*

$$t_{\text{June 7}} = 15 + \frac{37}{31}(+45)$$

$$+ \frac{\left(\frac{37}{31}\right)\left(\frac{37}{31} - 1\right)(+5)}{2!} + \frac{\left(\frac{37}{31}\right)\left(\frac{37}{31} - 1\right)\left(\frac{37}{31} - 2\right)(-120)}{3!}$$

$$= 15 + 53.6 + 0.565 + 3.66,$$

$$= 9 : 15 \text{ P.M.}$$

4(b). *Amount of minimum peak*:

$$P_{\text{June 7}} = 8.2 + \left(\frac{37}{31}\right)(-1.35)$$

$$+ \frac{\left(\frac{37}{31}\right)\left(\frac{37}{31} - 1\right)(1.75)}{2!} + \frac{\left(\frac{37}{31}\right)\left(\frac{37}{31} - 1\right)\left(\frac{37}{31} - 2\right)(-0.9)}{3!}$$

$$= 8.2 - 1.61 + 0.1975 + 0.0275,$$

$$= 6.82 \times 10^5 \text{ watts.}$$

The minimum peak power load for the summer occurred at 9:15 P.M. on June 7th and had a magnitude of 6.82×10^5 watts.

EXAMPLE 3

A certain power station has a maximum load capacity of 60 000 kW. This power is being supplied by three turboelectric generators—one with an output of 30 000 kW, and each of the other two with an output of 15 000 kW. The load requirements vary throughout the day, and it is not necessary to operate all three turbines continuously. Say that the load requirements vary much the same within a 24-hour cycle. There is a certain schedule available, telling the engineer in charge what turbines must be used at any particular time of day.

Say that the period of lowest output occurs during the middle of the night, from 1:00 A.M. to 5:00 A.M., and that the heaviest demand occurs during mid-afternoon, between 1:00 P.M. and 4:00 P.M. Let x be equal to the time of day, and $f(x)$ be equal to the power load at that particular time. In the following, the values of x and $f(x)$ along with the successive application of the difference operator Δ are tabulated, and, following the tabulation, the interpolation formulas are used to determine the exact time of day at which the demand is a maximum, or a minimum.

Case I: Minimum power demand (see Table V). If we add to the independent variable x a number n of equal increments, we obtain a new function $g(x)$, such that

$$g(x) = E^n f(x) = f(x) + n f(x) + \frac{n(n-1)}{2!} \Delta^2 f(x) + \frac{n(n-1)(n-2)}{3!} \Delta^3 f(x) + \dots .$$

TABLE V

Time of day x	Load (kW) $f(x)$	$\Delta f(x)$	$\Delta^2 f(x)$	$\Delta^3 f(x$
2 A.M.	16 400	−1200	500	1700
3 A.M.	15 200	− 700	2200	—
4 A.M.	14 900	−1500	—	—
5 A.M.	16 000	—	—	—

By taking the first-order derivative of this equation and setting it equal to zero, we can find the value of x for which the equation is a maximum or minimum:

$$g(x) = 16,400 + x(-1200) + \frac{x(x-1)}{2!}(500) + \frac{x(x-1)(x-2)}{3!}(1700),$$

$$g(x) = 16,400 - 1200x + 225(x^2 - x) + \frac{850}{3}(x^3 - 3x^2 + 2x),$$

$$\frac{d[g(x)]}{dx} = 0 - 1200 + 225(2x - 1) + \frac{850}{3}(3x^2 - 6x + 2) = 0,$$

$$\frac{d[g(x)]}{dx} = 90x^2 - 150x - 103 = 0,$$

and $x = 2.19$ hr = 2 hr, 11 min.

Adding this to the initial time, 2:00 A.M., we find that the time of minimum load is 4:11 A.M.

Substituting the above value of x into the initial equation, it is now possible to determine the minimum load:

$$g(x)_{min} = 16\,400 + (2.19)(-1200)$$
$$+ \frac{2.19(1.19)(500)}{2} + \frac{2.19(1.19)(0.19)}{6}(1700).$$

Thus the minimum load is 14 495 kW.

Case II: Maximum power demand (see Table VI). Proceeding as before,

TABLE VI

Time of day x	Load (kW), $f(x)$	Δ	Δ^2	Δ^3
1 P.M.	28 000	8500	−3800	−8100
2 P.M.	36 500	4700	11 900	—
3 P.M.	41 000	−7200	—	—
4 P.M.	34 000	—	—	—

$$g(x) = 28\,000 + x(8500) + \frac{x(x-1)}{2!}(-3800) + \frac{x(x-1)(x-2)}{3!}(-8100),$$

$$g(x) = 28\,000 + 8500x - \frac{3800}{2}(x^2 - x) - \frac{8100}{6}(x^3 - 3x^2 + 2x),$$

$$\frac{d[g(x)]}{dx} = 0 + 8500 - 1900(2x - 1) - 1350(3x^2 - 6x + 2) = 0$$

$$= 405x^2 - 430x - 770 = 0,$$

and $x = 2.01$ hr $\simeq 2$ hr, 1 min.

Adding this value of x to the initial time, 1:00 P.M., we obtain, for the time of maximum load, 3:01 P.M.

Solving for the maximum load,

$$g(x)_{\max} = 28\,000 + 2.01(8500) + \frac{2.01(1.01)}{2}(-3800) + \frac{2.01(1.01)(0.01)}{6}(-8100).$$

The maximum power demand, therefore, is 41 225 kW.

CHAPTER 23

The TVA Power Simulator

Introduction

The objective of an economic loading simulator is to determine the most efficient loading of generating stations in order to produce the lowest delivered power cost to electric utility customers. Its use on a utility system can result in savings in respect to system operation.

The first mathematical simulator ever developed for a power system has been designed by TVA,[1] and it is run every hour on the hour on a large scale electronic digital computer. Through this operation TVA establishes exact schedules for its entire power production and distribution network. Though much has yet to be perfected before arriving at a real-time control application, the present day achievements present a significant contribution to the state of the art in simulation and computer control. The complete model is known as the *Economic Loading Program*. To better follow the workings of the Economic Loading Program, a number of points should be carefully considered. These include the meaning of economic loading, the structure of the mathematical model, the operation of an economic program and its implementation by means of a computer, the power system on which the computer is used, and the results that have been achieved. We would start our discussion with a consideration of the power company and its network, in order to give to the reader some understanding on the range of this application.

The TVA System

TVA revenues range at the level of 250 to 300 million dollars per year. It covers an area of 80 000 sq. miles. One of the principal functions of the Authority is the operation of 9 major and 3 minor steam plants

---

[1] TVA = Tennessee Valley Authority. All numerical data on power production and consumption are with reference to 1958, when the digital control system described in this chapter was installed.

and of 37 hydroelectric plants with a total capacity of 12 000 megawatts or 10 % of the total power generation in the United States.[2] Average loads on the system run at the level of 7500 to 8000 megawatts, two-thirds of the corresponding power is generated by steam, the balance by hydroelectric plants. The peak load is 9700 MW. The two atomic laboratories and the *Air Force Experimental Station* in the Tennessee Valley consume the 51 % of the total power production. Since this is taken on a steady and well-predetermined basis, it has not been taken into consideration in the making of the mathematical simulator. Hence, the average load handled by the simulator is at the level of 3750 to 4000 megawatts. Furthermore, the three minor steam plants are normally not on production and some of the 37 hydroelectric installations are tightened one to another, only 32 of these are considered independent. The Tennessee Valley Authority embraces seven states, or portions thereof, with a total area of 140 000 square miles. TVA has 12 interchange points with neighboring power concerns, namely : *Kentucky Utility*, *Virginia Power*, *Georgia Power*, and *Arkansas Power*. Within its boundaries, the TVA network consists of 104 busses. Given that the already established production points are 41 and the interchanges are 12, the remaining 51 are power sinks. The network has a total of 11 728 miles of transmission lines.

TVA supplies 50 major industries, 150 farm cooperatives, and 4 large municipalities—Memphis, Nashville, Knoxville, and Chattanooga—a total of 204 major loads. Several of these loads are grouped together, being fed by the same bus. Although the number of TVA customers is at the level of 140 000 many of these are grouped together into the cooperatives, hence relieving the Authority both of a major billing job and of getting into too much detail into its decision-making in respect to power distribution. This too is an important point which should be taken into consideration in the discussion on the power simulator which follows.

Profits from power distribution are only part of the total picture. The Authority has other activities which can also be substantially assisted by a rationally designed and electronically processed power simulator. For instance, normally, the Tennessee valley has 55 inches of rainfall. North of the Chattanooga valley over the drainage area, an inch of rain is worth about one million dollars. If this inch can be simulated by a mathematical optimization of the hydrodynamic usage, TVA would derive a net million dollar profit. Hence, gains in one subject

---

[2] The steam plants range in size from 240 to 1440 MW. The hydroelectric power generation stations range in size from 10 to 436 MW.

within one small section of the whole area will be enough to equate all expenses associated with the electronic computation center. A mathematical programming job for optimal hydraulic allocation is currently under work over and above the already existing power simulator, which will be discussed in the following sections.

Economic Loading

Economic loading differs from what might be called normal dispatching in that the cost of transmission losses is included. Until the introduction of a new technique, which utilizes a transmission loss formula, most electric utilities loaded generators so that all were operating at equal incremental bus-bar cost; little consideration was given to the system load pattern and cost of power delivery from the generator to the load. Since, however, the forementioned method offered a very crude approximation to reality, a great deal of effort went into the development of a loss equation, from which system electrical transmission losses could be determined from the known power output of each generating station. This equation, or formula, is determined by utilizing an ac network calculator to obtain basic system data, and a digital computer to reduce this data to the formula constants. For example, the economic loading equation for the ith station in an n-station network can be written as

$$\frac{dF}{dP_i} + \lambda \frac{\partial L}{\partial P_i} = \lambda,$$

where P_i is the power output of the ith station, dF/dP_i is the incremental production cost for station i, $\partial L/\partial P_i$ is the incremental transmission loss with respect to P_i, and λ is the incremental delivered power cost, and is the same for each of the n equations for the system.

Transmission loss can be expressed in terms of the n power stations as

$$L = B_{11}P_1^2 + B_{22}P_2^2 + \dots + 2B_{12}P_1P_2 + 2B_{13}P_1P_3 + \dots ,$$

where L is total system loss, P_1 is power output of station 1, and the B constants are a measure of the self and mutual resistance between the various generating stations and the equivalent load pattern of the system. All are determined from the transmission network involved. Since the incremental losses are needed for the economic loading equation, we can take the first partial derivative of the latter equation with respect to each station's power, yielding incremental transmission loss equations for each station of the n-station network of the form

$$\frac{\partial L}{\partial P_i} = 2P_1 B_{i1} + 2P_2 B_{i2} + \ldots + 2P_i B_{ii} + \ldots + 2P_n B_{in}$$

for station i. These incremental transmission loss formulas substituted in the coordination equations for each station (economic loading) form the system coordination equations:

$$\frac{dF}{dP_i} + \lambda(2P_1 B_{i1} + 2P_2 B_{i2} + \ldots + 2P_i B_{ii} + \ldots + 2P_n B_{in}) = \lambda$$

for station i. The latter system of equations will be computed by the data processor.

Hence, the incremental production cost, or bus-bar cost, at each generating station can be combined with the incremental transmission loss determined from the loss formula for that station to produce a system of simultaneous equations. For n variable stations, there are n coordination equations of the form

$$\left\{\begin{array}{l}\text{Station}\\\text{incremental}\\\text{production}\\\text{cost}\end{array}\right\} + \left\{\begin{array}{l}\text{Incremental}\\\text{transmission}\\\text{cost}\end{array}\right\} = \left\{\begin{array}{l}\text{Incremental}\\\text{delivered}\\\text{power cost}\end{array}\right\}.$$

Transmission losses can be charged at the λ rate. Therefore,

$$\left\{\begin{array}{l}\text{Station}\\\text{incremental}\\\text{production}\\\text{cost}\end{array}\right\} + \lambda\left\{\begin{array}{l}\text{Incremental}\\\text{transmission}\\\text{loss}\end{array}\right\} = \lambda.$$

One of these coordination equations exists for each station on the system. Equations of this type are quite simple in themselves, and, for the time being, sufficiently accurate. They have been used in a variety of fields. For instance, in production control, inventory optimization can be made on the basis of a relatively simple mathematical model:

$$\left\{\begin{array}{l}\text{Foot day}\\\text{in storage}\end{array}\right\} = \left\{\left|\begin{array}{l}\text{Weighted receipt}\\\text{date of inventory}\end{array}\right| - \left|\begin{array}{l}\text{Present}\\\text{date}\end{array}\right|\right\}\left\{\begin{array}{l}\text{Foot}\\\text{sale}\end{array}\right\},$$

where inventory costs are expressed in foot-days. This simple model allows experimentation on optimal allocation of space which can be done by means of a simulator that gives total sales during a certain time period, by warehouse. The storage in each warehouse is expressed in foot-days. The simulator also gives the distribution of intervals between sales and distribution of sales in quantity per item.

Base Constants

The basic matrix of the power production and distribution simulator, as used on the hourly prediction basis, is 104×104 with complex numbers. Two versions of this network matrix exist—one known as the "exact solution" and the other as the "B-method" or matrix of the "B-constants".[3]

In either case, the matrix in question is symmetric. Hence, it occupies only 5408 words in the high speed memory of the data processor. The exact solution, as developed by the research office of TVA, takes into account real and reactive loads, calculates lines losses, economically weights hydroelectric vs. steam production for different plant sizes, and finds the optimum solution subject to minimum and maximum power production levels for each plant as established with the input data. Such levels may change as a function of time. For the economic evaluation of the different alternative load distributions, the simulator considers the relative efficiency of each generator, the cost of coal at each location, the price of the kilowatt, transmission drops, etc. Upon introduction of the digital control system, in 1958, the exact solution has worked only with a reduced system of a 10×10 matrix involving the major power production centers; a larger matrix of 26×26 being under development.

The B-constants solution is essentially an approximation to the exact one. The matrix of complex numbers is converted by approximation into a matrix of real numbers, each element of the latter being known as a "base" or B-constant. This matrix is affected by changes in the configuration of the network, and therefore such changes necessitate a recalculation of B. This recalculation requires one and a half hours of processing time on the large scale computer. Examples of changes that may affect B is the installation of new power production units and the installation or removal of busses from the network.

New distribution of loads and heavy seasonal variations also affect the values of the B-constants. As an example of seasonal variations one

---

[3] The former was developed by Shipley and Hochdorf of TVA and will be described in a later section of this chapter. The B-method was designed by Westinghouse. The nature of the B-coefficient has already been stated.

should consider that the Tennessee Valley has a severe flood problem. To avail for efficient flood control, during the first 3 months of the year, power production is considered a matter of only secondary importance. Such seasonal variations can be handled effectively by a set of four different B-matrices. Hourly variations would not affect the values of the constants within each matrix.

The Equation of the Exact Solution

The fundamental equations of the model (exact solution) are as follows:

1. LOAD FLOW EQUATION[4]

$$p_k = (e_{\text{ref}} - zi_k)i_k,$$

where

p_k is the power in the kth buss

z is the impedence matrix

i_k is the kth buss current

e_{ref} is the reference voltage.

2. ECONOMICS EQUATION

$$p_{\text{ref}} + p_1 + p_2 + \dots = D + L,$$

where

p_{ref} is the reference generator

p_i is the output of the generating station

D is the demand on the system

L are the system's losses.

Then the functions $f_{\text{ref}}(p_{\text{ref}})$, $f_1(p_1)$, $f_2(p)$, ... are functions of the variable generating cost. The reference power is selected once. This combines a generating lens near the electrical center of the system (impedence standpoint) and a plant that always stays in business. The reference bus is essentially the zero row in the z matrix. The $f_1(p_1)$ curves are

---

[4] See Shipley and Hochdorf, Economy Dispatch—Digital Computer Solution, in Power Apparatus and Systems, December 1956, No. 27, AIEE.

determined on the basis of the operating costs at each plant. These are a composite of the cost of the generating units and of other costs (Fig. 1).

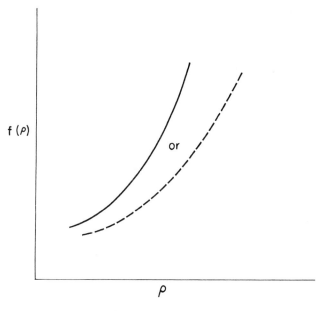

f (p)

or

p

FIG. 1

3. COST FUNCTION

In these terms, the total cost function takes the form

$$T = f_{\text{ref}} + f_1 + f_2 + \dots .$$

Minima and maxima can be used for the treatment of this function. For minimization, we take the partial derivatives

$$\frac{\partial T}{\partial p_{\text{ref}}} = 0, \qquad \frac{\partial T}{\partial p_1} = 0, \qquad \dots .$$

We experiment with variations in the output of both the reference plant and the one which is going to be optimized. This calculation has to be repeated often times since the plant to be optimized might be any and all of the power production plants in the network. For every case, we have

$$\frac{dT}{dp_{\text{ref}}} = \frac{df_{\text{ref}}}{dp_{\text{ref}}} + \frac{df_1}{dp_{\text{ref}}} = 0$$

or

$$\frac{dT}{dp_{\text{ref}}} = C_{\text{ref}} + C = 0.$$

The simulator considers next the equation

$$C_{\text{ref}} = C \left(1 - \frac{2}{C_{\text{ref}}} Ri_r \right),$$

where

$$R = R(z)$$
$$i_r = \text{the current vector}$$
$$C_{\text{ref}} = \text{a column matrix.}$$

The variations in C_{ref} can be used to estimate the incremental costs in the system. The current vector i_r contains all currents in the system (both load and generator). The voltage regulator equation is

$$i_G = f(e_{\text{ref}} - zi, e_n).$$

Using the Simulator

Given the station costs, loss-formula coefficients (B-constants), and desired total generation, the data processor adjusts itself to show most of the economic loading for each of the system stations. Processing of the simulator is done every hour on the hour. It requires about 6 minutes of computer time, or a maximum of 10 minutes with input-output considerations. Hence, each day during the first eight-hour shift the computer is available for 50 minutes per hour to process other work. The processing of the power simulator does not interfere seriously with other projects run in the computation center.

All program runs processed on this machine have an interrupt feature, so that they would be automatically dumped on tape and the economic loading program will take on without delay. Data-collection and data-distribution delays largely account for the fact that at present the computer does not operate on real time for power control. The complete cycle of operations involved in this process takes exactly one hour, and therefore the simulator needs to work on an hourly forecast basis.

To follow the computer operations, consider a "typical job" at the dispatching center. Intake of local information is being done from 71 locations. Sixteen of these telemeter the data while the remaining 55 give them in by telephone. Two operators are used in the dispatcher's office for telephone communication on a three shift per day basis, seven days of the week. This activity takes about 25 minutes, including the "setting of dials"; its rationale is quite interesting.[5]

Data taken in from the load points need to be transcribed on punched cards. Obviously, this might have been done by a human operator on a key punch machine. Two distinct reasons, however, made this approach unfeasible. First dispatchers are unionized, and the local labor union objected to their use as keypunch operators, while, for instance, there was no objection in switching dials.

Second, because of their past experience in jobs of the latter type, management felt that accuracy-wise it would be better off by having the operator manipulate a switchboard. A section of the dial board is shown in Fig. 2.

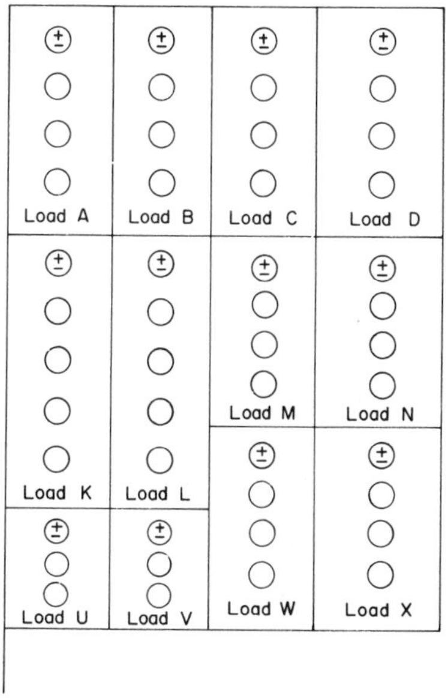

FIG. 2

Notice that each load point has two, three, or four switches corresponding to the number of digits necessary to express the load in megavolt-amperes. The symbol $+$, $-$ preceding each number is not a sign but an indication of whether the corresponding station is a power spring or sink point. The reason for the distinction should be found in the fact

---

[5] Here, reference is made to the practice followed in late 1958, when the writer had visited the installation.

that the system includes 12 power interchanges while at times some of the major consumers who have power production equipment of their own may be contributing to the network. The load is taken as normally positive, hence a negative sign would indicate power production.

Reactive data are not used with the B-constants, hence as long as this approach is in effect information in columns 6 to 20 (Fig. 3) of the card layout is of no concern to the simulator. However, information given by the individual load station contains both real and reactive power, and the dispatcher has available a second tableau through which he can store this information in "automatic production recording" unit.[6] This unit automatically fills in information such as the identification of the load station, the card sequence, and the card code.

A card code is necessary because four types of cards are used in relation with this work: (1) A "date card," for identification of date, month, year, hour, minute. This is used as a heading card. (2) Maximum-minimum cards. The maximum and minimum limits between which a plant can produce varies. This is particularly true for the hydroelectric plants where the variation may be a function of the season, of the rainfall level, of irrigation or flood control needs, etc. Maximum and minimum limits for all plants are held by the simulator in a special table, hence this card needs to be inserted only when there is a change in either limit for a certain plant. (3) On-off cards. These are used in relation to changes effected in the network configuration. (4) Load cards, which have been already discussed.

The described punched cards are to be sent through a transceiver hookup to the location of the data processor. At the sending place, the transmitter produces a hard copy of the forwarded information for review by the load dispatchers. Subsequent to computer processing, final load schedules are produced in punched cards at the general area of the data processor. These are then sent via the transceiver back to the dispatching office. While the transceiver is receiving these cards, a hard copy is also produced of this output information. There are approximately 40 cards in the data group under discussion corresponding to the power production centers.

The data transmission job is done at fixed intervals, and time is essential. Figure 4 indicates the time distribution of the various operations. The operations, on the whole, involve the following steps:

(1) data collection from load points,
(2) automatic recording,

---

[6] "Automatic production recording," the unit used in that instance, has since been withdrawn from the market by its manufacturer.

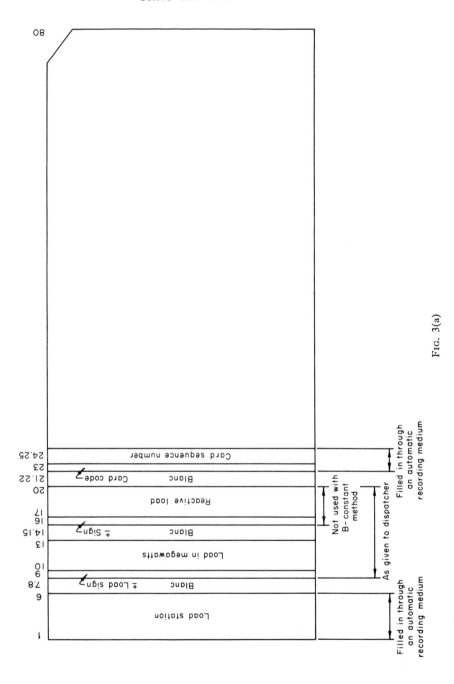

Fig. 3(a)

(3) transmission-in (to the data processor by means of the transceiver),
(4) computation by the data processor,
(5) transmission-out (to the dispatcher by means of the transceiver),
(6) communication of information to the power stations.

LIST FORMAT						
Station	Abbreviation	Symbol	MVA	Sign	Reactive MVA	Card sequence
K25	K25	±	XXX	±	XXX	01
Memphis City	MEM	+	XXX	±	XXX	02
East Kentucky	EKY	+	XXX	±	XXX	03
Chattanooga	CHA	+	XXXX	±	XXX	04

FIG. 3(b)

Output data are taken in a format similar to that given in Fig. 5. The output is by plant location and a double schedule is given: one based on a one-hour forecast, the other on an hour and a half. The simulator forecasts demands through the usage of the actual hour data and of a load curve which is stored on its memory. The shape of the load curve

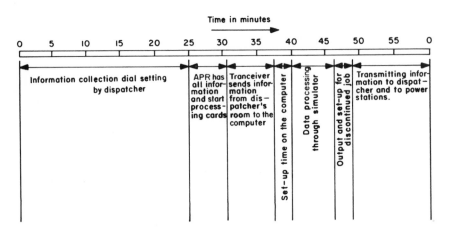

FIG. 4

varies as a function of the time of the day. Some seasonal variations are also taken into account. Since the forecasts are made every hour on the hour, essentially the simulated data are given to the individual power plants with a timely precision of half an hour.

POWER GENERATION SCHEDULE			DATE: XX.XX.XX	HOUR: XX.XX	
Plant	I hr Schedule	I ½ hr Sched.	Max	Min	Unrestricted
01 S. Holston	35	35	35	35	21
02 Fontana	140	140	140	47	93
03 Wilson	300	289	300	100	289
04 Kingston	950	950	950	400	1766

Fig. 5

The power generation schedule also includes the maximum and minimum power production limits and the allocation which the simulator finds as the optimal one. However, this optimal might have been only a suboptimal of the over-all operation because of limits which have been set on the production level of each plant. Notice, for example, that the South Holston plant (Fig. 5) would have been allocated 21 KVA if there was no lower limit of 35 KVA. Inversely, the optimal solution without restricting boundaries would have involved greater power production allocations for both the Fontana and the Kingston plants. It follows that the closer the limits are set the further the sub-optimal solution might be from the optimal.

The hydroelectric station can be handled by the economic load simulator in several ways, depending on system conditions and the amount of water available. Because the hydro station can pick up or drop load quickly, it is often used in the load-frequency control system to keep the frequency and tie-line loadings to their scheduled values.[7] In this case, the administration can feed into the machine factors representing the hydro station at a value in the middle of the band over which the unit is set to regulate.

Another method of hydro-station operation is to use it in economic loading by assigning a value to its power. It is assigned a cost value that does not vary with power and can be adjusted by the cost-factor dial, the same as the cost of a steam station can be adjusted. This cost is set by experience at a value that will just use the available water in the time period, say one day. In this method of operation, the hydro generators come on during times of high-cost operation, and go off during periods of low-cost operation, as the cost varies during the day. If the water is not entirely used up, the dispatcher merely reduces the cost of hydro generation, which makes it come on earlier and stay on longer. This process dispatches the available amount of water in the most efficient

---

[7] Examples of computer outputs of city loads and generation schedules are given in Fig. 6 (sheets 1, 2, and 3).

SHEET 1

MONTH 11 DAY 28 SCHEDULE FOR 1100 TO 1200

			APR	APRMAX	APRMIN	
3	MEMPHIS CITY	1	321.00	500.00	2.00	34
47	KNOX (HS BANK)	2	113.00	200.00	2.00	40
48	LONSDALE (LS BANKS)	2	141.00	300.00	2.00	
41	CHICKAMAUGA 46KV (+VALDEAU)	3	147.00	200.00	5.00	
42	OGLETHORPE (HS BANK)	3	125.00	250.00	2.00	43
43	MOCCASIN (HS BANK)	3	109.00	200.00	2.00	
33	BOWLING GREEN (HS BANK)	4	48.00	75.00	1.00	34
50	MARTIN (HS BANK)	5	62.00	150.00	1.00	26
55	SO JACKSON (HS BANK)	6	63.00	200.00	1.00	34
44	RADNOR (HS BANK)	7	104.00	200.00	2.00	
45	S NASHVILLE (HS BANK+OHNES)	7	196.00	300.00	2.00	33
46	W NASHVILLE (HS BANK)	7	144.00	300.00	2.00	
69	HUNTSVILLE (HS BANK)	8	63.00	100.00	0.	38
56	WILSON 44KV (WIL CONF+SHO)	9	89.00	200.00	1.00	36
51	WEST POINT (HS BANK+MIDWAY)	10	96.00	200.00	1.00	36
29	NE JOHNSON CITY (HS BANK)	11	23.00	50.00	1.00	51
2	LG+E (PADDYS RUN)		−15.00	250.00	−250.00	
5	AEP (BOONE)		80.00	150.00	−150.00	
6	AEP (NOLICHUCKY)		14.00	150.00	−150.00	
7	AEP (NO BRISTOL)		4.00	150.00	−150.00	
8	PINEVILLE (KU+AEP'		25.00	150.00	−150.00	
9	AEP WALTERS		25.00	150.00	−150.00	
10	EAST KY RECC		16.00	150.00	−150.00	

FIG. 6(a)

fashion to reduce the total fuel input to the system. It can also happen during the processing of the simulator that the computer does not find enough power supply to meet the demand. Then, through the on-line printer the machine will type:

"Call dispatcher and ask for higher plant generation tops. You need-181.0MW Date xx xx xx." it is the function of the dispatcher to make the proper changes in the established maximum limits. Among other information given by the data processor is the buildup of nonconforming loads (for the B-constants matrix), the buildup in systems capacity, and the differences between the total system generation and the total systems load.

From the foregoing, it becomes rather obvious that although the system is considerably sophisticated there still exists much room for improvements. For instance, data collection can be improved by having each load point telemeter-in the information now given to a human operator. An automatic recording unit can be used to collect the individual data and then transmit the collected package to the computer.

Program-interrupt features or data synchronizer accepting interrupt signals may also provide a basis for converting this system into a real time control operation. An integrated data-handling system will probably necessitate a transducer-telemetering and a telemetering-actuator set-

SHEET 2

```
MONTH 11 DAY 28 SCHEDULE FOR 1100 TO 1200
72 TAPE 6 CODE
73 FACTORS ON TAPE 2
                    1.120000   1.100000   12.
AMAT     28.17        26.83      350.13      126.44      136.55      26.55      13.91      74.60
AMAT     55.63        72.07      124.78      109.19      180.49      20.05      17.83      52.37
AMAT     22.28        15.60       49.15       15.36       47.62      21.50      84.48       9.22
AMAT     56.21        15.43       35.27       73.97       43.25      98.63     215.08     127.40
AMAT     36.99        58.91       34.25        8.72       43.84      32.88      34.25      10.96
AMAT     60.64        44.10       51.82       12.13       67.25      38.59      22.05      83.41
AMAT     46.79        93.10       53.76        7.87        7.87      22.40      26.88      21.28
AMAT     19.04         6.72       12.32       24.64       11.20       2.24       6.72      10.08

AREA  9 LD SP WILSON          48.49   130.19   127.87    3.86
AREA 10 LD SP WEST POINT      50.53   162.59   159.69    4.82
AREA 11 LD SP NE JOHN CITY    54.65   180.32   177.10    5.34
KNOXVILLE (CITY LOAD)                 262.99 AND 258.29
CHATTANOOGA (CITY LOAD)               414.46 AND 407.06
NASHVILLE (CITY LOAD)                 441.11 AND 433.24
MEMPHIS (CITY LOAD)                   350.13 AND 343.88
TOTAL CONFORMING LOAD                3376.00     3315.72   100.00
NET INTERCHANGE                       169.
TOTAL INDUSTRIAL LOAD                4494.
TOTAL SYSTEM LOAD               6.   . AND          7978.72

GENERATION MINUS LOAD        -4.94

GENERATION MINUS LOAD         3.22
SYSTEM LOSSES ARE           168.1070 AND        164.6549
SYSTEM GENERATION          8202.0000 AND       8146.0000
```

Fig. 6(b)

SHEET 3

DIVISION OF POWER OPERATIONS - GENERATION SCHEDULE

11 MONTH 28 DAY SCHEDULE FOR 1100 TO 1130

PLANT	1100 SCHEDULE	1130 SCHEDULE	MAXIMUM CAPACITY	MINIMUM CAPACITY	UNRESTRICTED
01 SOUTH HOLSTON	35.	35.	35.	35.	21.
02 WATAUGA	71.	71.	71.	71.	50.
03 BOONE	64.	60.	85.	60.	48.
04 FT PATRICK HENRY	36.	36.	36.	36.	16.
05 CHEROKEE	55.	55.	55.	55.	39.
06 NOLICHUCKY	10.	10.	10.	10.	27.
. . . .	. . . . .	. . . . .	. . . . .	. . . .	. . . .
. . . .	. . . . .	. . . . .	. . . . .	. . . .	. . . .
. . . .	. . . . .	. . . . .	. . . . .	. . . .	. . . .
37 JOHNSONVILLE	820.	820.	820.	299.	1134.
38 KINGSTON 1-4	258.	258.	258.	80.	551.
39 KINGSTON 4-5	950.	950.	950.	400.	1766.
40 SHAWNEE	1294.	1294.	1294.	360.	1851.
41 WIDOWS CREEK	52?.	520.	520.	140.	567.

LAMBDA WAS 7.4940 AND 7.3860

T.V.A. SYSTEM GENERATION ... 82?2. AND 8146.

SYSTEM CAPACITY   8358.0

MINIMUM CAPACITY   3982.0

FIG. 6(c)

up. Eventually transducers and remote control may replace dispatchers, however, as late as 1958 such substitution was rather improbable. Improvements in respect to the simulator may involve abandonment of the B-constants method in favor of the exact solution; substitution of the average hydrodynamic storage cost, presently used in the economic analysis, with exact specific storage data; improvement in the load prediction curves, a mathematical model for the calculation of maximum and minimum production limits; and a tie-in with a simulator for flood control and irrigation.

Another problem that can be tackled by electronically processed simulators in the same applications area is systems planning for further expansion. This can be subdivided into more specific subjects as, for instance, load flow for network expansion, allocation of new generators, capacity increases for dams, discontinuance of operation of certain nonprofitable plants, studies on new transformer installations and on transformer replacement. Statistical jobs such as the computation of moving averages in power consumption and forecast on electricity sales are already handled to advantage by electronic data-processing means.

Upkeeping the TVA Simulator

Some additional work has been done on the iterative portion of the load flow solution required in the exact model. This has included experimentation with Stagg's method, Newton's method (applied to the solution of the system of quadratic load flow equations), and Bauer's method. Nevertheless, no major effort has been placed on this part of the program because the magnitude of additional savings afforded by an exact model over the approximate approach can not be ascertained, particularly when the unavoidable inaccuracies of input data are considered.

Regarding the computation for hydro-storage control and releases, a weekly estimate of the relative value of the stored hydro energy in each reservoir is now being used. This results in an indication of the total amount of water to be used from each source, during a one-week period, in combination with the supplemental steam needed for the total anticipated power requirements for that week. A new program, which will afford better coordination of power production from hydraulic and steam sources, is in the works. This program will use incremental water rates for hydro control in combination with incremental heat rates for steam units.

It may be of interest to point out that the TVA applications of the loss coefficient method to economic dispatch is somewhat different than the conventional application described in various technical papers.

The application here is unique in that all load busses are treated as negative generators, and the conforming load block which assumes that all loads vary in the same pattern has been elinimated. This treatment is entirely feasible with a large scale digital computer; whereas, it is impractical if some other approaches are used due to the number of elements required to represent the loss coefficient matrix.

As the simulator becomes more sophisticated, emphasis is placed on the economies which could be realized through its usage. The amount of dollar savings derived from economic dispatch computations depends on the efficiency of the methods of dispatch and also the characteristics of the particular power system involved. Hence, dispatch conditions are continously reevaluated to assure that economies are being effected. This is made necessary by continually changing circumstances such as

(i) abnormal unit conditions which might not constitute emergencies, but do make temporary unit close-down for maintenance desirable;

(ii) unexpected manipulations of hydro releases, due to unusual precipitation, flash floods, etc;

(iii) fluctuating interchange arrangements with adjoining power system due to abnormalities or emergencies;

(iv) coal miners' strikes, railroad delays, and happenings with attendant impact on fuel reserves at particular locations;

(v) other items of this general nature which have a direct bearing on specific scheduling decisions.

The use of the simulator helped uncover various sources of error. For instance, some significant errors in metering, due to previously unrecognized voltage drops in long potential transformer leads, have been identified by comparing the results of computer studies with recorded information from system operating logs. The careful analysis which has been necessary to establish input data for certain studies and to reconcile differences between the study results and system records has brought to light discrepancies which would not have been detected otherwise.

Management is confident that tangible improvements in systems operation have been realized through the use of the computer-processed simulator for economic dispatch studies. Some facts are now known which have brought about changes in scheduling from what was considered in the past to be "normal." The over-all effect of losses on the relative costs of power from optional sources has been evident from the computer solutions.

PART VII
Simulation by Analog Means

CHAPTER 24

Introduction to Analog Simulation

The use of models for the simulation of physical and technological systems has already been duly discussed. In this discussion, reference was made to the use of computational media for the processing of the mathematical simulator. The use of digital means for problem solution was either directly or indirectly referred to. The structure of electronic digital computers and their utilization in computation and data processing will not be discussed in the present book.[1] Instead, certain aspects of analog computing will be presented, with emphasis on simulation work.

Dynamic analogy, or the correspondence between the equations of motion of mechanical, electrical, and acoustical systems, allows the use of mechanical devices for the study of electrical principles or the use of electrical networks for modeling complex mechanical and electromechanical equations. The laws of Kirchhoff provide the basis for the analysis of electrical systems, the laws of Newton for problems in dynamics. They both are versions of the more general concepts of equilibrium and continuity. Voltage and force, current and velocity, inductance and mass, electromagnetic energy and kinetic energy seem to be analogous quantitites; voltage is analogous to force, current is analogous to velocity, and resistance is analogous to a "shock absorbtion" coefficient. There exist well-defined analogies between mechanical and electrical systems which account for the representation of the one in the form of the other.

Evolution in the Use of Analog Media

As an introduction, we will trace analog computation to its very beginning. In doing so, we will keep close to the meaning we give today

---

[1] The reader is referred to other works by the author on this subject. For instance: "Traite des Ordinateurs." Hermann, Paris, 1960; "Les Applications des Ordinateurs." Éditions de l'Entreprise Moderne, Paris, 1961; "Programming Systems for Electronic Computers." Butterworths, London, 1962; and "Control Systems Functions and Programming Approaches" Academic Press, 1966.

439

to "analog computation," for otherwise the text would be lost in a labyrinth of historical data.

Most probably, the earliest attempt at analog computation was the surveying and map-making of Babylonia, in 3800 B. C., for the purpose of taxation. By 1300 B. C., surveying and map-making were common in Egypt. Nevertheless, the earliest record we find close to the "present-day" concept is in 1614 when John Napier described his invention of logarithms, and in 1615 when John Briggs, in collaboration with Napier, converted them to the base 10. In 1617 John Napier devised a method of multiplication utilizing numbering rods. Edmund Gunter utilized Napier's logarithms in 1620 to create a slide-rule with no moving parts. This was subsequently improved upon, in 1632, by William Oughtred's conception of the "astrolabe," which was the forerunner of the slide-rule and nomogram with a sliding scale.

The planimeter, an analog device, first appeared in 1814; its inventor was J. A. Hermann, a Bavarian engineer. Between 1814 and 1854 when Amsler invented the popular modern polar planimeter, many new and improved types of planimeters were introduced. The early art of analog devices was active during the time of Lord Kelvin. Kelvin's brother, James Thomson, had invented an integrating mechanism. In 1816, Lord Kelvin conceived the idea of connecting these devices together to solve differential equations.

The network analyzers for the simulation of power networks appear to be due, principally, to the developments of two major electrical manufacturers. The dc network analyzer was the first of these devices to appear, in 1925. Since this is a resistive analog, it is limited to steady-state problems which are either purely resistive or purely reactive. The ac network analyzer, introduced in 1929, is a much more versatile machine. It includes three types of linear impedances, which make it usable for the simulation of alternating current power networks showing both phase and magnitude. The most recent development in this family of devices is the "transient network analyzer." Its component values are readily changed, and nonlinear elements can be simulated. This flexibility makes the machine a true general-purpose computer.

Mechanical integrating devices were improved on when Hannibal Ford, during World War I, increased the torque output of the ball-and-disk integrator to make a naval gun-fire computer. This was followed by more experimentation, in the 1920's, at M.I.T. which led to the completion (in 1931) of the first large scale mechanical differential analyzer. Further work in this field brought more improvements until at the present time there are several large scale mechanical machines in operation. Simultaneous equation solvers and harmonic analyzers of many types appeared in the 1930's. Among these were a mechanical method of solving simultaneous algebraic equations, an electrical machine for the same purpose, an adjuster-type equation solver, a mechanical harmonic analyzer, and the like.

From the slide-rule to the network or the harmonic analyzer we are dealing with devices able to simulate and to compute. These are two fundamentally distinct concepts, in spite of the fact that, by and large, this distinction has not been recognized, both in literature and in the minds of their users. We could divide these concepts in the following way: "The mathematics behind the calculation" constitute the model. But this should not be confused with "the process of the calculation" which is an entity in its own right. Once this distinction has been made, we can then talk about digital and analog media to which will be assigned the computing aspects.

Digital and analog computers differ substantially in accuracy, versatility, and cost—the differences arising primarily from matters concerning the modes of computations. Though these two modes of computation are, in several respects, complementary to one another, rarely can a specific problem be solved with equal facility and speed on either machine. Digital computers are inherently more accurate than analog machines. If solution time permits, high digital precision is attained simply by increasing the number of pulses used to represent a number, or what we call the "word length." Depending upon the complexity of the problem, higher order precision and substantial functional accuracy can readily be developed. Although less accurate, the analog computer is much faster for some problem classes than the digital machine. For a simple problem it is generally the cheaper of the two, even if less flexible. But initial analog machine cost rises rapidly with the precision that is demanded.

Analog machines range in size from one-man desk models, incorporating ten to fifteen amplifiers, to large installations using hundreds of amplifiers, with considerable associated equipment, and requiring a substantial staff for maintenance and operation. The analog computer is especially suited for limited-accuracy design studies of dynamic systems. Parameters and coefficients basic to the problem, as well as initial conditions and forcing functions, can be rather simply varied while the problem solution is in progress. This feature is of particular value in design studies requiring trial solutions for design parameters.

The analog devices operate with physical variables such as shaft rotations or electrical voltages. We distinguish two types of analogy. The direct analogy is characterized by those cases where problem variables and problem parameters are represented directly by variables and parameters on the machine. An example is the direct analogy which exists between the energy storage in a mechanical spring and the energy storage in an electrical capacitor. Analogies of this kind are discussed in a later section of the present chapter.

By applying the principle of duality, it is also possible to construct a computer which operates as the dual of the problem. The mechanical direct analog computers are most generally scale models, such as wind-tunnel models. The electrical direct analogs include such instruments as the network analyzers. In the fluid analog we distinguish the model dams and stream beds which are found in many hydraulic laboratories. The indirect analog computers are of a type which can carry out or assist in the solution of algebraic or differential equations.

While it is generally accepted that the most common example of a mechanical indirect analog computer is the slide-rule where lengths on a stick are analogous to numbers, nomograms and various charts should also be taken as falling in this category. The fluid type of indirect analog computer is the least common. This is so presumably because of the difficulty of measurement in the fluid system. The electrical (or electronic) indirect analog computer is probably the most common of the indirect type. It normally employs high gain amplifiers and, when applied in appropriate feedback loops, performs mathematical operations.

A Closer Look at the Analog Approach

Analog devices—whether computers, simulators, or analyzers—share a common family characteristic: numbers in the problem to be solved are represented by corresponding physical quantities in the machine. A slide-rule, for example, represents problem numbers by scale lengths that are proportional to the logarithms of the numbers. Similarly, the dc analog computer translates problem numbers into corresponding network voltages, either constant or varying with time. Such practice is based on the fact that there exist certain "analogies" between the real system and its model. As in digital simulation, the term "analogy" should be interpreted as meaning similarity of properties or relations without identity. For most cases, such analogy does not need to exist with respect to every characteristic describing the simulator and the simulated system. It suffices to have a working analogy with respect to the characteristic(s) under investigation.

In the sense used in engineering and science, dynamic analogy refers to the correspondence between the equations of motion of mechanical, electrical, and acoustical systems. Throughout this work we have emphasized that it is exactly this well-established analogy which allows the use of mechanical systems for studying electrical principles, or the use of electrical networks, for modeling complex mechanical and electromechanical systems. Again, as with digital simulation, when analogous systems exist, experiments and measurements made on one of them can be used to predict the behavior of the others. To make this point clearer, we consider the particular example of electromechanical analogies.

The term *electromechanical analogies* is applied to that area of scientific study which relates the existence and behavior of certain elements in the mechanical systems to analogous elements in an electrical system — made possible by the fundamental analogies which exist between electrical and mechanical systems, and which have their ultimate foundation on the fact that electrical properties and mechanical properties satisfy the same type of differential equations.

Maxwell's view that electrical actions are finally dynamic led to notable advances in science. It was an approach widely accepted by most of the early authorities. In support of his thesis, Maxwell showed that the forces on any system of charged bodies could be attributed to a system of stresses in the medium in which they are embedded. Today, we use these concepts in analyzing the behavior of mechanical and acoustical structures by means of a simple electrical circuit. In this respect, some of the more prominent applications involve vibration studies, shock mounting, damping, and dynamic response.

The mechanical systems are composed of active and passive elements. The active elements are the energy sources of which there are two kinds, force and velocity sources. The passive elements are the masses, springs, and friction devices. If the force applied to a point is given, then a force source is considered as existing in the system. If the driving velocity of some point in the system is known, then a velocity source is considered as existing in the system. The mass M is the inertia element. In the network diagram mass is always referred to ground potential. This is a logical action because inertia force depends on acceleration relative to ground. Springs provide the restoring forces of the system. The degree of the tension or compression force of the spring depends upon its elastic constant K. In the translational motion system, the frictional resistance B represents the energy sink, and it is independent of the velocity differ ence across it.

In rotation there are two particular kinds of active elements, torque sources and angular velocity sources. Of importance is the polar moment of inertia $J = Mr^2$, in which r is the radius of gyration about the axis of rotation. In rotation, the spring-like bodies exert restoring torques as a result of the angular twist. The magnitude of the torque depends upon the rotational stiffness K of the body. The frictional torques are considered as proportional to the angular velocity difference between the surfaces in frictional contact. The constant of proportionality is B, the rotational resistance.

In the electrical network, also, there are present both active and passive elements. The active elements are the voltage and current sources. The passive members of this system are the electrical resistance R, the self-inductance L, and the capacitance C. Considering the differential equations of both the mechanical and the electrical systems:

$$M \frac{d^2x}{dt^2} + B \frac{dx}{dt} + Kx = F \cos \omega t \qquad \text{Translational mechanical,}$$

$$J \frac{d^2\theta}{dt^2} + B_r \frac{d\theta}{dt} K_r\theta = T \cos \omega t \qquad \text{Rotational mechanical,}$$

$$L \frac{d^2i}{dt^2} + R \frac{di}{dt} + \frac{i}{C} = \omega E \sin \omega t \qquad \text{Series electrical,}$$

$$C \frac{d^2e}{dt^2} + \frac{1}{R} \frac{de}{dt} + \frac{e}{L} = -\omega I \sin \omega t \qquad \text{Parallel electrical.}$$

We observe the following "series analogies":

$$\text{mass or moment of inertia} \sim \text{inductance } L,$$
$$\text{friction} \sim \text{resistance } R,$$
$$\text{springs} \sim \text{elastance } 1/C,$$
$$\text{force or torque} \sim \text{voltage,}$$
$$\text{velocity} \sim \text{current}$$

and the "paralell analogies":

$$\text{mass or moment of inertia} \sim \text{capacitance } C,$$
$$\text{friction} \sim \text{conductance } G,$$
$$\text{springs} \sim \text{suspectance } 1/L,$$
$$\text{force or torque} \sim \text{current,}$$
$$\text{displacement or velocity} \sim \text{voltage.}$$

In forming the electrical analog, either of these two systems can be used. The mechanical system can be set up in a pictorial diagram and then converted to a symbolic diagram using the symbols shown in Fig. 1.

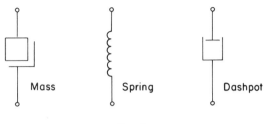

Gardner and Barnes[2] have established certain useful rules to be followed in constructing the symbolic diagram:

(1) Identify the two terminals for each element.

(2) Connect at a common junction those terminals that move together.

(3) Connect to the reference junction all terminals that remain stationary with respect to the reference frame.

(4) Mark each source element with an arrow to show the positive direction.

(5) Assign a coordinate to each movable junction, and show with an arrow the positive direction of motion.

After completing the mechanical symbolic diagram comes the task of writing the differential equations of motion. These equations are based on Newton's second law and D'Alembert's principle. Newton's second law states: "If a body is acted upon by several forces it is accelerated in the direction of the resultant of these forces, and the magnitude of the acceleration is proportional to this resultant and inversely proportional to the mass of the body." Notice that this law resembles Kirchoff's current law. D'Alembert's principle states: "The sum of the instantaneous external forces acting on a body in a given direction and the body's reaction force in that direction due to inertia is zero."

The electric analog for a mechanical system can be formed by finding an electric network having the same set of differential equations as the mechanical circuit. In forming this analog it pays to keep in mind the following two rules:

(i) Rewrite the equations of the mechanical circuit using electric network constants and variables.

(ii) Interpret these equations by drawing the electrical network that they describe.

[2] Gardner and Barnes, "Transient in Linear Systems." Wiley, New York, 1942.

One of the valuable concepts in analyzing electrical circuits is that of "duality." When an inspection of two mathematical equations reveals that those equations are of the same form, the circuits which these equations represent are duals of each other. In considering the equations of two dual electric networks it can be seen that the loop currents in one system and the node voltages in the other system are analogous, dependent variables; conductance is the dual of resistance, capacitance is the dual of inductance, voltage is the dual of current. If the original network cannot be mapped out in two dimensions without any crossovers, then this network will not have a dual.

In a number of cases, it is useful to express one network by its dual. This process has special importance in electromechanical analogies. In forming an electrical analog, for instance, either the series or the parallel analogy can be used. In the event that one of these is on hand, the other can be found by an application of duality. Figure 2 presents an example of dual circuits.

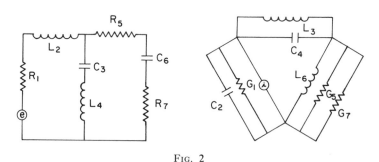

FIG. 2

Correspondingly, Fig. 3 presents a two-coordinate translational system; Fig. 3(a) is the the mechanical physical ensemble, Fig. 3(b) the mechanical symbolic diagram, and Fig 3(c) the electrical circuit diagram, supplemented with both the mechanical and electrical equations.

The analysis of a linear servomechanism is a classic example of analog computer use in design. The aircraft and missile autopilots would never have reached their present high state of development without the aid of the analog machine. The mathematical and functional similarity between the linear servomechanism and the simulator is so complete that the application is almost straightforward, except for the linearization process itself. This is so because any real servomechanism is linear only over a limited range of inputs, hence a great deal of ingenuity must be exercised in determining the appropriate transfer function of each component. Once this is done, however, the operational amplifiers

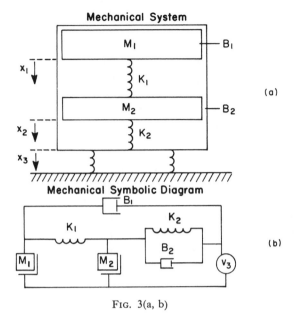

Mechanical System

(a)

Mechanical Symbolic Diagram

(b)

FIG. 3(a, b)

Mechanical equations:

$$M_1 \frac{d^2x_1}{dt^2} + B_1 \frac{dx_1}{dt} + K_1 x_1 - K_1 x_2 = B_1 \frac{dx_3}{dt}$$

$$-K_1 x_1 + M_2 \frac{d^2x_2}{dt} + B_2 \frac{dx_2}{dt} + (K_1 + K_2) x_2 = B_2 \frac{dx_3}{dt} + K_2 x_3$$

Electrical circuit diagram

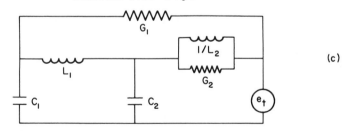

(c)

Electrical equations:

$$C_1 \frac{d^2e_1}{dt} + G_1 \frac{de_1}{dt} + e_1 L_1 - e_2 L_1 = 0$$

$$C_2 \frac{d^2e_2}{dt^2} + G_2 \frac{de_2}{dt} + e_2 L_2 - e_1 L_1 = 0$$

FIG. 3(c)

of the computer can be easily connected to simulate the gain and integrations of the servo-system.

On an analog computer the performance of the servo can be determined by introducing input functions, or commands, often of a stylized and arbitrary nature. When known, we use simulations of the inputs that will be applied in actual operation. The advantage of the analog computer in linearized servo-system design is not immediately obvious, since once a relatively simple equation is derived in the linearization process (for the closed loop dynamics) the response to a step function or to a sinusoidal input can be readily calculated by a number of algebraic and graphical techniques. The contribution of the computer in this case lies in its ability to

(i) handle a relatively complex multiloop situation with the same degree of facility as a simple one;

(ii) permit introduction of completely arbitrary input functions rather than the stylized step or sinusoid;

(iii) permit rapid changes of transfer function, corresponding to changes in the operating environment or to adjustments of the design itself.

As an example of an application, consider the suspension system of the automobile. This system is basically a means of attaching the chassis of the car to the wheels with the objective of reducing the passenger's vibration to a minimum. If the chassis were rigidly attached to the wheels, the passenger would vibrate just as the wheels vibrate with every bump on the road. Therefore, the chassis is attached to the wheels through springs, and the springs take up much of the vibration transmitted from the tires. However, it is not sufficient to allow the springs to vibrate freely—there must be some restriction in the form of damping in order to control them. On the automobile this damping is the shock absorber, connected in parallel with each of the springs. It curbs the vibration. Figure 4 presents the entire system in (a) mechanical and (b) electrical form.

Garner and Barnes describe this passage from physical to mathematical or informational systems quite clearly by stating: "When passage is made from physical to mathematical system it is discovered that many different physical systems lead to the same abstract system, i.e., to the same mathematical problem . . . The correspondence of analogous physical systems with each other and with the mathematical system, if fully used, results in an enormous saving of work."

In developing these analogies, several assumptions need to be made.

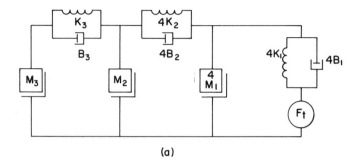

(a)

FIG. 4. Analysis of automobile suspension: (a) mechanical symbolic diagram,

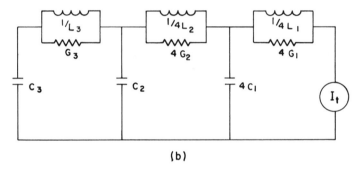

(b)

FIG. 4. (b) electrical circuit diagram.

For example it must be assumed that the system allows only vertical freedom of motion, although many degrees of freedom are actually present. It must also be assumed that the resistance of the tires and of the springs is small, and the like. As soon as the system is clearly visualized, the mechanical symbolic diagram can be drawn [Fig. 4(a)], and then the electrical equivalent circuit can be made [Fig. 4(a)]. The following are the equations which govern the system behavior:

$$C_3 \frac{d^2 e_1}{dt^2} + G_3 \frac{de_1}{dt} + L_3 e_1 - G_3 \frac{de_2}{dt} - L_3 e_2 = 0,$$

$$C_2 \frac{d^2 e_2}{dt^2} + G_3 \frac{de_2}{dt} + L_3 e_2 + 4L_2 e_2 + 4G_2 \frac{de_2}{dt} - 4G_2 \frac{de_3}{dt} - 4L_2 e_3 = 0,$$

$$4C_1 \frac{d^2 e_3}{dt^2} + 4G_2 \frac{de_3}{dt} + 4L_2 e_3 + 4L_1 e_3 + 4G_1 \frac{de_3}{dt} - 4L_1 e_4 - 4G_1 \frac{de_4}{dt} = 0,$$

$$4G_1 \frac{de_4}{dt} + 4L_1 e_4 = I_t .$$

A low-frequency oscillation takes place due to the resonance of the mass of the body M_2 and the spring effects in K_2 and K_1. This oscillation is excited by a rough road bed, and it becomes particularly violent when it reaches the resonant frequency. The resonant frequency is computed from the mass of the car body, wheels, and axles, along with the K_1 and K_2 of the tires and springs. This resonant oscillation is of a rather high frequency, and it is excited by sharp discontinuities in the road, such as cobblestones.

Since we have built an electrical analog of the mechanical system, we can study these oscillations on the electrical circuit diagram. In Fig. 4(b) it can be seen that series resonance takes place between C_2 and $4L_2$ and between C_1 and $4L_1$, where C_2 is the electrical equivalent of M_2, $1/L_2$ is the equivalent of K_2, etc. Changes in the size of the parameters on the mechanical system can be interpreted as changes in the equivalent parameters on the electrical circuit. For example, the formula to compute the frequency of series resonance is

$$f = \frac{1}{2\pi} \frac{1}{(LC)^{\frac{1}{2}}},$$

which shows that if either L or C increases, the frequency of resonance will decrease.

In the absence of damping, the resonance might become so violent that the wheels would leave the road. This means that damping must be incorporated into the system in the form of shock absorbers. This member is represented by conductance or resistance on the electrical diagram. The introduction of resistance to the series resonance circuit does not change the frequency, yet it reduces the amplitude of oscillation and makes it difficult for resonance to be reached. This analogy enables the designer to select the proper amount of damping by considering the introduction of resistance to a series circuit.[3]

Broadening the Horizons of Analog Studies[4]

Cases of analog simulation range widely as to field of interest and tools used. A recently constructed dynamic mathematical model of the human heat transfer system emphasizes blood as a major heating and

---

[3] In Italy's prestigious Alfa Romeo, for instance, 50% of the Scientific calculation on their digital computer are simulation studies for car design. The "Julia TZ" sport car has been tested in this manner, in respect to stability, safety, and running performance on a curve. The practical results, obtained after a prototype was built documented the digital experimentation.

[4] Jointly written with H. A. Tas.

cooling factor. This model has been developed by E. I. du Pont de Nemours in an effort to predict human work levels under varying environmental conditions. The system is capable of simulating six main factors of human heat exchange through the use of four analog computers. The computers can be interconnected and operated as one unit to provide a total of 130 nonlinear algebraic and differential equations describing

   (i) the flow of heat within the body and to its environment,

  (ii) the distribution of metabolic heat generation,

 (iii) the convective transport of heat by the blood stream,

 (iv) the conductive transfer of heat through the tissues,

  (v) the storage of heat in the tissues,

 (vi) the loss of heat through the respiratory tract,

(vii) the loss of heat from the skin by radiation, conduction, and evaporation.

While this is not the only example of analog studies in biotechnology, it could well be considered as one of the good cases. The results obtained in the industrial field make one wonder why simulation methods have not been used for other biological functions. This is said with full understanding that there is a big difference between an electromechanical system and a biological system. In a mechanical system inputs and outputs are, in most cases, completely known; the system's components are also known [Fig. 5(a)]. A biological system contains many components, most of which are unknown. In most cases only an incomplete knowledge is available on the processing or the "throughput" of a biological ensemble [Fig. 5(b)].

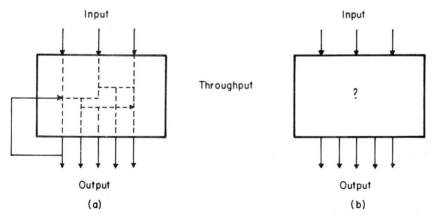

FIG. 5.   (a) Electromechanical black box; throughput know completely. (b) Biological black box; throughput know only partly or not know at all.

To start with, we will investigate the advantages to be gained by using the "black box" approach in setting up the model or equations which will describe a biological system. The problem of the black box[4] arose at first in electrical engineering. Briefly, it can be defined as follows: Given a sealed box with terminals for input and terminals for output, both of which can be observed, one has to learn everything possible about the contents of the black box. Though the problem originally arose in a purely electrical form, its range of application is far wider. The clinician studying a patient with brain damage and aphasia may try, by means of tests and the observations of speech patterns, to deduce something about the mechanisms involved. In fact, the location of traumata in neurology is a kind of black box technique.

The current state of the art in systems analysis practice gives us possibilities of answering such questions as

(i) How should an experimenter proceed when faced with a black box?

(ii) What properties of the box's contents are discernable?

(iii) What methods should be used if the box is to be investigated efficiently?

In the begining we shall make no assumptions at all about the nature of the box and its contents, which, for instance, might be something that has just fallen from a flying saucer. What we need to make is a protocol which, at a number of times, describes exactly at what state the input and output are. Mathematically speaking the black box is described at these different times by a vector with two components: input state and output state. The "throughput" can then be defined as the mathematical transformation that changes input into output.

Knowledge available from a black box is such that it can be obtained by recording the protocol in terms of these vectors. In some cases, in fact in a great number of them, it will be found that the behavior of the box is machine-like. That is to say that a certain input always gives way to the same output. In this case it is possible to make a model which will act like the "machine" and which then is given by a certain set of equations describing the "canonical representation" of the system. If, for example, we use this approach to a model of the functions of the kidney, it turns out that we have to use a very large system consisting

---

[4] By "black box" is meant a certain device which, regardless of its complications, is treated as one component. Usually we are interested in certain properties of this component that relate it to the system of which it is a part.

of a number of black boxes to describe all of them. A few of the functions to be considered are

(1) tubular reabsorption of several solutes,

(2) tubular excretion,

(3) clearances involving neither tubular reabsorption nor excretion,

(4) urea excretion,

(5) the control of strong electrolytes,

(6) the control of water diuresis and antidiuresis,

(7) the acid-base equilibria of blood and urine, etc.

In this short discussion it is not possible to give a complete model incorporating all the functions mentioned. Therefore, we will consider in detail only one of these functions, the hydrogen ion balance. The H^+ concentration is one of the most carefully guarded homeostatic states of the body fluids. There are several considerations which stress the importance of H^+:

(a) The universal solvent in biological systems in H_2O which dissociates into H^+ and OH^-.

(b) Biochemical reactions often involve compounds with prototropic groups (groups which can give off or accept a proton or H^+), and compounds of the type RCOOH are highly reactive because of the ease with which they dissociate into the ion pair $RCOO^-$ and H^+.

(c) In general, oxidation and reduction systems are highly sensitive to H^+ concentration. The configuration of the amphoteric structure and functional proteins is highly sensitive to H^+ concentration.

(d) Oxidation leads to the formation of acids which are again easily dissociative.

Treating the hydrogen ion balance function as a black box has another advantage: we already know something of the "contents" of this black box as the "throughput" is partially determined by physico-chemical laws. One of these laws, the mass law,

$$HA \rightleftharpoons H^+ + A^-,$$

$$[H^+] = \frac{[HA]}{[A^-]} k_a \qquad \text{(Mass law (weak acids), where}$$
$$k_a = \text{acid dissociation coefficient),}$$

$$\gamma[BA] = [B^+] = [A^-] \qquad \text{(Mass law (electrolytical dissociation), where}$$
$$\gamma = \text{activity coefficient),}$$

leads to the Henderson-Hasselback approximation which is as follows:

$$pH = \log \frac{[BA]}{[HA]} + pK^1, \qquad pH = -\log [H^+],$$

$$pK^1 = -\log \left(\frac{k_a}{\gamma}\right) = \log \left(\frac{\gamma}{k_a}\right).$$

Approximation of HENDERSON

$$pH = \log \frac{[BA]}{[HA]} + pK'$$

Equation of HASSELBACH

$$[H^+] = \frac{[\text{Total HA}] - [BA] - [H^+] + \frac{k_w}{[H^+]}}{\gamma [BA] + [H^+] - \frac{k_w}{[H^+]}} k_a$$

k_a = acid dissociation constant

k_w = k [HOH]

pK' = log $\frac{\gamma}{k_a}$

pH = - log [H$^+$]

This makes it possible to determine what happens if a certain disturbing input, for instance a pH change, occurs. In this case the kidney will react, trying to balance out this disturbance by using a feedback mechanism: absorption, reabsorption, or excretion of $NaHCO_3$ (Fig. 6).

The Henderson equations are easily applied, in practice, to H_2CO_3 : $BHCO_3$ solutions. Total CO_2 is determined by the Van Slijke/Neill manometric apparatus and [BA] is computed as equal to [total CO_2] — [HA]. Here [HA] is calculated from the partial pressure of CO_2 or P_{CO_2} of the gas mixture with which the fluid is in equilibrium, utilizing the solubility coefficient α of CO_2 at the equilibrium temperature. The solubility coefficient α is conventionally expressed as the number of cubic centimeters of gas, at standard temperature and pressure, dissolved by one cubic centimeter of fluid at a partial pressure of 760 mm Hg and at a specific temperature. At $380°C$, $\alpha(CO_2) = 0.510$ per cm^3 plasma, and $\alpha(CO_2) = 0.524$ per cm^3 urine. This is an average figure, which will vary slightly with the composition of the urine.

The concentration of dissolved CO_2 at any partial pressure is given by

$$P'_{CO_2} = \frac{\alpha P_{CO_2}}{760}.$$

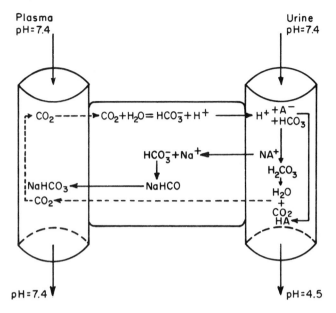

FIG. 6.   The exchange mechanism applied to reabsorption of $HCO^3\bar{u}$ and acidification of urine buffers. The system is carbonic hydrase dependent.

To obtain the concentrations in millimoles/liter, we combine the fixed terms:

$$[HA] = 0.0301 \, P_{CO_2} \text{ (plasma)} \qquad \text{and} \qquad [HA] = 0.0309 \, P_{CO_2} \text{ (urine)}.$$

These equations, together with the chemical data of the model, enable us to compute the influence of a disturbance.[1]

---

[1] I discuss Human Engineering in my book "An Introduction to Product Planning" (Cassell, London, 1967). Digital computer usage in research is covered in "Managing Industrial Research for Profits" (Cassell, London, 1967) and data load calculation for machine choice in "Selecting the Computer System" (Gee and Co., London, 1967).

CHAPTER 25

Considering the Analog Computer

As with all calculating machines, the basic elements for a mechanical analog computer are

(i) input devices,
(ii) devices which perform the mathematical operations,
(iii) output devices.

The basic function of the input device is to transport the characteristics under study into units of energy of motion which will cause the computer to function or operate according to the implied conditions. Human operators, input tables, function generators, or error-sensing devices can be used to input information in an analog machine. The output is usually taken in the form of an xy graph made by a graph plotter, or in a digital form by using an analog-to-digital converter. Although visual displays are used mainly for outputing computer information, other types of displays are not impossible.

For initial economical studies of systems on the analog simulator, sources of direct current voltage for step and pulse excitation and an audio-frequency oscillator for harmonic excitation are sufficient. For more advanced work, some means of generating arbitrary voltage inputs may be desirable. These may range from simple motor-driven nonlinear resistances to expensive phototube cathode-ray tube follower devices which are on the market. For recording input and output voltages, a good cathode-ray oscilloscope will suffice for frequency-response studies. It is often convenient to have some type of direct recording oscillograph when transient responses to pulses and step input are studied, and there are recorders on the market which will plot directly the output of a simulator as a function of time or frequency.

The Mechanical Differential Analyzer

The differential analyzer is a mathematical machine used in the solution of systems of differential equations, to which it proceeds by the

457

method of mechanical analogy. For instance, the multiplication of a variable by a constant can be accomplished with simple mechanical elements. In linkage computers the mechanical advantage of a lever arm serves to ratio a displacement up or down. Shaft rotations are changed with simple gear couplings. For every variable, or function of a variable, in the equation to be solved, there exists in the machine a corresponding rotating shaft. The position of this shaft at any given time determines the value of the parameter which it represents. Known scale factors are assigned to each shaft, so that, by means of an attached counter, it is possible to record the value of any function or variable at any time. For instance, in the solution of a certain problem, the scale factor of one second per revolution might be assigned to the shaft representing time. Thus each revolution made by this time shaft represents the passage of one second in the solution of the problem. Each fractional part of a revolution identifies the same fractional part of a second.

In the operation of a mechanical computer, the instantaneous value of each variable or derivative, of each of the numerous combinations of variables and derivatives occuring in the solving process, is represented by the number of turns of a particular shaft. At any time the number of turns from a specified origin will give the value of the assigned variable at that instant, subject to a predetermined scale factor.

Scale factors may vary widely from problem to problem. An experienced operator is required to assign these factors so that optimum performance may be obtained. This type of machine solution of an equation is also known as the continuous variable method, since shafts representing variables rotate continuously. The solution emerges from the machine in uninterupted manner. This is opposed to digital methods of computation in which values of the solution are obtained at discrete intervals.

Let's consider, as an example, an analyzer consisting of fourteen bays, each containing about twenty freely rotating longitudinal shafts. The axis of rotation of any given shaft in the bay is aligned with the corresponding shafts in all the other bays. Thus, by means of couplings and connecting shafts, one of them can be made to run the whole length of the machine. The spacing between the centers of rotation is fixed and is such that adjoining shafts may be coupled by means of gears or mechanical adders. The input and output shafts of the integrators, function tables, and the output tables run across the machine perpendicular to the longititional shafts and may be coupled to them by means of gear boxes.

In the diagram of Fig. 1, as in every analyzer set-up, the independent variable shaft t is driven by a constant-speed motor which furnishes the power for the machine. This is commonly called the time shaft, since time appears very frequently as the independent variable. In this solution, t is fed into the function table and to the rotating disks of both integrators. As the reference point is kept on the curve drawn on the

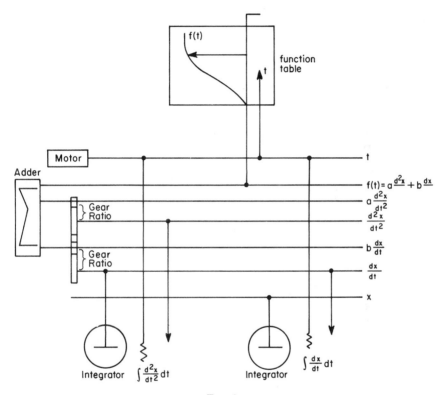

FIG. 1

function table by means of a crank, the output represents $f(t)$. This is coupled directly to the shaft of an adder representing the sum of

$$a\frac{d^2x}{dt^2} + b\frac{dx}{dt}.$$

When the t shaft begins to rotate, $f(t)$ also begins to turn as dictated by the function table and drives d^2x/dt^2 through the adder and gear ratio a.

The shaft dx/dt will turn only as allowed by the integrators, since it is not possible to drive back through the torque amplifier. In turn,

d^2x/dt^2 is fed into the integrator generating dx, which is multiplied by a gear ratio and is fed into the adder dt. Thus a feedback path is set up

Considering the rather limited range of its ability in problem solving, the mechanical differential analyzer is an expensive machine. Contrasted to this device, the digital machine can solve equations more accurately and more rapidly, and it can also solve partial differential equations which the analyzer cannot handle.

We will not consider digital computers in this book, but we do treat the subject in question in "Control Systems Functions and Programming Approaches." For a discussion on computer usage in research see "Managing Industrial Research for Profits" and for computer choice and data load calculations: "Selecting the Computer System."

The Electrical Analog Computer

Although mechanical computing elements have the advantage of simplicity and to a large extent of dependability, they also have the disadvantages of bulk, required extensive set-up, lack of flexibility, and weight. For a large range of computational operations electrical analog computers seem to better suit the purpose. The basic linear computing elements of an electrical analog machine are composed of operational amplifiers and resistors or amplifiers, resistors, and capacitors. Operational amplifiers are high-gain dc feedback amplifiers with impedances in series with the input and with a feedback loop such that the amplifier will perform certain mathematical operations on an incoming signal voltage, such as solving differential equations.

An electrical analog computer particularly designed for the solution of differential equations is also called an electrical differential analyzer. An electrical analog computer has direct application in many fields. There are literally thousands of problems in both engineering and nonengineering fields that can be set up and solved with relative ease through its usage. Not only is time saved in the initial solution, but also, if necessary, the constant may be varied without necessitating a new set-up of the problem.

In order to solve a problem with an electrical analog machine, relationships must be established between voltages (the dependent variable) and real time (the independent variable) that are equivalent mathematically to the variables of the problem. Figure 2 shows the main elements of the operational amplifier in block form. The amplifier should be directly connected, with the gain as high as possible.

An operational amplifier is a very high gain device with an uniform response to frequencies from zero up to the kilocycle range. The output of the amplifier is connected back to the input through a feedback element, which, if the amplifier is to be used for summing, is a resistor. In an electrical-electronic device, when input voltages are applied to the grid of the first tube through resistances equal in magnitude to the feedback, the output is the sum of the inputs (reversed in sign), and the over-all gain is unity.

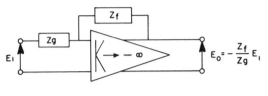

FIG. 2

With these devices, the high internal gain and heavy feedback result in good stability and broad frequency response, in addition to complete decoupling of input from output loads. The transfer function (dynamic variation of output with respect to input) is determined almost entirely by the feedback elements and not by the amplifier characteristics, owing to the stability and the broad frequency band. If the input resistors of the operational amplifier are a fraction of the feedback resistance, the outputs are multiplied by the inverse of that fraction. Substitution of a calibrated or "coefficient" potentiometer for the input resistor allows considerable freedom in multiplication by a constant coefficient.

Substituting a capacitor for the feedback resistor in the operational amplifier can integrate the sum of the input voltages. The current through a capacitor is a function of the rate of change of the voltage applied across it. With the electrical-electronic device, the high gain of the amplifier tends to keep its input grid at ground, hence the output voltage must rise continuously to balance the input and keep the sum of the voltages at the grid close to zero. Approximate integration is an inherent property of any capacitor fed through a resistor, but the operational integration amplifier is more accurate and has less attenuation of voltage than the simple RC quasi-integration network (see Table I).

Equivalent relations for a particular problem are established using computing elements which perform the operations of addition and multiplication by a constant. Differential equations are solved by simulating the equations with these computing elements, setting the variables (voltages) to the proper initial conditions, and then placing the computer into operation, causing the voltages to vary in a manner prescribed by the differential equation. The voltage variations are recorded with respect to time (independent variable) by means of a recorder. In reality, the

TABLE I

THE BASIC ANALOG COMPUTING ELEMENTS

I. ADDER:

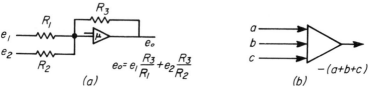

$$e_o = e_1 \frac{R_3}{R_1} + e_2 \frac{R_3}{R_2}$$

(a)

$$-(a+b+c)$$

(b)

Alternative notation and input-output relation:

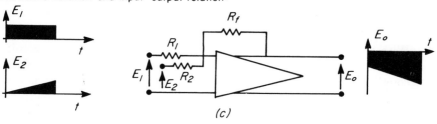

(c)

2. INTEGRATOR:

$$e_o = \frac{1}{C_3 R_1} \int e_1 \, dt$$

(a)

Block diagram

C (inital value)

$$-(a+b+c)\,dt+c$$

(b)

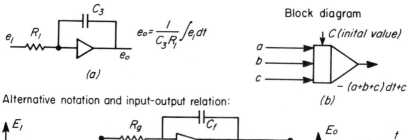

Alternative notation and input-output relation:

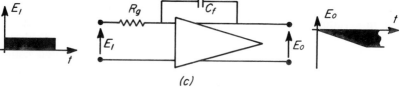

(c)

TABLE I *(continued)*

3. DIFFERENTIATOR:

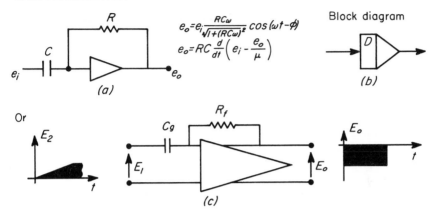

$$e_o = e_i \frac{RC\omega}{\sqrt{1+(RC\omega)^2}} \cos(\omega t - \phi)$$

$$e_o = RC \frac{d}{dt}\left(e_i - \frac{e_o}{\mu}\right)$$

Block diagram

(a)

(b)

Or

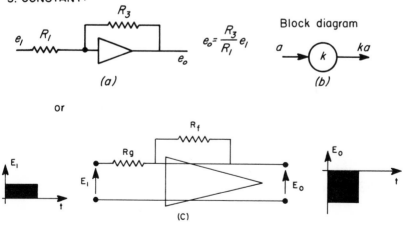

(c)

4. MULTIPLIER:

Block diagram

5. CONSTANT:

$$e_o = \frac{R_3}{R_1} e_i$$

Block diagram

(a)

(b)

or

(C)

computer is an analog, an electronic model, which by manipulation is made to simulate the dynamic characteristics of the problem under study.

It is known that for a high-gain amplifier with a series impedance z_g and a feedback impedance z_f the output voltage is related to the input by

$$E_0 \approx - \left(\frac{z_f}{z_g} \right) E_1 .$$

The constant multiplier, or scale changer, is formed by using resistors for z_f and z_g. This device is merely an amplifier whose gain is determined by the ratio R_f / R_g. When this ratio is set on a value of two, it will operate on a square wave. An adder is formed by using two or more inputs, which will have a negligible effect on each other due to the fact that the large amount of feedback gives a very low input impedance. The output for two time-varying voltages is

$$E_0 = - \left(\frac{R_f}{R_1} \right) E_1 - \left(\frac{R_f}{R_2} \right) E_2 .$$

Should these resistances be all equal, the output is merely the negative sum of the inputs. This is known as an adder, though it may also function as a scale changer. If capacitive feedback is used, the device becomes an integrator. This may be shown by examining the operational form of the expression for the output:

$$E_0 = - \frac{1}{SC_f R_g} E_1 .$$

The operator $1/S$ is equivalent to an integration in the time domain, where we may write

$$E_0 = - \frac{1}{C_f R_g} \int_0^t E_1 \, dt.$$

The response of such an integrator to a square wave is a linearly falling curve which corresponds to the negative of the steady increase in area under the square wave with time. By reversing the resistor and capacitor in the operational integrator, the resulting device is called a differentiator. In this case, the gain equation takes the form

$$E_0 = -SC_g R_f E_1 .$$

In the time domain, the operator S becomes a differentiation, so that

$$E = -C_g R_f \frac{dE_1}{dt} .$$

The differentiator will restore a linearly rising function to stepwave form.

The operational amplifier can be considered as the core of the electrical analog computing elements. In Fig. 3, the forward gain is $-\mu$, where

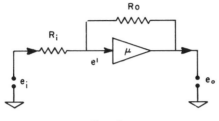

FIG. 3

$|\mu| \gg 1$. The relation of the output potential e_0 to the input potential is the gain of the amplifier:

$$e_0 = -\mu e' \quad \text{or} \quad e' = \frac{e_0}{-\mu}.$$

A reasonable maximum value for e_0 is 50 to 100 volts. The gain μ can go up to 100 000 but usually for dc amplifiers is at the level 10 000. For $\mu = 10\,000$ the largest value e' can have is 0.01 volt.

Using integrators, analog computers can solve differential equations and can generate many mathematical functions. Integration is one of the most important operations in the computing machinery field, and it is rather difficult to perform in an accurate manner. An all-purpose integrator must be able to square both negative and positive numbers. The differentiator is also an important element in an analog computer. The differentiation of displacement with respect to time forms the basis of many devices that are in common use, such as generators and speedometers. The utilization of time differentiators to produce differentiation with respect to some other variable may be accomplished by dividing dx/dt to produce dx/dy. Also, an important requirement of an analog machine is the generation of trigonometric functions, particularly sine and cosine.

In setting up a differential equation on an analog computer, the usual practice is to transport to the left side of the equation the highest derivative of the independent variable, and the balance to the right side. For example, consider the equation

$$y'' - ay' + by + c = 0.$$

This can be rearranged to read

$$y'' = ay' - by - c.$$

Then the output of the first integrator would appear as $-y'$ and could be converted to the first term of the right-hand side of the equation either by multiplying by a constant a or by judicious choice of a scale factor to result in ay'. Notice that because of the phase inversion characteristic of electronic operational amplifiers, the output of the first integrator would appear as $-y'$ for an y'' input. Insertion of the constant coefficient a would then be made as was convenient, using a positive value for a. By feeding the output of the first integrator into a second integrator, the variable y can be obtained. The various outputs may be attached to recording or display devices as desired and in turn fed to other points in the system where that particular value is required. Combining the symbols for the basic computer elements in the solution of the foregoing equation, we obtain the analog diagram in Fig. 4.

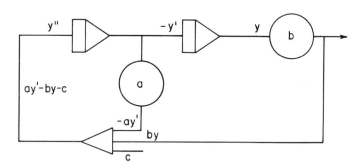

FIG. 4

In drawing the block diagram for the computer setup, it is recommended to use as few operational units as possible, from the standpoint of economy, ease of operation, and speed of computation. It is the programmer's responsibility to devise the simplest approach for problem solution. Sometimes operational error can result from an overloading of the various amplifiers because of exceeding the rating of that particular unit. This is usually taken care of by using neon lamps, which will conduct when the rating is reached, or sensitive relays connected to warning lights or bells. A more careful choice of scale factors can then be made to restore the problem so that it falls into the boundary conditions imposed by the amplifiers. Choice of a suitable time scale is another important factor in the problem solution. Rarely does the situation exist where a one-to-one time relationship can be used.

When it becomes necessary to depart from the use of a unit time base, the resulting choice of a computing period would probably be made using the nature of the display equipment as the primary consideration. To achieve good resolution it is necessary to adhere very closely to the frequency response characteristics of the recording apparatus. One display apparatus used is the cathode-ray oscilloscope from which it is possible to make photographs in accordance with the writing rate used.

Let us consider the solution of a second-order linear differential equation as an example of the use of operational amplifier computer components. This equation, which applies to an R-L-C circuit or to a mass-spring-damper mechanical system, has the form

$$A \frac{d^2x}{dt^2} + B \frac{dx}{dt} + Cx = f(t),$$

where A, B, and C are constant coefficients and $f(t)$ is the driving voltage or force and is some given function of time. To facilitate solution, we write the equation with the highest derivative on the left:

$$A \frac{d^2x}{dt^2} = f(t) - B \frac{dx}{dt} - Cx,$$

This may be solved by the arrangement of computer elements shown in Fig. 5. Notice that the operational unit on the extreme right is an adder that gives the sum of three voltages corresponding to the three terms on the right side of the above equation. These will add to give the second-derivative term on the left side of the equation, but with a minus sign.

The second-derivative term $-A \, d^2x/dt^2$ in Fig. 5 is multiplied by $-1/A$, in a scale changer, to give d^2x/dt^2. Then an integrator reduces it to the first derivative and reintroduces a minus sign. Another scale changer multiplies the output of this integrator by $-B$ to give the term $B \, dx/dt$, which is changed in sign by a sign changer before being fed into the adder. The negative first derivative $-dx/dt$ is also integrated and multiplied by $-C$ to supply the $-Cx$ term to the adder. A voltage $f(t)$ which has the same form as the voltage or torque applied to the system under study is also applied to the adder. Once the computer loop is closed and $f(t)$ is applied the solution x begins to appear at the output of the second integrator, and may be recorded.

For example, assume each of the R-C constants of the integrators as equal to, say, one second. If the units of time in the equation being solved are also in seconds, the computer will operate at the same rate as the system it represents and is said to operate on a one-to-one time scale. This may be an advantage in cases where the computer represents only a part of some mechanical system which is to be solved. Thus, if the equations of flight of an aircraft are set up on a computer with a one-to-one time

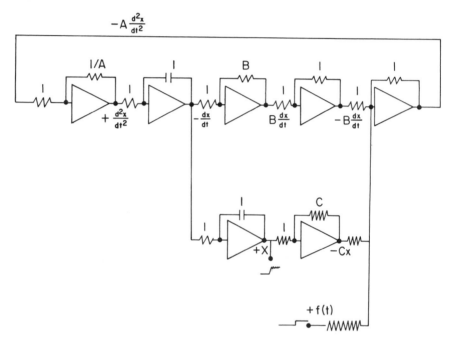

FIG. 5.   Block diagram of an analog computer setup for the solution of a second-order differential equation. Resistance is given in megaohms and capacitance in microfarads.

scale, an autopilot may be tested by connecting it to the computer before installing the former in the aircraft for a flight test. If the R-C time constants of the integrators are made much smaller than one second, the problem will be solved in a correspondingly shorter time. In high-speed or "repetitive" computers, the solution is made repetively at a 60-cycle rate, and can be conveniently viewed on a cathode-ray oscilloscope. In these computers the integrator R-C time constants must be somewhat smaller than 1/60 sec.

The differential analyzer type of computer may also be used to solve sets of simultaneous differential equations. Of still greater importance is its application to the solution of the nonlinear differential equations. Such devices as multipliers, limiters, and function generators must be used in conjunction with operational amplifiers in the computer solution of such equations. The basic nonlinear computing elements are shown in Fig. 6.

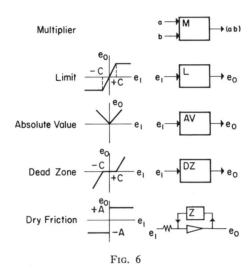

FIG. 6

Examples of Analog Computer Usage

We said that the analog simulator is useful in determining the response of systems which may be described by linear differential equations. The basic operations which the analog machine must perform in this process of solving a linear differential equation are

(i) addition of several terms,
(ii) multiplication by a constant,
(iii) integration of a variable with respect to time.

The time building blocks necessary for the performance of these operations have already been discussed. In the following we will be concerned briefly with the process of setting up the machine.

Solution of differential equations, such as those representing the motion of a damped vibrating body, can be carried out on the analog simulator by either of two methods. One is the mathematical method, which is basically a step-by-step copy of conventional pencil and paper solution techniques. The other is the method of direct simulation, which has the advantage of reducing the number of operational amplifiers required.

A PROBLEM INVOLVING TRANSFER FUNCTIONS

The preliminary steps required for the solution of a problem by analog computation are very similar to those utilized in a numerical integration solution, As an example, consider the second-order relation

$$\frac{\theta}{\alpha} = \frac{1}{1 + 0.098s + 0.019s^2} .$$

In differential equation form, this can be written

$$0.019\ddot{\theta} = \alpha - \theta - 0.098\dot{\theta}.$$

Figure 7 shows an analog computer block diagram for the solution of this problem. It is assumed that the voltages representing each unit have been so chosen that the magnitude of the variables (in volts) is

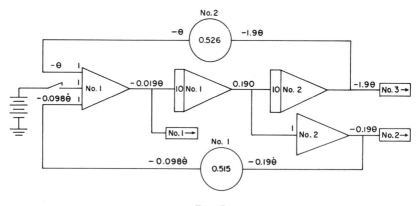

FIG. 7

neither so high as to saturate computer component levels nor so low as to be lost in the signal-to-noise level. The sum of the inputs to amplifier 1 is 0.019 $\ddot{\theta}$. Since inverting action takes place, the output of amplifier 1 is $-0.019\ddot{\theta}$. The $\ddot{\theta}$ signal to integrator 1 is at an input point which has a gain of 10. Therefore, the output of integrator 1 is 0.19$\dot{\theta}$, which is the negative of 10 times the integral of the input. Since one input to amplifier 1 is $-0.098\dot{\theta}$, amplifier 2 serves to change the polarity of 0.19$\dot{\theta}$, and potentiometer 1 selects the proper magnitude of $\dot{\theta}$. Integrator 2 functions in a manner similar to integrator 1. The output is 10 times the integral of the input. Potentiometer 2 selects the proper magnitude of θ to be fed back to amplifier 1. Recorders 1, 2, and 3 monitor the signals $\ddot{\theta}$, $\dot{\theta}$, and θ, respectively.

The operation of the system in Fig. 9, in response to a unit step α signal is as follows: When the switch is closed, a voltage representing α is applied to amplifier 1. This causes $\ddot{\theta}$ to have an immediate value. Integrator 1 integrates the $\ddot{\theta}$ signal, and the proper magnitude of the $\dot{\theta}$ signal is applied through amplifier 2 and potentiometer 1 to amplifier 1. Integrator 2 integrates $\dot{\theta}$ and enables the proper magnitude of θ to be applied to amplifier 1. Equilibrium is reached when the sum of the inputs to amplifier 1 is zero.

Sometimes simplifications are possible in analog computer setups. Thus the block diagram in Fig. 8 shows a simpler method of solving the

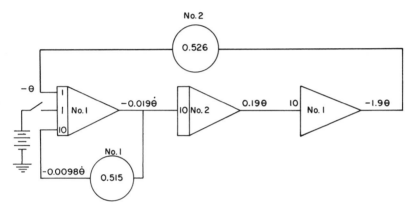

FIG. 8

same problem as that in Fig. 7. The sum of the inputs to integrator 1 is $0.019\ddot{\theta}$. However, since an integrator instead of an amplifier is used, the output is $-0.019\dot{\theta}$, permitting a saving of one amplifier unit. In complicated control systems considerable savings are often possible by using similar techniques.

As another example of analog computation, consider the control system shown in Fig. 9. The equations which describe the operation of this control system are

$$\theta_e = \theta_i - \theta_0 , \tag{1}$$

$$y = 18.9 \frac{(1 + 0.448s)}{(1 + 2.24s)} \theta_e , \tag{2}$$

$$x = \frac{1 + 0.185s}{1 + 0.037s} y , \tag{3}$$

$$0.01 \dddot{\theta}_0 = z - \dot{\theta}_0 - 0.1\ddot{\theta}_0 . \tag{4}$$

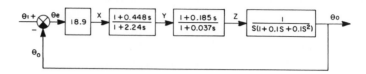

FIG. 9.   Control system block diagram.

Amplifier 1 in Fig. 10 solves (1). Amplifiers 2 and 3, together with their frequency-dependent input and feedback functions, solve Eqs. (2) and (3). Integrator 1 solves (4), and integrators 2 and 3, together with amplifier 4, provide the other signals needed in the simulation. Potentiometer 1 provides a method of setting the system gain. If the designer

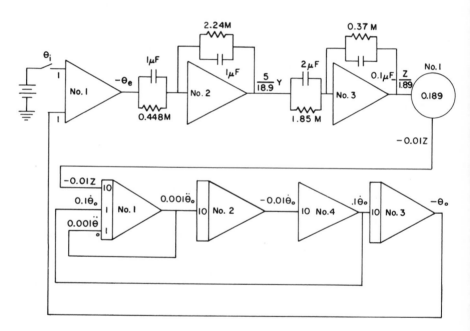

FIG. 10.   Analog computer block diagram for the simulation of the control system shown in Fig. 9.

choses to observe the system operation when the gain is either higher or lower, he may do so by merely changing the potentiometer setting. (see Table II).

TABLE II

EXAMPLES ON THE SOLUTION OF DIFFERENTIAL EQUATIONS
BY MEANS OF ANALOG COMPUTER ELEMENTS

$$\frac{dx}{dt} = -ax$$

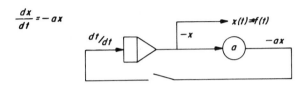

$$\frac{d^2x}{dt^2} + \omega^2 x = 0$$

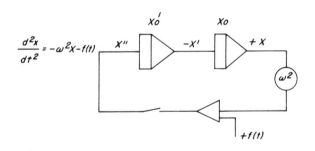

$$\frac{d^2x}{dt^2} = -\omega^2 x - f(t)$$

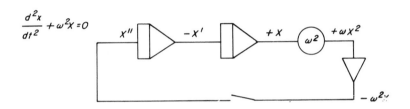

$$x'' + kxx' + \omega^2 x^2 = -f(t)$$

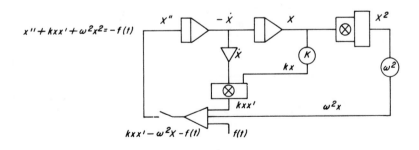

TABLE II (*continued*)

$y'' = y + g$

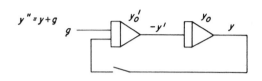

$my'' + ry' + ky = 0$

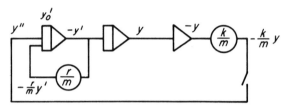

$\dfrac{dy^2}{dt^2} + \omega y^2 = 0$

$y(o) = 0$

$y'(o) = 0$

Solution:

$y = \dfrac{l}{\omega} \sin \omega t$

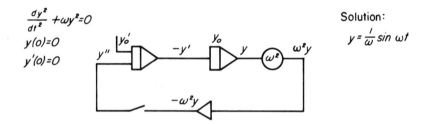

$my'' = mg - cy'^2$

$y(o) = 0$

$y'(o) = 1$

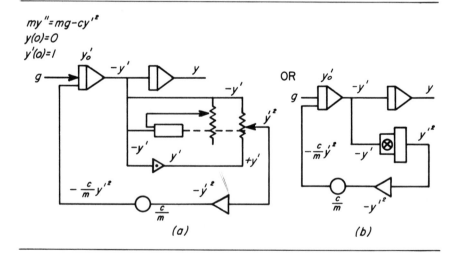

(a)   OR   *(b)*

TABLE II (*continued*)

$y'' + ay' + by = f(t)$

$y'(o) = 0$

$y''(o) = 0$

OR

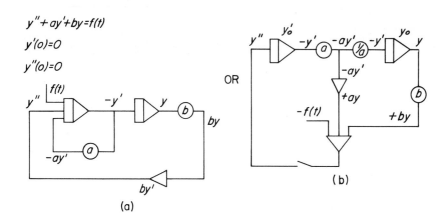

(a)

(b)

$\frac{C}{R} = \frac{-\tau}{\tau p + 1}$

or $-\tau R = \tau C' + C$

or $C' = -R - \frac{C}{\tau}$

OR

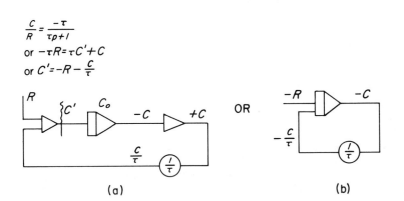

(a)

(b)

TABLE II (continued)

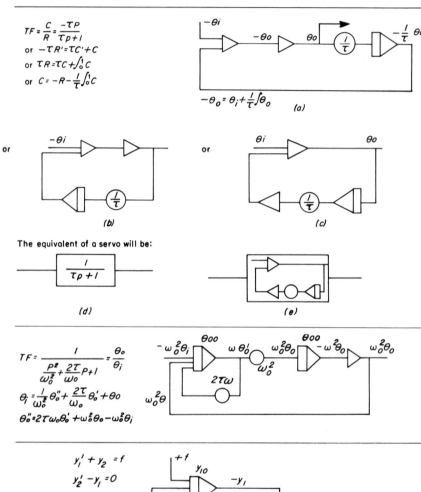

$$TF = \frac{C}{R} = \frac{-\tau p}{\tau p + 1}$$

or $-\tau R' = \tau C' + C$

or $\tau R = \tau C + \int_0^t C$

or $C = -R - \frac{1}{\tau}\int_0^t C$

$$-\theta_0 = \theta_i + \frac{1}{\tau}\int \theta_0$$ (a)

or   (b)   or   (c)

The equivalent of a servo will be:

$$\frac{1}{\tau p + 1}$$

(d)   (e)

$$TF = \frac{1}{\frac{p^2}{\omega_0^2} + \frac{2\tau}{\omega_0}p + 1} = \frac{\theta_0}{\theta_i}$$

$$\theta_i = \frac{1}{\omega_0^2}\theta_0'' + \frac{2\tau}{\omega_0}\theta_0' + \theta_0$$

$$\theta_0'' = 2\tau\omega_0\theta_0' + \omega_0^2\theta_0 - \omega_0^2\theta_i$$

$$y_1' + y_2 = f$$

$$y_2' - y_1 = 0$$

$$y_1(0) = 1, y_2(0) = 0$$

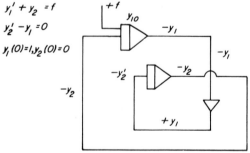

BUILDING RESPONSE TO AN EARTHQUAKE[1]

This study was conducted to investigate the possibility of determining building strains and deflections during an earthquake by an analytic method. The differential analyzer was used to mathematically determine strain and deflection by solving idealized equations of motion of a certain building A. An accelerograph record for the California earthquake in August 1952 was used as a driving function for the equations. Strain and deflection measurements were made at the time of the earthquake to permit subsequent comparison.

The equations of building motion as submitted to the differential analyzer are as follows:

Translation equations:

$$\ddot{y}_1 = a_1 y_0 - a_2 y_1 + a_1 y_2 + a_3 \dot{y}_0 - a_4 \dot{y}_1 + a_3 \dot{y}_3 , \tag{5}$$

$$\ddot{y}_2 = b_1 y_1 - b_2 y_2 + b_1 y_3 + b_3 \dot{y}_1 - b_4 \dot{y}_2 + b_0 \dot{y}_3 , \tag{6}$$

$$\ddot{y}_3 = c_1 y_2 - c_1 y_3 + c_2 \dot{y}_2 - c_3 \dot{y}_3 , \tag{7}$$

Rotational equations:

$$\ddot{\theta}_1 = -k_1 \theta_1 + k_2 \theta_2 - k_3 \dot{\theta}_1 + k_4 \dot{\theta}_2 - k_5 \ddot{y}_1 , \tag{8}$$

$$\ddot{\theta}_2 = r_1 \theta_1 - r_2 \theta_2 + r_3 \theta_3 + r_4 \dot{\theta}_1 - r_5 \dot{\theta}_2 + r_6 \dot{\theta}_3 - r_7 \ddot{y}_2 , \tag{9}$$

$$\ddot{\theta}_3 = s_1 \theta_2 - s_1 \theta_3 + s_2 \dot{\theta}_2 - s_2 \dot{\theta}_3 - s_3 \ddot{y}_3 , \tag{10}$$

where

y_0 = ground displacement,

y_1 = translatory displacement of the first floor,

y_2 = translatory displacement of the second floor,

y_3 = translatory displacement of the third and fourth floors,

θ_1 = first-floor rotational displacement,

θ_2 = second-floor rotational displacement,

θ_3 = third- and fourth-floor rotational displacement.

The masses, spring constants, and damping constants of the third and fourth floors were lumped together to reduce the number of equa-

---

[1] This study was made on an analog computer at the Department of Engineering, University of California, Los Angeles, as were the studies in the following two examples.

tions. The strain and deflection equations for a particular column in the building frame were written as follows:

$$\delta = (y_1 - y_0) + A\theta_1 , \tag{11}$$

$$\epsilon = C(y_2 - y_1) + B(\theta_2 - \theta_1). \tag{12}$$

Figure 11 shows where strain and deflection were measured experimentally on a typical column.

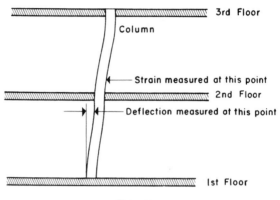

FIG. 11

Solving the foregoing on a differential analyzer, the researchers obtained plots of translational displacement, rotational displacement, strain, and deflection. Translational displacement of the different floors was found to decrease very slightly with higher floors, displacement of the top floor being about 95 % of that of the first floor. The rotational displacement on the other hand showed an increase with higher floors, the rotational displacement of the first floor being about 40 % of that of the top floor.

The magnitude of strain as computed from the equations was within 20 % of the values recorded by the strain gauges. The natural frequency of the strain equation was established at 8 cps which did not compare with the 3 cps indicated on the strain gauge recordings. The discrepancy between the measured and computed frequencies is attributed to the inability to closely estimate such things as mass distribution, location of center of mass of the building, type and magnitude of stiffness, location of center of rigidity, damping magnitude and linearity, and the like.

THE LINEAR TRANSFER STUDY

A simulation on thermal effects for aircraft was conducted by means of an electrical analog. A set of linear differential equations was written to describe the system under study. The nonlinear nature of the driving functions and the large number of solutions required made the differential analyzer especially useful in the solution of these equations.

The electrical analogs of two alternative systems considered are indicated in Fig. 12.

Node voltages were assumed and the following equations were written:

Alternative I.

$$T_1 = \int [Q - \tau_1 T_1 - \tau_{12}(T_1 - T_2)]\, dt,$$

$$T_2 = \int \tau_2(T_1 - T_2)\, dt;$$

Alternative II.

$$T_1 = \int [Q - \tau_1 T_1 - \tau_{12}(T_1 - T_2)]\, dt,$$

$$T_2 = \int [\tau_2(T_1 - T_2) - \tau_{23} T_2]\, dt,$$

where

$Q = I/C_1$,

$T_1 = $ voltages across C_1

$T_2 = $ voltage across C_2

$\tau_1 = R_1/C_1$

$\tau_2 = R_2/C_2$

$\tau_3 = R_2/C_1$

$\tau_4 = R_3/C_2$.

The differential analyzer was set up in three independent sections, with each section representing the equations for alternative I. This approach permitted three different solutions of the equations each time the independent variable was "swept" through the interval under consideration. The time per solution was thus reduced. Approximately 900 solutions were completed for different values of the parameters. Due to a limited number of components, only two independent sections could be set up for alternative II. Two hundred solutions were completed

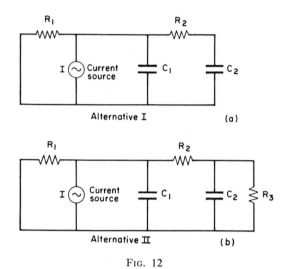

Alternative I   (a)

Alternative II   (b)

Fig. 12

for this system with the same parameters being varied as had been varied previously.

The output information was in the form of plotted curves of T_1 and T_2 as functions of time. A typical T_1 response is illustrated in Fig. 13.

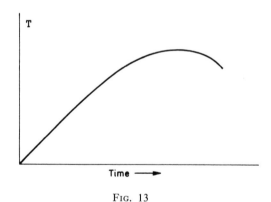

Fig. 13

Aircraft Air Conditioning

This project was concerned with the analysis of the operational characteristics of certain standard air conditioning equipment. These units find their application in jet aircraft. They are used to counteract the accumulation of heat due to accessory equipment in the personnel cabin, which contributes to the heat load.

In the hand calculation of the desired characteristics, an iteration method is used, which requires that the operator assume the result and then by a series of arithmetic and graphical operations compute the error in his assumption; thereby the operator may make a new assumption and repeat. The differential analyzer was used essentially to complete this circular process in such a way that the initial condition was necessarily, being mechanically linked, always equal to the result, thereby eliminating the iterative process. Seven graphs of performance data were used: two of the turbine alone, one of the heat exchanger alone, and four of the physical interrelations between these two when connected.

The schematic diagram of the air-conditioning unit under consideration is shown in Fig. 14. High pressure air is bled from the engine

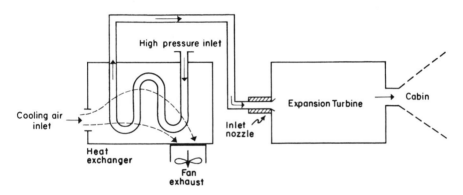

FIG. 14

compressor into a heat exchanger using outside air. It is then further cooled in an expansion turbine of given characteristics and led into the cabin where an assumed temperature (say 80°F) is to be maintained. A fan is used to draw cooling air through the heat exchanger.

The arithmetical and graphical operations on the differential analyzer were essentially the same as applied in the hand computation, the main difference being that logarithms of functions were often used to simplify the multiplication of two functions. This necessitated, then, that there be seven graphical input tables, besides the functions generated arithmetically by the machine. In each case the input function was derived from a graph which was a function of three variables, i.e., a family of curves over which the operator of the table interpolated the input function from member to member. For example, the drop in temperature of the air across the turbine was obtained as a function of both the revolutions per minute of the turbine and the adiabatic heat across the turbine.

In run No. 1 the flow rate of air (in lb/min) through the turbine and the output temperature of the turbine were plotted versus the input nozzle area of the turbine. The altitude parameter was held at sea level, on the assumption that the worst possible heating conditions are encountered at sea level for a given aircraft velocity. Run No. 1 was made to help in optimum aircraft performance at this level. Its objective was to determine the size of input nozzle area A_n for which maximum heat is removed from the cooling air.

A value of A_n was then chosen at or near (for other considerations) this optimum, and, in run No. 2, A_n was held fixed and the altitude was allowed to vary up to 50 000 ft. Output temperature and flow rate of the turbine air were plotted versus altitude. The resulting plots indicated that weight of air per minute decreased steadily with greater altitude. Output temperature versus altitude is shown in Fig. 15.

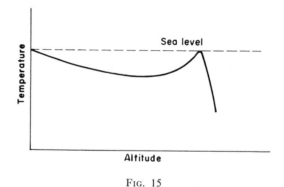

FIG. 15

Simulating a Nonlinear Economic System on an Analog Machine[2]

An analog computer was used in a research project concerning the behavior of a nonlinear economic system. Twelve equations were studied, describing the interaction of the banking system and the production market within the United States. No attempt was made to include the

---

[2] See Chapters 12, 13, and 14 of this volume and also D. N. Chorafas, "Nouvelles Méthodes d'Analyse Économique" Éditions Dunod, Paris, 1963.

securities market or the effect of international relations. The basic quantities employed in these equations were

Y	National income, taken equal to PX, where P is the price factor a X the aggregate production level
L	Total loans of the banks
M	Total money supply
B_1	Total bank reserves
B_2	Currency held by the public
B	Monetary base (total money controlled by the authorities)
R	Actual bank reserve ratio
$R*$	Desired bank reserve ratio
C	Total bank deposits
A	Aggregate demand for all products
I_e	Rate of new loan extensions.
I_0	Rate or loan repayments
r	Loan conditions (a factor including interest rates, downpayments, and repayment conditions).

Several of the equations are simply mathematical statements of basic definitions. Thus, the total bank deposits are composed of the total loans and bank reserves:

$$D = L + B_1 . \tag{13}$$

The monetary base is defined as the sum of bank reserves and currency held by the public:

$$B = B_1 + B_2 . \tag{14}$$

The reserve ratio is defined as the ratio of bank reserves to bank deposits:

$$R = \frac{B_1}{D} . \tag{15}$$

The total money supply is composed of bank deposits and currency held by the public:

$$M = D + B_2 . \tag{16}$$

The total outstanding loans are the time integral of the difference between loan extensions and loan repayments, l_e and l_r , respectively:

$$L = \int (l_e - l_r) \, dt + L_0 , \tag{17}$$

where L_0 is the amount of loans at time t_0 .

The "banking decision" equation relates the loan conditions to the actual and desired bank reserve ratios:

$$\frac{dr}{dt} = k_1 (\log R^* - \log R). \tag{18}$$

The "production decision" equation relates the aggregate demand to the rate of production through the National Income, Y:

$$\frac{dY}{dt} = k_2(A - Y). \tag{19}$$

Thus, if demand exceeds the rate of production, the production will be stimulated, though in the long run, this might have disastrous effects on prices.

The remaining five equations are behavior hypotheses, relating the production market to the monetary system:

$$\log R^* = (a_0 + a_1 \log Y), \tag{20}$$

$$\log I_c = a_4 + a_s \log r + a_6 \log Y + a_7 \log \frac{A}{Y} + a_8 \log M, \tag{21}$$

$$\log I_r = a + a_2 \log L + a_3 \log \frac{A}{Y}, \tag{22}$$

$$\log A = b_0 + b_1 \log r + b_2 \log Y + b_3 \log M + b_4 \log L + b_5 \log \frac{A}{M}, \tag{23}$$

$$\log B_2 = d_2 + d_0 \log Y + d_1 \log D. \tag{24}$$

In all cases the initial conditions were average figures for the economic status of the U. S. in 1952-1953, when the subject study was made. Each run extended for some twelve years into the future. Integrators were used to take logarithms and antilogarithms of the various quantities.

An output curve showing the variation of total national income is presented in Fig. 16. The parameters that were varied included conditions, effect of production rate on the bank reserve ratio, the "tightness" of production-decision equation, and the like. In almost every case during this experimentation, the 1952 data pointed to a "slump" within one to two years, to be followed by a much larger rise in national production. This is in accord with the subsequent real behavior of the American national economy.

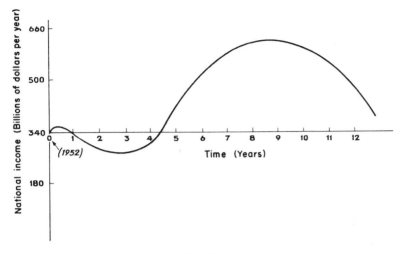

FIG. 16

The Future of the Analog Computer

The first designs of a general-purpose analog computer were those in which the manufacturer tried to guess the applications to which it would be used or could be used. He then designed an instrument flexible enough to solve most of the problems. As time went on, the better features were kept and poorer features were dropped. For example, such features as long busses were dropped while removable patch boards were added. Currently several electrical analog computers provide really general purpose facilities. Such machines are made up of building block assemblies which are mounted together to meet the need of a particular application. These building blocks (such as amplifiers, multipliers, and function generators) may vary in design, quality, and accuracy, but functionally maintain their identity.

There exists a trend in the analog computer business to reduce cost and increase accuracy, maximizing convenience and flexibility. An increasing number of small computers is being sold in the over-all market. It is becoming apparent that low cost analog computers with a high degree of acceptable accuracy must be designed, flexible enough to avail themselves to "on-line, off-line" switching to a central digital computer unit.

Given the competitive advantages of the analog computer for small size problems, conceivable areas of usage for small, low cost, units might be those of a desk-top unit, complete in itself, to solve equations of more than usual difficulty. Such devices would enable the engineer to try out simple circuits, portions of loops, or transfer functions before tying up the time of a large facility. Similarly such devices could be used as an auxiliary to a large installation, whereby the unit will be slaved to operation of the larger unit, offering additional amplifiers or a transfer function of the system; as one of several subcomputers in a computer network direct by a digital computer primary; as an educational and research tool for use in universities; as an auxiliary patch board and smaller computer whereby amplifiers of an existing facility might be sectioned off into the smaller unit; and, as a means for testing physical units such as controllers, meters, etc.

Furthermore, in laboratories and other research and development institutions that use digital computers, which have limited capabilities for the handling of certain problems these organisations are faced with, the treating of fractions of problems on analog machines has often proved to be of considerable advantage. In fact, this may well be the case not only in what concerns the usage of analog computers but also in connection with scale models to assist in the undertaking of simulation work for relatively large-scale projects.

A good example of the foregoing is the joint use of scale models and a digital computer made by a major hydraulic works laboratory in Western Europe. The digital machine in question had a relatively limited memory capacity for the handling of the project this laboratory had in process, hence the decision for this combined approach to simulation. In the study of the Escaut River waterway to the harbor of Antwerp, laboratory engineers used mathematical simulation in connection with the digital computer in representing the present conditions and in experimenting on feasible technological changes. They then constructed scale models in order to study specific results and variations.

Though the relationship between analog and digital means in this precise example was, so to speak, off-line, and scale models rather than an analog computer have been used, it is nevertheless fair to say that the case in question constitutes an excellent example of the possible advantages of on-line coupling of analog and digital units, each used to its fullest potential.[3]

---

[3] Reference is made to the work accomplished by Mr. A. Sterling, and his associates, Director of the Waterbouwkundig Laboratorium, of the Belgian Ministry of Public Works, in Antwerp.

An analog computer, like its digital counterpart, may be classified by means of four criteria:

(i) cost,
(ii) accuracy,
(iii) convenience,
(iv) flexibility.

Cost has a relationship to quality of components, complexity of design, and size of facility. Accuracy depends upon the quality of the components, quality of units such as power supplies, reference standard, and passive R-C components. Convenience, in general, is inversely proportional to the time necessary to set up and reach a solution to a particular problem. A computer is considered more convenient with features such as predetermined integrators, summers, push-button potentiometers setting, and removable patch board. These features, in turn, tend to increase cost. Flexibility refers to the availability of these computing elements. A computer is more flexible if the passive resistors and capacitors are not associated with a certain amplifier and may be used as any computing impedance.

The flexibility and the applicability of an analog computer can be further increased by incorporating into it function generators and other nonlinear units. Several types of nonlinear function generators are manufactured and any may be used. One of the most flexible is the bias diode straight-line single-function generator. Other nonlinear units, such as servomultipliers and special purpose units may also be used in conjunction with this computer. The utility of the device would be improved if the computer were capable of being "slaved to" or "mastering" other machines.

Index

489